Outside an Army Headquarters Signal Office.

# WORK OF R.E.

## IN THE

## EUROPEAN WAR, 1914–19

---

# THE SIGNAL SERVICE
# (FRANCE)

**The Naval & Military Press Ltd**

Reproduced by kind permission of the Central Library,
Royal Military Academy, Sandhurst

Published by

**The Naval & Military Press Ltd**

Unit 10, Ridgewood Industrial Park,

Uckfield, East Sussex,

TN22 5QE England

Tel: +44 (0) 1825 749494

Fax: +44 (0) 1825 765701

**www.naval-military-press.com**

© The Naval & Military Press Ltd 2006

*In reprinting in facsimile from the original, any imperfections are inevitably reproduced
and the quality may fall short of modern type and cartographic standards.*

Printed and bound by Antony Rowe Ltd, Eastbourne

# AUTHOR'S PREFACE.

It has been the endeavour of the compiler of the following account of the activities of the British Signal Service during the European War of 1914 to 1918, to present as clearly as possible an understandable picture of the evolution of signal policy, organization, and practice during these five fateful years. The fact that previous historical accounts of army signal communication have been carried only so far as the South African War of 1899-1901 has, however, caused a slight enlargement of the scope of the present History.

The formation of the Signal Service in 1912 as a separate and integral branch of the Royal Engineers, was undoubtedly the greatest step forward in the evolution of signal policy previous to the European War. As such it has been used here as the foundation upon which the account of the subsequent history of the Service has been built up.

In the present volume the development of the Signal Service in France is dealt with. A companion volume is at present under consideration, which will outline the salient features of signal evolution in other theatres of war, emphasizing especially any particulars in which the conditions of campaigning were such as to cause special local applications of signal practice radically different from those of the main battle front.*

Thus, the amphibious nature and the cramped condition of the warfare in Gallipoli ; the barren, rocky, and precipitous nature of the *terrain* on the Salonica front ; the extreme mobility and the desert conditions of the campaigns in Palestine and Egypt ; the tropical country and the vulnerable lines of communication in East Africa ; the arctic conditions in North Russia ; etc., all gave a special, and in some cases a unique, direction to the evolution of signal policy and the modification of signal practice, while all also caused certain very definite alterations in signal organization. The general principles on which forward and rear intercommunication systems were built up and the means employed, remained to a certain extent the same, but variations in the method of application were numerous and interesting.

A detailed account of the work of individual signal units, or, indeed, of the intercommunication services as a whole in the different theatres of war is impossible, and, in the opinion of the author, undesirable. Such a description is given in some degree in dealing with the French campaigns, and here a general connected account of the evolution of a signal system under the continually varying conditions of modern warfare can be read. Space does not, however, permit, and records are not sufficiently full to allow of, such a description being given for all the subsidiary campaigns. The confines of a single volume can only contain the salient characteristics in which signal policy, organization, and practice differed essentially from those described as being in operation upon the French front.

* Whether this second volume will ever appear must necessarily depend largely upon the reception of its predecessor.

The History has been compiled from various documents collected during March and April, 1919, in France ; from accounts and documents sent home from the various Expeditionary Forces at about the same date or later ; from personal accounts—unfortunately far too few in number—of officers who have played a distinguished part in making the history which is now being recorded ; and from the war diaries of signal units.

The records are, however, very far from complete, for many essential documents had been destroyed before the decision to preserve the remainder was taken and the request for their submission to War Office or G.H.Q. had been formulated.   To this fact must be attributed any omissions which may be noted in the narrative.   If critics will forward to the author or to the President of the Signals Association Publications Committee their account of any incidents or variations of policy or practice which they consider should have been inserted, such omissions may be remedied in a later edition of the book.

The most disappointing feature of the available records has undoubtedly been the comparative uselessness of the war diaries of the majority of units.

The difficulties in the way of writing a full war diary were many and great, but its value to the historian and to the successors of the intercommunication service of the time is such that considerable sacrifices should be made in the endeavour to do justice to the happenings of each day.   The ideal war diary should contain a record of all vital changes in policy, practice, and organization, together with an account of the matter discussed, the opinions expressed, and the decisions arrived at at conferences of signal officers.   All departures from previous or normal practice should be recorded ; the reasons for the adoption of the new methods should be explained ; the results of experiments and the degree of persistence of innovations should be noted.   Such a record would be invaluable from many points of view, and is in itself an indelible witness to the efficiency of the officer who has caused it to be kept.

In view of the practical difficulties certain to be encountered, however, there is much to be said for the practice of keeping as full an account as possible of events from day to day, attaching duplicate copies of all signal instructions, operation orders, circulars, memoranda, maps and diagrams to the war diary each month, and summarizing the chief developments of policy and organization at the close of the month.   One thing, in particular, seems quite clear.   The diary at Army and Corps headquarters should be kept in the office of the chief signal officer of the formation.   An additional record of construction kept by the O.C. Army or Corps Signal Company is useful, but the latter is in no position to record changes either in signal policy or in forward practice, while he is often entirely ignorant of the more interesting details of the process by which such changes have been arrived at.

———— ————

The present narrative deals principally with the story of the British Signal Service in France.   Throughout the chapters devoted to this narrative, three main *motifs* can be detected.   All three are woven together in a connected thread whose continuity is due to a chronological arrangement of facts which has been adhered to as far as possible. The three main themes are, respectively :—the evolution of signal policy, of signal organization, and of signal practice.

Several definite phases of the war as it affected the Signal Service can be recognized, and of these the most important are :—(1) The early mobile phase ; (2) The long-continued stationary warfare which characterized the years 1915 to 1917 ; (3) the retreats of the spring and early summer of 1918 ; and (4) The final advance in the autumn of 1918, which brought about the decision of the long struggle.

Each phase reacted on signal policy, organization, and practice alike, but the first was affected to a less extent than the other two. Running through the whole of the 52 months which intervened between the landing of the Expeditionary Force in France and the signing of the Armistice, certain main principles of signal policy which were tenaciously pursued by the Signals Directorate can be recognized.

The two chief of these were :—(1) The determination to consider mobility the essential feature of decisive warfare which must override all other considerations, no matter how urgent these latter might appear at any one time. (2) The decision to direct all efforts at reorganization towards the one supreme object of making the Chief Signal Officer of each formation an advisory member of the formation Staff rather than an executive officer.

The tenacity with which these two policies were pursued ; the difficulties which had to be overcome ; the success which finally attended them ; are all well displayed in the history of the Service to which they gave the final form. To these two principles, more than to any other factor, the Signal Service may attribute the very substantial measure of success which attended its efforts to adapt itself to every set of conditions met with during the war, and yet to play a worthy part in the final decisive phase.

Signal organization, on the other hand, owed its chief modification to the stationary warfare phase of the war. With the formation of a comparatively rigid line across France and Flanders, an entirely new type of warfare set in, where movement was slow and technical development correspondingly rapid. For many months, the Signal Service struggled manfully with hopelessly inadequate numbers to supply the ever increasing demands for intercommunication. The formation of the stationary warfare signal service with its special personnel to deal with area responsibility, is a chapter in Signal Service history by itself, and has necessarily been dealt with in stages which are to a certain extent inimical to the purely chronological sequence aimed at in the book. Certain definite reorganizations, all directed towards similar ends, can be traced. The final result was the formation of a much modified series of signal units which were capable both of dealing with the greatly increased responsibilities of intercommunication in position warfare, and, at the same time, could revert at need to the comparatively simple system most suitable to the needs of the army in mobile warfare.

Intimately wrapped up with questions of reorganization was the development of a great organization for the construction, maintenance, and working of the rear signal system and for the supply and control of stores and reinforcements.

The chief points of the evolution of the intercommunication service of rear areas may be summarized as the organization of construction units on a large scale and the adoption of a policy of concentration of signal responsibilities along certain main routes arranged on a " chessboard " pattern.    The latter policy persisted until late in the war when it was necessarily modified to counteract the disastrous effects of the enemy bombing raids and long range shelling.

The policy of control of signal stores by the Signal Service was early worked out and the necessary organization created ;  the supply and control of reinforcements was catered for by the formation of a Signal Depôt.

––––––––

Perhaps the most fascinating and most vital of all the aspects of signal development is to be seen in the study of the evolution of forward signal practice and forward signal policy.    It was of course near to the immediate scene of infantry and artillery action that signal policy and practice were most decisively affected by the presence of an ingenious and highly-skilled enemy.

The evolution of forward signal policy was affected above all by the increase in the intensity of the warfare, particularly as regards artillery action.    As the storm of shot and shell poured by the enemy upon the British lines increased, the maintenance of an efficient line system became a matter of the greatest difficulty.    As the batteries, groups and brigades of our own artillery multiplied in numbers, a greater measure of control of our own forward communications by the Signal Service became more and more essential.    The final effect of the latter factor was to vest the control of forward signals entirely in the Signal Service's forward representatives.

The former factor, meanwhile, caused the extension of the " danger area " further to the rear, with the result that the Chief Signal Officers of the rear formations gained a progressively greater degree of responsibility for, and power over, forward signals generally.

At the same time, as one method after another proved uncertain, the policy of co-ordination of different means of signalling into combined schemes became more and more a feature of their employment.    In 1915, we see the period of evolution of alternative means of signalling ; 1916 was the experimental period of the combination of all these means into schemes.    In 1917 (which saw the culmination of position warfare) the necessity for economy of energy, personnel, and stores, resulted in the adoption of the single forward route perpendicular to the front of each formation.    With the publication of S.S. 148 and its successor S.S. 191, the General Staff set its seal upon the forward signal policy, and, at the same time, admitted the Signal Service to the status of a collaborator rather than an executive servant.    The final reversion to mobile warfare in 1918 came only to prove that the lines along which evolution had taken place had been sound ;  to crown the efforts of the Service with decisive success ;  and to cement firmly the good relations which had been set up between the Staff and the organization to which the former must look for the conveyance of information and the distribution of their instructions.

———————

Finally, a summary of the evolution of the Signal Service would be incomplete without a survey of the effect of war conditions upon the means of signalling used. It is to these means that the greater portion of the detail of the narrative is devoted. In August, 1914, the Expeditionary Force went to France equipped for a short sharp trial of strength and relying entirely on the telegraph, visual, despatch riders, and orderlies, and upon *liaison* officers, for all intercommunication. The telegraph form and the message book reigned supreme and, in the hands of the experienced officers of the Regular Army, were potent means of collecting and distributing information.

With the decimation of the original Expeditionary Force and the increasing intensity of stationary warfare, conditions underwent a decisive change. This was first shown by the almost complete suppression of visual and by the extraordinary rise in importance of the telephone which were the chief characteristics of the warfare of 1915. As time passed and artillery fighting continued to increase in intensity and in range of action, the telephone proved inefficient to cope with all circumstances in spite of the adoption of the shallow bury.

The latter portion of 1915 and the early months of 1916 saw the inception of experiments in many directions with the object of reinforcing what was becoming a very unsafe method of intercommunication. The beginning of forward wireless, the formation of the pigeon service, and the rehabilitation of visual, were the outstanding features of a period peculiarly prolific in the evolution of means of signalling.

The battle of the Somme, in later 1916, afforded an opportunity for testing the new means and showed up the good points and shortcomings of them all, while it was also the means of demonstrating the undoubted success of the deep bury and thus illustrating the possibility of the adequate protection of forward lines.

The forward telephone system had, however, received its deathblow in 1915 by the discovery of the extent of enemy overhearing. The consequent slow strangulation of the service in the grip of the precautions and restrictions imposed upon it in the endeavour to minimise this new danger was a feature of the two succeeding years.

In 1917, we see position warfare reach its maximum intensity with, as a corollary, a still further evolution of means of signalling under intensive warfare conditions. The evolution of the message-carrying rocket ; the first tentative experiments with continuous wave wireless for forward work ; and the practical success of the Power Buzzer and Amplifier—perhaps the most exotic of all means of signalling—are the characteristics of the year, though its early months were also marked by the general adoption of the daylight signalling lamp which had made its debut, and had at once proved itself a decided success, in the previous autumn. In this year, also, occurred a great extension of the use of the fullerphone as the standard method of forward telegraphy.

The close of this year was signalized by the battle of Cambrai which possessed many particularly interesting aspects from a Signal Service point of view and has therefore appeared to merit special treatment in a chapter by itself. This miniature essay in semi-mobile warfare both in attack and defence, was followed in 1918 by the great reversion to mobile warfare conditions which characterised the final, decisive phase of the war.

In the retreats of the spring and early summer, and the advances of the late summer and autumn of 1918, a marked reversion to type took place. Once more, we see the Armies retreating or advancing at speed with a restricted skeleton signal system closely allied to that of the autumn of 1914.

The greater efficiency and variety of the means in use, however, and the possession of a well considered signal policy, attest the value of the dearly bought experience of the past four years, while the rise of wireless from a somewhat discredited monopoly of the Independent Cavalry to a valued primary means of intercommunication throughout the whole force is perhaps the most striking visible result of the revolution in signal policy which has taken place.

November 11th, 1918, when the signing of the Armistice brought to a close the militant phase of the greatest international struggle the world has ever known, showed a British Expeditionary Force of some 40 Divisions, closely knit together by an intercommunication service which could guarantee the delivery of an urgent message from any one unit to another, from front to rear or from flank to flank of the force, by at least one of several available alternative channels, within a time which need be measured in minutes only. The closely compact and highly specialized Service—already a Corps in all but name—was none too large to cope with its responsibilities, but was as efficient in its day and generation as the personnel of the highly trained signal units of the original Expeditionary Force had been in theirs.

---

One aim of any History of the Signal Service should be to set forth the basis of tradition. It has been the author's desire to emphasize, without exaggerating, the admirable spirit of determination, co-operation and adaptability to constantly changing circumstances which, above everything else, characterized the Signal Service in the critical years 1914–1918. The standards of self-sacrifice and devotion to duty set by the young Signal Service in these years will doubtless be emulated and improved upon by the Royal Corps of Signals of the future. The record of these five strenuous years should do much towards the maintenance of an *esprit de corps* which is already beginning to shine as a guiding light to officers and rank and file alike.

R. E. PRIESTLEY.

Christ's College, Cambridge.

# CONTENTS.

# CONTENTS OF CHAPTERS.

## CHAPTER XII.

General Remarks.—Horses of Cable Sections a Problem.—Universality of Training Aimed at.—Motor Cyclists.—Visual in the Division.—Wireless in the Division.—R.A. Signals.—Brigade Signals.—Forward Signals in the Attack.—Pushing forward the Buried Cable.—General Policy of Forward Signals Compared with S.S. 148.—Forward Lines.—Forward Visual.—Message-carrying Agencies.—Decentralization of the Pigeon Service.—Formation and Organization of the Messenger Dog Service.—Runners.—Forward Wireless.—Loop Sets.—Continuous Wave Wireless.—The History of the Power Buzzer and Amplifier.

## CHAPTER XIII.

First Battle of Cambrai.—Signals in the Surprise Attack.—Cavalry Line System in Addition to Command and Artillery System.—Use of Area Personnel.—" Camouflage " Line System of Poled and Trench Multicore Cables.—Effect of Tanks on the Line System.—Precautions to Ensure Secrecy.—Testing with Galvanometers and Fullerphones.—Alternative Methods.—Problems Caused by the Depth of the Advance.—Cavalry Signals.—Decreased Telephone Facilities.—Congested Transport Prevents Line Stores from being brought forward.—Twisted Cable in Mobilization Equipment.—Cable Dumps.—Visual :   Two-way   Working.—Wireless.—Other Methods of Forward Signalling.—Brigade and Battalion Signals.—Use of Enemy's Lines.—Pigeons and Runners.—Stabilization of the Situation.—Consolidation of the Signal System.—The German Counter-attack.—S.S. 191, like S.S. 148, Ignores the Possibility of a Retreat.—Emergency Divisional Route Saves the Situation.—W/T Very Useful.—Signal Personnel Engaged in the Fighting.—Guards Division Counter-attack.—Lessons of the Battle.—History of Tank Signals.—Evolution of Tank Wireless.—A.D. Signals, Tank Corps.—Trench Warfare again.—Increase of Enemy Bombing Causes Modification of Rear Routes and Signal Offices.—Second Great Re-organization of the Army Signal Service.—No. 5 Section of a Divisional Signal Company.—Strength of Signal Service and Economy of Personnel.—Army Conference Considers Possibility of Retrenchment.

## CHAPTER XIV.

The General Situation in March, 1918.—Buried Cable Absent or Incomplete on the Critical Front.—Poled Cable and Airline Relied upon Divisions and Brigades.—Visual and Wireless Relied upon to a Great Extent.—Too Little Attention Paid to the Signal System of the Rear Defence Zones.—The Opening of the Attack.—Fog Prevents Observation and Visual Signalling.—Line System Destroyed within a Few Minutes.—Two Main Phases of the Retreat.—The Fighting Retreat through Prepared Positions.—Arras and the North.—Safe Buries and No Retreat.—The Situation South of Arras.—Excellent German Long-range Artillery Preparation.—Loss of Forward Signalling Apparatus and Signallers.—Importance of Wireless and Visual and Message-carrying Agencies in the First Phase.—Formation of a Rear Emergency Carrier-pigeon Service.—The Second Phase :  The General Retreat.—Extent of the Withdrawal.—Characteristics of the Retreat.—General Signal Policy.—The Divisional Route.—A Contrast in Staff Methods and its Effect on Signals.—The Need for Concentration of Headquarters.—Chief Difficulties Encountered.—Hurried Movements.—Laterals.—Congestion of Traffic.—Supply.—Filling Up at Dumps.—Destruction of Routes.—Lessons Learnt during the Retreat.—Line Signalling in Retreat.—Permanent Lines and Ground Cables.—Effect of Tanks, Traffic and Horse Lines.—Cables Used.—Instruments Used.—Emergency " Grid " of Ground Cable.—Wireless.—Practice in Stepping Up Required.—Supply of Accumulators.—Interception.—Rise in Importance of Wireless.—Visual.—Differences in procedure.—Message-carrying Agencies.—Battalion Inter-communication.—Loss of Stores.—The Lys Retreat.—The 9th Corps in the Marne Retreat.—Signal Personnel in the Fighting Line.—Carey's Force.—The Retreat Reflected in Rear Signals.—Special Instructions for Future Similar Emergencies.—Special Training for Mobile Warfare.

## CHAPTER XV.

Effect of the Retreat on the New Stationary Warfare System.—Buries Back to Corps Headquarters.—The Signal System of the G.H.Q. Reserve Line.—Shortages of Material Produce a Relatively Slender Line System.—The Human Element in Buried Cable.—Education of the Working Parties.—The Bury of the Future.—General Characteristics of the 1918 Summer Signal System.—Development of Wireless.—C.W. W/T *liaison* with the French.—Silent Days.—The Signal Service thoroughly Efficient.—G.H.Q. and L. of C. Signals.—Traffic Statistics for 1918.—Standardization of Stores.—Field and Armoured Cable.—The Four-plus-three Buzzer Exchange and the Test Panel.—Signal Repair Workshops.—Air Force Signals.—

# THE WORK OF THE ROYAL ENGINEERS IN THE EUROPEAN WAR, 1914—1919.

## SIGNALLING.

### CHAPTER I.

#### SYNOPSIS.

Comparison of the Signal System of an Army and the Nervous System of an Organism.—Signals in the Nineteenth Century.—The South African War.—The First Official Tribute.—Suggested Co-Ordination of Telegraphs and Signalling.—The Need for an Organized System of Orderlies.—Appointment of Committees to Study Intercommunication Problems.—Experiment.—Alternatives Considered.—The Formation of the Signal Service.—Co-Ordination of all "Message Routes" under One Director of Army Signals.—The Duties of the New Service.—Signal Practice, 1904 to 1914.—Introduction of the Telephone and Motor Cyclists.—Early Criticism of the Telephone.—Army Wireless Telegraphy in its Infancy.—Visual : Semaphore *versus* Morse.—Lessons of the Russo-Japanese War.—The Signal Service in 1914.—Mobility the Premier Consideration.—No Control of Artillery Signals.—Total of the Signal Service at the Outbreak of War.—Its Responsibilities.—Looseness of Organization and Absence of the Magneto Telephone.—Summary of the Position as Regards Signals in August, 1914.—Battalion Signallers.—Individual Influence of Commanding Officers.—Initial Shortage in Establishment Particularly of Motor Cyclists.

JUST as the student of the comparative anatomy of animals can trace a gradual complication and elaboration in the nervous system of the various types as he ascends the evolutionary tree, so the student of military history will find a system ever increasing in complexity as he reads the pages of a history of the Signal Service. Just as the primitive organisms have only simple and scattered nervous connections, so the army of the Middle Ages relied for its *liaison* entirely upon mounted orderlies or esquires—or at the most on very primitive visual appliances.*

The zoologist finds, however, that the higher forms of animal life have nervous systems which reach a high degree of complexity and sensitiveness and are controlled by a central body (the brain).

Similarly, in the modern large and specialized army, the signal system which carries the orders correlating the activities of the parts, becomes more varied and more complex, and has its main trunk system centreing at one point (G.H.Q.) to which all important information is carried and from which all important instructions emanate.

The likeness does not end here, however. Just as the nervous system of the human body is liable to disease through parasites or

---

* Such primitive visual arrangements still persist in the rude code of smoke or flare signals used by certain primitive tribes to this day.

through abuse, and to destruction through accident ; so the army signal system needs the exercise of constant care and thought. Continual attention is necessary to prevent its interruption either by the forces employed against it by the enemy, or from the more insidious troubles which may arise from lack of organization or conscientiousness within the service itself. Diseased nerves will convey the instruction of the brain incorrectly, as in " locomotor ataxia," or may fail to convey them at all, when paralysis sets in. In a similar fashion, a message transmitted by an inefficient Signal Service may arrive at its destination altered out of all recognition, in which case wrong action may result* ; or may not arrive at all, when plans may be marred by the immobility of the formation affected.

Efficiency can only be ensured by constant study of the successes and failures of the past, and by constant research to forestall and avoid the dangers of the future.

An impartial history provides the means by which the former study may be carried out, and, at the same time, the foundation upon which all future researches should be based.

---

The story of intercommunication within the British Army to the date of the conclusion of the South African War has already been written in the general history of the services of the Royal Engineers in that and preceding campaigns. Upon the experience of the Army in South Africa was based the reconstruction which resulted in the formation of the Expeditionary Force as it existed prior to the European War.

Intercommunication personnel was vitally affected by these reforms and the formation of the Army Signal Service was the immediate result. In 1920, it appears likely that the European War just completed will be followed by a similar sweeping reform which will terminate the existence of the Army Signal Service as at present constituted.† A fit period for treatment in a single unit would therefore seem to be the history of the Army Signal Service from its formation in 1912 to its abolition and the creation of the Royal Corps of Signals, in 1920. It is this period that it is intended should be the main theme of the present work. In order, however, that the

* A classical example which has value as a powerful and amusing illustration is offered by a story current in the present day Signal Service. A chain of orderlies was being exercised in conveying verbal messages from the front line to battalion reserves. One message started as " Going to advance ; send reinforcements." It is stated to have been received by a mystified Adjutant at Battalion Headquarters as " Going to a Dance ; lend me three-and-fourpence."

† Since this chapter was written this reorganization has become an accomplished fact.

# OXFAM

VAT: 348 4542 38

**Volunteer here: Have fun,
meet new people & learn
new skills**
Sign up in store or at
www.oxfam.org.uk/join.he.eam

| VJF | SALES | F3622/POS1 |
|---|---|---|
| WEDNESDAY 31 MAY 2023 | | 11:21 201352 |
| 1 C10 - HISTORY | | £11.99 |

1 Items

TOTAL **£11.99**
CREDIT CARD £11.99

Oxfam Shop: F3622
25 Maidenhead Street
Hertford, SG14 1DR
01992 583221
oxfam.org.uk/shop

# THANK YOU

Every item you buy or donate
helps beat poverty.

We are happy to offer a 30 day refund policy for items returned to
the store in the same condition they were sold in, with proof of
purchase and with a valid price ticket attached to the item.
View full T&C's in store or at: www.oxfam.org.uk/shopfaqs
This does not affect your statutory rights.

Oxfam is a registered charity in England and Wales (no 202918) and Scotland (SC039042).
Oxfam GB is a member of Oxfam International.

Find thousands of unique
items in our online shop
www.oxfam.org.uk/shop

# THANK YOU

Every item you buy or donate
helps beat poverty.

We are happy to offer a 30 day refund policy for items returned to formation of the Service may be understood, it is necessary that a summary should be given of the previous history of intercommunication in the British Army. In particular, some account should be written of the steps which led up to these reforms and of the considerations which guided the responsible authorities in determining the exact form that the new Signal Service was to take.

In the early days of the nineteenth century, opposing forces were of so small a size, and scientific signalling equipment was so little developed, that an army's requirements in the way of intercommunication could be efficiently met by the judicious use of mounted officers attached to Staffs for the purpose of carrying orders.

In the smaller units, mounted or foot orderlies, or visual signalling were employed.

Since this time, until the South African War, the British Army had been engaged only in wars against uncivilized tribes and nations in inaccessible, sparsely populated, and hostile countries. In such wars, the striking forces usually consisted of a single column or of a number of columns acting independently. Communication between such columns was impossible save when they were advancing on parallel lines, or during the final stages of a converging movement. Then visual was employed, usually with conspicuous success.

Within the columns themselves, distances were so small that visual with the heliograph, with flags, or with the primitive signalling lamps then available, proved ample for the requirements of the force. Along the lines of communication, the succession of small armed posts or blockhouses, rendered necessary by the presence of a hostile population, served admirably the purpose of relay posts for intercommunication purposes. Communication in the latter case was by visual, by runner, or by mounted orderly, or—in the later years of the nineteenth century—by telegraph along a route which followed the line of advance of the troops.

With a highly trained Staff who required the minimum of information and instruction from the rear, and with an enemy who was technically inefficient and therefore unable to interfere with, to obscure the meaning of, or to tap, the primitive signalling apparatus then in use, the post of signal officer would have been a sinecure. It was not until the introduction of the telegraph brought in its train constant increase in the complexity of this branch of army work, that the Staff were unable to find time to look after their own intercommunication problems. When this state of affairs arose, however, a specially trained signal service was at once required.

Considerable developments in army telegraphy had taken place during the years which immediately preceded the South African War. Telegraph Sections had become a recognized part of the establishment of civilized armies. In November, 1899, the British forces landed in South Africa included a complete Telegraph Division which was followed shortly afterwards by a reinforcement of one hundred linesmen and telegraph operators.*

As the Boer resistance was gradually overcome, and the various columns moved forward, communication with the bases in Cape Colony or Natal was kept by cable and airline with great success. In the later stages of the war a good system of rapid communication along the line of blockhouses which divided up the country for the better isolation of roving bands of Boer guerillas played a dominant part in the extermination or dispersal of these bands and the final pacification of the country.†

In Lord Roberts' report occur the words :—

" The main line telegraph was extraordinarily well done, and the way repairs were made, lines renewed, and new lines started was quite admirable throughout."

This was probably the first official recognition of the value of the signal arm as a separate entity in the operations of the modern army.

Thus, at the conclusion of the South African War, the value of the signal detachments of the Royal Engineers had become generally recognized. During the succeeding years a normal system of inter-communication based on these experiences and on subsequent yearly manœuvres was evolved.

This normal system will be described later in the chapter, but it is now necessary to consider the radical changes in signal organization which were brought about as a corollary to the reorganization of the British Expeditionary Force which was the outstanding feature of army development in the early years of the 20th century.

As reorganized, the Field Army consisted of Army Troops, one Cavalry Division, six Infantry Divisions, and a Lines of Communication organization. To serve this the " Director of Telegraphs " had at his disposal a relatively strong complement of Telegraph Companies, and the " Director of Army Signalling " controlled in some measure an entirely separate organization of signallers who were trained solely under regimental arrangements.‡ There was no co-ordination between the two branches of the inter-communication

---

* These men were largely drawn from the permanent staff of the G.P.O. They did excellent work in the field under unaccustomed conditions. An army reserve of Post Office operators existed prior to the South African War.

† Many telephones were utilized in this inter-blockhouse signal system.

‡ In the South African War a miniature Signal Service of trained battalion signallers was formed to supplement telegraph lines. These men were distributed all over the Transvaal and Orange Free State on kopjes. They were equipped with heliographs, lime lights, etc., and their duty was to keep touch with mobile columns and to take up messages if the Boers cut the telegraph lines—as they frequently did.

service, while an equally unsatisfactory feature of the unco-ordinated scheme was the entire absence of any central organization for the provision of the necessary quota of orderlies to convey messages to and from signal offices and stations.

As it stood, the disadvantages of the intercommunication scheme were obvious alike to Staff and Signal officers. At each of the yearly manœuvres its drawbacks were emphasized. As early as 1906 a committee appointed to report on the intercommunication services made strong recommendations for the organization of all " Message Routes," whether telegraphs, telephones, signalling, or orderlies, under one central controlling authority. The formation of the Signal Service was foreshadowed by the resolution that the committee " recommend the provision of communication units for each formation to work under the General Staff of the formation." It was proposed that one common " Director of Telegraphs and Signalling " should be appointed and that communication detachments should be formed with brigades. Indeed, the committee of 1906 were so far in advance of their time that they strongly advised that the " Communication Service " should take over artillery signalling as far forward as battery headquarters, a degree of prevision which was afterwards nullified by considerations of economy and simplicity.

Experiments with communication units were at once commenced, first in the Irish Command which afforded the maximum facility for extended manœuvre, and later in the Aldershot Command. The new departure involved, however, a relatively considerable increase in expenditure. The history of the embryonic and experimental Signal Service of the next few years is therefore one of constant readjustment in the endeavour to strike a balance between the minimum of intercommunication services considered necessary by the General Staff and the maximum expenditure which could be admitted by the Finance Member of the Army Council. It was not until 1912 that, as a result of further strong representation of a committee which met in 1911, the new Service was recognized in fact and the provisional establishments approved.

The alternatives considered by the committee of 1911 were the formation of a Signal Corps, the creation of an intercommunication branch of some already-existing Corps, and the formation of signal companies by the selection of the most suitable men from any branch of the Service.

The first and last alternatives were ruled out by considerations of precedent, economy, and difficulties affecting the promotion of officers, and the Signal Service was finally created in 1912 as a branch of the Royal Engineers. A feature of the scheme as finally adopted was the seconding of subalterns with suitable experience as brigade signal officers. This provision was made with a view to linking up the intercommunication services of regimental units with the Army

'Signal Service. Officers so selected remained with the Signal Service for a period of four years, while remaining on the promotion roster of their own units. At the conclusion of their period of attachment they returned to their regiments. In due course this policy would have had the result of distributing throughout the Army in consider-able numbers officers with a technical knowledge of intercommunication problems and with close and cordial relations with the Signal Service. This was undoubtedly one of the most valuable features of the revised intercommunication organization and as such is being incorporated in the regulations governing the constitution of the Signal Corps.

It was this committee which reversed the decision of the committee of 1906 as regards artillery signalling, while it agreed with the latter body in leaving unit signalling in battalion, regiment, battery, etc., in the hands of the units concerned. The dividing line was fixed through the recognition of the fact that the regimental signaller was a soldier first and that his signalling duties were of secondary importance. This being admitted, it was essential that the control of such men should be vested in their commanding officers. Consideration of the provision of extra-regimental personnel to be responsible for unit signals was ruled out on the score of economy, a negative decision being strengthened by the obvious evils of a divided command within such small units.

The reorganized service was much as it remained in 1914. Continued experiment resulted in various minor changes, but the main reforms were regularized by an Army Order published late in 1911.* In this Order, the duties of the responsible officers of the new Signal Service were defined and the scope of the responsibility of the service and of regimental signalling organizations was laid down. The division of the new cable and airline signal companies into sections was foreshadowed by the ruling that " the unit for employment is the section of two detachments." The sequel to this was the break-ing up of these companies into cable and airline sections, the head-

* Interesting paragraphs of this Army Order were those specifically defining these duties and responsibilities. The Director of Army Signals was made the supreme arbiter of the Signal Service and he was given power to " communicate direct with his representatives on all matters of administrative and technical detail connected with the Army Signal Service." The commanders of the different companies were his representatives at the headquarters of the lower formations. They were empowered to " act as technical advisers to their commanders and to be responsible under his (the D.A.S.'s) orders, for the general organization, maintenance and efficiency of the service of intercommunication other than the Postal Service." Finally, the regimental signal personnel were " (1) to provide such visual signal stations as may be necessary to complete the intercommunication between themselves and their superior commander and neighbouring units. (2) to arrange for intercommunication within their unit."

quarter detachments forming the nucleus of what became the G.H.Q., and Army Corps Headquarter Signal Companies.

With the acceptance of the recommendations of the committee of 1911, the old R.E. telegraph units disappeared. A comparative picture of the nomenclature of the intercommunication units in 1904, 1907, and 1911, is given below in Table I.

Having summarized the chief features of the reorganization which brought the Signal Service into existence, it is now necessary to review shortly the means at the disposal of that Service at the date of the outbreak of the European War. Two principal advances in signal practice during the period under consideration were the introduction of the telephone for forward work in 1907 and the addition of motor cyclist despatch riders to the establishments of signal units which took place in 1911. As regards the former, an interesting report on its use during manœuvres shortly after its introduction strikes at once a note of criticism. The writer of the report first refers to its inaudibility due to the noise of the artillery firing, and he concludes with a summary of certain moral objections to its use. His conclusion is :—

" It is not difficult to realize the many situations in which it would not be advisable to call verbal messages down the telephone in the hearing of all and sundry in the neighbourhood, whereas the most secret messages could be transmitted in the Morse code without any moral effect upon the bystanders. Nor is the employment of the Morse code considered to contain any insuperable difficulties."

It was very slowly, indeed, that the telephone won its way to the respect and confidence of the General Staff* who distrusted the new instrument particularly because it did away to a great extent with a written record of their instructions. From this opposition much comfort might have been drawn by the discouraged supporters of wireless telegraphy during the early years of the war. Indeed, in signalling as in every other branch of human activity, pioneers will always be faced with the problem of overcoming the distrust with which the normal conservative human being views the introduction of anything new. They must draw their inspiration and courage

* One factor which perhaps militated against the popularity of the telephone to some extent was the fact that in the Russo-Japanese War of 1904–1905, the Japanese on more than one occasion suffered seriously from over-reliance upon a field telephone system. In considering such cases, however, a distinction should be drawn between defects inherent in the telephone itself and others due to the employment of an ill-balanced intercommunication scheme. The instances quoted were due to a failure to supplement the line system by other more reliable, if slower and more expensive, means. This was a lesson that was to be taught to the British Signal Service, also, in the critical years 1914 and 1915. It should not, however, be held to detract from the value of a good field telephone system which, in the Japanese Army, was normally the safe basis of a signal system which was unusually efficient for its day.

TABLE I.

| Army Formation. | 1904 Signal Units.* | 1907 Signal Units.† | 1911 Signal Units.‡ |
|---|---|---|---|
| (a) Lines of Communication | | 2 Telegraph Companies | Signal Company (L. of C.) |
| (b) Advanced Base to Army H.Q. | Three Telegraph Divisions | 2 Airline Telegraph Companies | Signal Company (Airline) |
| (c) Army Headquarters ... | Three Lines of Communication Telegraphs | 2 Cable Telegraph Companies | Signal Company (Cable) |
| (d) Divisional Headquarters | | 6 Divisional Telegraph Companies | Signal Company with each Division |
| (e) Cavalry Division ... ... | Three Cable Sections (as part of Field Troops) | Three Cable Sections (as part of Field Troops) | Signal Squadron |
| (f) Army Headquarters to Cavalry Headquarters | | 2 Wireless Telegraph Companies | Signal Company, Wireless. |

* In addition three Volunteer Telegraph Sections and a "Nucleus" to remain at home for P.O. requirements.
† In addition a small establishment of signallers sufficient to man one visual station at each headquarters.
‡ Contain a proportion of Visual Signallers, Motor Cyclists and Orderlies, in addition to telegraph and telephone personnel.

from the successful outcome of similar battles waged by their predecessors in the past.

By the end of 1910, the buzzer telephone had, however, fairly won its place as a recognized part of the signal equipment of all linemen in rear of Divisional Headquarters. By 1914 it was firmly established as an essential portion of the equipment of all pack cable detachments : further forward it was not to penetrate until position warfare set in.

There was, however, one more direction in which a revolution in signal practice was foreshadowed. The development of wireless telegraphy had appealed to the imagination of the more enthusiastic army Signal officers and as early as 1903* a small experimental staff had commenced work at Aldershot on the development of this branch of signalling along lines suitable for army work. In 1905, wireless telegraphy was accepted definitely as a distinct part of the army signal organization and the first Wireless Section was formed. By August, 1914, however, this science had not proved its value as applied under the restrictions inseparable from army work. Its use was, therefore, confined to certain definite functions particularly concerned with the operations of independent cavalry. It was looked upon with suspicion and dislike by the General Staff as a whole.

This attitude was justified to a certain extent, wireless in its then state of development having two main drawbacks which reduced its value for army purposes. The primitive types of portable army stations were unreliable. The fact that the enemy could overhear every word or group sent made it necessary to use code or cipher for any messages of importance. These objections to the use of wireless telegraphy have, indeed, militated against its effectiveness throughout the war, though special methods of employment which were never contemplated in these early days have been found for it.

Of the two methods of flag signalling—semaphore and Morse—the latter was the favourite of the signal officer himself. It was foreseen that future technical signal developments would inevitably involve the use of the Morse alphabet, the latter being applicable to almost any type of instrument which could be devised. The other arms of the service, however, and particularly the artillery, preferred the quicker semaphore method, ignoring or overlooking the fatal fact that this means of signalling could only be made use of for visual work and involved a considerable measure of exposure to hostile fire and observation. This divergence of opinion was the cause of much trouble during the earlier months of the War before the universality of the Morse alphabet carried the day and semaphore signalling was relegated to a less important place in the Training Manual and in army signalling generally.

* Wireless was also tried in South Africa in 1899.

The experience on which the British Army Signal Service had been formulated and built up, had all tended to emphasize the importance of mobility. In the last fifty years—since the Crimean War in fact—the British Army as a whole had not been engaged in any prolonged and great sieges. The lessons of the Russo-Japanese War, when for the first time nation-sized armies confronted each other for weeks and months across intricate systems of trenches, had not been sufficiently driven home to Western European nations. The possibility that the war for which our little Expeditionary Force was intended might resolve itself into a protracted struggle between two nearly equal forces snugly ensconced behind earthworks or burrowing in trenches, saps, or dugouts, was not visualized either by our own Staff or by those of other European nations. Many considerations pointed towards the likelihood of the next European War being a short sharp campaign where the army most mobile, and therefore most ready to take advantage of the opportunities presented by a rapidly changing situation, would win. Financial experts believed that a European War could not last many months without universal bankruptcy; statesmen believed that the Balance of Power could not be accurate enough to produce a deadlock for any long period of time; generals knew that—to be decisive—war must be a war of movement.

It was this last consideration that carried most weight, and justly so as events have since proved. The immediate effect of cutting down equipment to obtain mobility at all costs was, however, to be seen in the second year of the War. The rapidly increasing demands from all branches of the army for more and better intercommunication to cope with the fast-crystallizing state of stationary warfare, then almost snowed under the service which was called upon to meet them with utterly inadequate resources.

If there was a period of the War when the Signal Service in France was within measurable distance of becoming inefficient, it was in late 1915 and early 1916, before the first reorganizations relieved the situation. That this position did arise was not the fault of the personnel of the Service but was unavoidable in view of the change in the functions which it was expected to fulfil.

Before the War, the Signal Service was designed to be the servant of the General Staff only. Its work (which lay practically entirely between G.H.Q. and battalion headquarters) was to ensure that a message written by the Staff was safely and rapidly delivered to the addressee. Long before the termination of the position warfare period this delimitation of responsibility no longer held good. To take a single instance of the growth of Signal Service activity, it may be mentioned that previous to the War, artillery communication, which was so soon to become a very major portion of the duty of the Army Signal Service, was outside the sphere of its activities.

Such primitive form of *liaison* between artillery and infantry as existed in those days was the responsibility of the artillery themselves, while communication within artillery units was also carried out by signallers provided, trained, and controlled by that arm.

The strength of the Signal Service proper on August 4th, 1914, is shown in the following two tables. Table IIA. shows the units which proceeded to France with the original Expeditionary Force, and Table IIB. the partially trained signal units of the Territorial Force.

TABLE IIA.

*Regular Signal Service Units, August, 1914.*

| Name of Unit. | Establishment. | | No. of units in E.F. | Total nos. personnel. | |
|---|---|---|---|---|---|
| | Offr's. | Men. | | Offr's. | Men. |
| " L " Signal Company | 5 | 263 | 1 | 5 | 263 |
| G.H.Q. Signal Coy. | 5 | 75 | 1 | 5 | 75 |
| Army Corps H.Q. Sig. Coy. | 4 | 63 | 2 | 8 | 126 |
| Divl. Signal Coy. | 5 | 157 | 6 | 30 | 942 |
| Cable Section | 1 | 35 | 8 | 8 | 280 |
| Airline Section | 1 | 57 | 5 | 5 | 285 |
| Cavalry Sig. Squadron | 8 | 198 | 1 | 8 | 198 |
| Sig. Troop with Cavalry Bde. | 1 | 23 | 3 | 3 | 69 |
| Sig. Trp. with Independent Cav. Bde. | 1 | 42 | 1 | 1 | 42 |
| Wireless Section (incl. Motor W/T Det.) | 2 | 66 | 1 | 2 | 66 |

August 4th, 1914.     Grand Total A.S.S. with E.F. ... ... 75 2346

TABLE IIB.

*Territorial Signal Service Units, August, 1914.*

| Name of Unit. | Establishment. | | No. of units in U.K. | Total. | |
|---|---|---|---|---|---|
| | Off'rs. | Men. | | Off'rs. | Men. |
| Divl. Telegraph Coy. | 2 | 57 | 14 | 28 | 798 |
| Army W/T Telegraph Coy. | 3 | 66 | 5 | 15 | 330 |
| Army Cable Telegraph Coy. | 6 | 159 | 5 | 30 | 795 |
| Army Airline Telegraph Coy. | 6 | 194 | 5 | 30 | 970 |

August 4th, 1914.     Grand Total A.S.S. with T.F. in U.K. 103 2893

N.B.—In addition to the above should be considered the Indian Telegraph units of the Indian Army and the Divisional Signal Company of the 7th Division which was then concentrating before completing its training with the Division.

In addition to the units shown in these tables, the signal companies of the University Officers' Training Corps (where such existed) might be considered as a source of reinforcements, particularly of motor cyclist despatch riders and of men likely to be suitable for training as junior commissioned officers. These latter, with such officers and men as could be spared from the engineering and telegraph departments of the General Post Office, might be looked to to relieve the situation in the future.

With the exception of the despatch riders, however, who required little further training, and who were in any case so urgently required that refinements of training had to be dispensed with, these reinforcements could not be considered as immediately available. Technical engineers who were admirably qualified to build telegraph routes and oversee telephone and telegraph offices, required training in military discipline and army methods of procedure. The partially trained cadets of the Officers' Training Corps, on the other hand, required in many cases further technical experience. In almost all cases, a further insight into army organization and a final polishing up in drill was necessary before such men could be considered fit to take command of regular sections or detachments.

Thus, on the landing of the Expeditionary Force in France and its advance until it obtained touch with the German armies at Condé, Mons, and Binche, the signal requirements of the Force had to be met by 72 officers and approximately 2,200 men. It is true that this personnel was exceptionally well-trained and efficient. The total, however, compared very unfavourably indeed with that of the signal units which would have been allotted in 1917 or 1918 to an Army of two Army Corps each containing three Divisions. (See Appendix IV.).

As can be seen from a study of the units in Table IIA and from the 1914 column of the Table of Comparative Establishments in Appendix II, the Expeditionary Force was served by "L" Signal Company, one G.H.Q. Signal Company, two Army Corps H.Q. Signal Companies, and six Divisional Signal Companies—that is, one signal unit for each formation of the Force. In addition, a Signal Squadron, and a Signal Troop served the Cavalry Division and an independent Cavalry Brigade. Wireless was represented by "Q" Wireless Section, consisting of three wagon and one motor wireless detachment, which was attached to G.H.Q. Signals.

These units were responsible for the intercommunication, not only from the Base on the coast of France to Battalion Headquarters, but, actually, owing to causes which will be mentioned later, the Divisional Signal Companies were soon obliged to exercise close supervision over, and, indeed, in many cases, to carry out line communication right up to the front line posts and trenches. This was an extension of their work which was never intended when they were formed and to cope with which their establishment was not suitable either as regards numbers or equipment.

Two important characteristics were common to the whole of the above units. These were the complete reliance on the telegraph and message work for all purposes, and the looseness of the organization. Each unit was self-contained, and its senior officer was of similar rank and equal standing with those of the units which succeeded it both up and down the chain of communication. The result of the latter feature of the organization was that, although all units worked loyally together, there was within the Signal Service itself nothing even remotely resembling the chain of command which is so necessary to the smooth working of the military machine.

At G.H.Q. was a senior Signal Service officer, the Director of Army Signals of the Expeditionary Force, who exercised technical control over the whole of the units under his supervision. It was, however, impossible for the latter, with the very small staff he possessed in 1914, to keep in personal touch with the signal units of so many diverse formations. In practice, therefore, commanders of signal units were responsible only to the General Staff of their formation for the technical working and efficiency of their units.

In dealing with intercommunication problems, affecting as they necessarily do not only the formation in question but those immediately superior and subordinate, the lack of technical control step by step up the chain of command was naturally very severely felt. A considerable portion of the administrative reform of the first two years of the War was directed towards putting this matter on a more satisfactory footing.

It is a little difficult to understand how, in view of the high degree of technical efficiency to which the civil telephone of the country, and indeed of civilized nations generally, had been brought, the telephone had been so completely subordinated in the scheme of signals evolved for the British Army. In this respect both our French allies and our German foes were far in front of us at the outbreak of war. The magneto telephone had already obtained an important position in their intercommunication services, although these were in many other respects far behind our own in efficiency.

Here, again, it seems probable that considerations of mobility had been allowed to overrule all other ideas of greater convenience and of the value of personal interchange of ideas between Staff officers of different formations. Be this as it may, certainly the outbreak of war found the British Army relying almost entirely on the telegraph for the transmission of orders, reports, and urgent information throughout the higher formations. It is true that forward signals relied to a certain extent upon a portable type of telephone,* but the

---

* The unpopularity of these instruments may have been due to the undoubted fact that in the case of the two earlier types efficiency had to a great extent been sacrificed to portability. Neither the D, mark I, nor the D, mark II, telephone was a satisfactory instrument to use, the latter especially, which had been issued in large numbers just previous to the outbreak of war, being particularly unpopular. This was largely due to the fact that both hands were occupied in using it, the one in holding the receiver to the ear and the other in the act of pressing down

instrument was not popular with the Staff, who preferred to do without conversation altogether, or, in the event of a personal explanation being considered necessary, to carry it out through the operators in the Signal Offices.

August, 1914, thus found the telegraph (Wheatstone and Duplex on the lines of communication, Simplex forward of G.H.Q., and Vibrator in divisions and brigades) in general use for all urgent messages. To deal with less urgent despatches, motor cyclists, mounted orderlies, and cyclists were used as occasion demanded, while packets and letters for the administrative services, together with the private correspondence of the troops, were dealt with by the Postal Section of the Royal Engineers whose activities were outside the sphere of the Signal Service. The not unnatural inability of this branch fully to live up to its responsibilities in this respect was later responsible for the commencement of the regular D.R.L.S.*

In addition to the above-mentioned methods of despatch which were relied upon to deal with all normal communications in the higher formations, other means of signalling over short distances and in face of the enemy were provided.

These first assumed prominence in the Divisional Signal Company where—although no men were available specifically for this purpose—certain of the mounted and cyclist orderlies were trained in visual signalling. A small amount of visual signalling apparatus—heliograph, night lamps, and flags—was also provided in the company mobilization store table. As the formation became of less size, and distances decreased, while proximity to the enemy increased, visual signalling assumed greater and greater prominence. Brigade signal sections were issued with pack cable-laying apparatus and a light cable of comparatively poor insulation. Each section had as part of its composition a telephone detachment which was responsible for laying lines to Battalion Headquarters on the occasions when it was considered necessary to link these up with the headquarters of the brigade. Here, however, the visual training of the men was of greater importance, and considerably more stress was laid upon visual work, the whole personnel of efficient brigade sections being exercised in this method of signalling.

In the battalion, which did not lie within the jurisdiction of the Signal Service, the battalion signallers under the control of the

the button which corresponded in this type to the more convenient pressel switch of the D, mark III, and the later types of hand telephones. Had the last mentioned type been in general use before the outbreak of war there is little doubt that its efficiency and comfort would have greatly enhanced the popularity of the telephone, and from the good buzzer telephone to the better magneto telephone is—as was proved by subsequent developments—a very short step indeed.

* Despatch Rider Letter Service.

signalling sergeant and under the nominal supervision of the adjutant, were expected to be efficient in visual alone. In certain battalions —whose officers later reaped the reward of their enterprise—the commanding officer had equipped his signalling section with cable and telephones at his own expense. This was, however, exceptional. In some such cases, a still further keenness for the maintenance of efficient intercommunication and a realization of its importance, had led to the unofficial retention of a signalling officer although such a post had been officially abolished. Such a sacrifice—for it was a very real sacrifice when the tendency was to withdraw more and more officers for courses as specialists and thus to limit severely the number available for regimental duty—was offset by the possession of an unusually efficient signalling section with a smoothly working regimental organization as a natural consequence. Alike in peace manœuvres and in war, the battalion with the well-trained and efficiently supervised signallers scored heavily over its less enterprising rivals. The money and care expended was, however, only destined to be repaid in full when, in the autumn of 1914, the deadlock between the rival armies became accentuated and the deadly monotony of trench warfare settled down across the north of France. Fortunate, indeed, then, was the commanding officer who had husbanded his signallers; doubly fortunate was he who had been far-sighted enough to retain his battalion signalling officer and so ensure the maximum of efficiency in what was to become a more and more vital specialist section of his battalion.

The signal units had been calculated, in common with the other branches of the British Army, on the absolute minimum with which it was possible to carry out the least amount of work compatible with efficiency. It was, therefore, to be hoped at least that these units would be complete, and, on mobilization being ordered, could be filled up at once with fully trained men. Owing, however, to a lack of trained signallers in the reserve—the result possibly of miscalculation of the number required, possibly of unexpected casualties —it proved extremely difficult to complete various units to their war strength with fully trained men of the requisite army trades. This was particularly felt in divisions where battalion commanders, themselves harassed with similar shortages, felt unable to spare to the Divisional Signal Company the battalion signallers destined by Army Order to help towards the complement of the brigade sections.

In some cases, the vacancies had to be filled with partially trained pioneers, in others with men who were beneath the age limit of twenty years. The latter alternative was preferred since it did not affect the technical efficiency of the company to any great extent, and in view of the European climate was not likely to cause trouble to the men themselves.

A more serious shortage still was that of motor cyclists. To ensure good service in this important branch during mobile warfare, men of exceptional intelligence, endurance and courage, and, especially, men possessing initiative of a high order, were required. In the event, there proved to be a sufficiency of such men in the country and, as casualties occurred, little difficulty was found in filling up vacancies with good men. In the early days, however, when all was hurry and every department was working overtime on unfamiliar problems, the shortage could not be made good at once. Although the University Officers' Training Corps came to the rescue with a particularly good type of men for the purpose, the mobilization and equipment of civilians took time. Many units suffered from the fact that the majority of their despatch riders were late in reporting, while some formations even departed overseas with a deficiency.

# CHAPTER II.

On August 20th, 1914, the landing and concentration of the Expeditionary Force being completed, the march northward was commenced under peace time conditions. Such communication as was required was carried out by motor cyclist despatch rider by day and telegraph by night. On the 22nd, the Force deployed along the line of the canal from Condé, through Mons, to Binche ; touch was obtained with the enemy, and a British force went into action on a large scale for the first time since the South African War. Ample time was available for the creation of a good system of signal communications. and the task of the forward sections in particular was lightened by the fact that the Army was operating in country which was the centre of a large French mining and manufacturing district. The gently undulating landscape was covered with small mining villages grouped round towns of larger size and greater importance. The whole district was connected up by a very efficient and complete telegraph and telephone system which was a great help to the brigade sections.

Thus, at the outset of the campaign, we have an intercommunication system where, through favourable circumstances, the forward circuits were more numerous than was again achieved until much later in the war.

Behind the divisions, also, permanent lines were used to a certain extent, though the advisability of making the fullest use of these was not at once realized by the higher formations, One reason for this was that the latter had the means of laying lines of their own which would be under their own personal control and would not give rise to the same necessity for *liaison* with the local authorities. A more weighty reason, perhaps, was the unwillingness of the French authorities to hand over the lines required and thus jeopardize their own traffic.

C

As will be seen from the diagram of corps communications for this battle (*Plate* I.), cable was used to a great extent. The consequence was that when the enemy broke through the British line and orders to retreat were received, it proved impossible to recover the greater portion of this cable and it had to be abandoned.

The presence of a good line system in this position was all the greater boon because of the enclosed nature of the country. Visual, except over very small distances, was impossible. Lamps and flags were both used by battalions to a small extent, but the major formations relied entirely upon the telegraph system which served satisfactorily through the action. Care was taken to cut all permanent lines running towards the enemy, the usual procedure being to destroy one complete bay in front of battalion headquarters.

In the retreat to Le Cateau which followed, the retirement was so hurried and units were so harassed by the attentions of the enemy's cavalry and artillery, that no attempt at line communication was of much avail. Already much cable had been lost at the Mons position, for, though the civilian exchanges and telephone systems which had given so much help to the Signal Service in that battle had been thoroughly destroyed, time to reel up the cable lines could not be spared. During the night succeeding the first day's retirement some sections did connect up their formation headquarters, but these lines also had to be abandoned the following morning, and the spectre of shortage of cable which was to haunt signal officers for several years was already beginning to appear.

No immediate supplies were to be expected from the Base, and, indeed, until conditions settled down, there would be no leisure to permit signal units to think of the replenishment of stores. It was quite clear that greater use must be made of the permanent system of the country. With this in mind, the Director of Signals and his staff at G.H.Q. were already improving the system of *liaison* with the French telegraph authorities. Arrangements were made to take over considerable responsibilities as regards the French telegraph system in the zone in which operations were being carried on by the British Army.

It was evident that the mainstay of the intercommunication system in a rapid retreat must be the despatch rider and the orderly, assisted to a small extent only by the occasional use of permanent lines which were connected to headquarters by short spurs of cable laid by the cable detachments in anticipation of particular spots being selected as command posts or billets.

On August 25th, the British Army turned to bay before the pursuing German Army Corps. A hotly contested battle fought on the Le Cateau line held the enemy up long enough to allow of the evacuation of the civil population in the threatened area. Le Cateau was more of an impromptu action than Mons and much less time was available for the preparation of an elaborate system of communication. General Headquarters and Corps Headquarters, retiring along railways and main roads, were comparatively easily accommodated with lines along the permanent routes, but news of the forthcoming stand was only received in the divisions late in the evening before the battle.

Fought in an agricultural district, there was no friendly system of telegraph lines with sufficient ramifications to enable it to be made use of for formations lower than divisions. Once more units were compelled to utilize their already diminishing stocks of cable. Time was of the utmost importance and immediately orders were received, cable detachments limbered up and, forgetting their natural fatigue after the previous day's gruelling work and marches, laid cable at the canter across country until all brigades had been linked up with divisions by line.

The importance of subordinate formations informing the superior under whom they are working of their exact location was here emphasized by the loss of a complete cable deatchment which was ambushed by the Germans and captured while proceeding to Le Cateau to lay a line to a brigade which was to act during the forthcoming action under the orders of its division. Thus, the first serious casualty to the Signal Service in the War was an avoidable one, the result of an absence of exact information which was often destined to give trouble during the early years of the campaign.

Intercommunication cannot be secured under moving warfare conditions unless signal commanders of each formation realize that it is a paramount duty to keep the signals of the formation under which their own is working constantly and accurately informed of their position and when possible of their immediate future movements. If this is not done orders and messages go astray ; personnel is exposed to unnecessary risk ; and often at critical moments of an action the best-laid plans may fail through failure to utilize reserves to the best advantage or to give needed assistance to troops in action. Such was the first great lesson of the War to the Signal Service. To keep touch, assistance must come from the lower formation as well as from the higher. It is not always possible to carry out orders as to future movements to the letter, but when instructions are not rigidly obeyed, it is essential that early information should reach the signal commander of the next higher formation whose duty it is to link up his own staff with subordinate headquarters.

Forward of Brigades at the Le Cateau battle, visual was used to a greater extent than at Mons.

Light cable* was laid out to battalion headquarters and buzzer

* "D1" cable.

communication was universal between brigade and battalion when the battle opened. Now, however, for the first time, the power and weight of modern artillery was felt with disastrous effect on the forward lines. The Germans had collected a considerable concentration of field guns and heavy howitzers, and, soon after the opening of the battle, lines from brigades to battalions were cut right and left. Although linemen exposed themselves fearlessly in the endeavour to keep the cables through, it was evident that more reliance would have to be placed on other means of sending messages.

The chief objection to visual signalling had always been the necessity for at least partial exposure on the part of the signaller in an advanced position, but men had been trained to make the most of the natural shelter available in the country. The Le Cateau district, consisting as it does of fine rolling downs, was ideal for visual purposes and extremely good work was done by the signallers during the critical and closing stages of the battle.

By the use of a blue flag, with the signaller in a ditch against a dark background, a station in a very exposed position in one battalion was kept in action throughout the fighting without being discovered by the enemy, although the latter came within 1,200 yards of the position. Signals were easily read by the aid of a telescope at the Brigade Headquarters 800 yards off. This case was typical of the initiative shown and by the use of such precautions visual proved adequate in many cases to deal with all messages of tactical importance. Where visual was impossible or circumstances were more favourable to the employment of orderlies,* these were used with success. The drawback, however, to this, the most reliable of forward methods of intercommunication, was, as it always has been, that it is unduly expensive both in personnel used and in casualties.

At the battle of Le Cateau the German advance was slowed down considerably and heavy losses were inflicted. After fighting had continued throughout the 25th and 26th, however, further reinforcements came to the assistance of the enemy forces and the British retreat was resumed. The fresh withdrawal continued without interruption until the whole of the French and British armies delivered the blow from behind the Marne which was destined to turn the triumphant advance of the Germans into a stubborn but decided retreat.

During this second very rapid phase of the retreat, communication did not radically alter in character; the same problems arose and were met in much the same way, though familiarity with service conditions was already beginning to exercise a beneficial effect on

* In one case, a covered way of approach existed between a brigade and a battalion headquarters and gave such good shelter to runners that this means of conveying messages was used almost to the exclusion of all others.

signal organization. On the one hand, the improved *liaison* with the French telegraph authorities enabled the higher formations to make more use of circuits on the permanent routes, as more diagrams were available. These circuits were examined beforehand by the personnel of the airline and cable sections and suitable lines on the routes which the retreating army was ordered to follow were " proved " and connected up by short lengths of cable to the châteaux, farms, and houses which were selected for occupation by the staff. When halts were made in towns, further refinements were possible. In such cases, the use of civil exchanges and local telephones much decreased the labours of the signal unit which was fortunate enough to have its staff located in a favourable situation for making the most extensive use of the already existing facilities.* In this respect the army was in a situation which was destined not to repeat itself during the whole of the war—a retreat over undamaged country occupied by a friendly population. In 1918 similar, though not quite so extensive, retreats took place, but the increased range of guns and the development of the bombing plane had considerably damaged the communication system as far behind our original lines as the retiring troops were forced.

In the rearguard, the divisions and brigades were subjected to pressure from the enemy which, though not nearly so great as in the earlier short retreat to Le Cateau, prevented very great use of telegraphy in any form. Many units made attempts to anticipate the movements of their headquarters and to drop offices at spots to which the staff had announced their intention of going. Movements were so uncertain, however, that this procedure was attended by very real risk of loss of personnel and instruments that could ill be spared. The chances of hitting off the future movements of the Headquarters Staffs proved to be so small that it was soon decided that the risk far outweighed any advantages that were gained. Resigning themselves to less rapid forms of intercommunication, the latter were well, and, under the circumstances, expeditiously served by efficient motor cycle despatch riders.

During the day, the cable wagons of the divisional signal companies were sent ahead of the division in order to leave a clear road free for the retreating fighting troops. At night, on some occasions, permanent line circuits with short cable spurs were used as in the Corps and at G.H.Q., but units reached their destinations so late, and had in many cases to leave so early, that it was not worth while to make the practice general. As a general rule, reliance was placed entirely on despatch riders for keeping touch between division and brigade. These men were, of course, reserved for messages affecting

* In 1914 the Staff did not always realise the advantage of selecting their H.Q. billets to suit signal requirements. As will be seen later, this lesson was thoroughly learnt during the next two years.

operations, and the equally urgent questions of the supply of ammunition and rations. Less important despatches had to be held over until the situation stabilized.

Even when the permanent line circuits were in use, implicit reliance was not placed upon them. Cases of malicious cutting of the wires occurred on several occasions and important messages were usually duplicated by despatch rider in order to make certain of their delivery.

The triumph of the despatch rider in the retreat and in the advance that followed was the triumph of the human element in Signals. The majority of the motor cyclists had been specially recruited from the University Officers' Training Corps at the outbreak of war. The men had attended the army manœuvres from 1911 onwards and had there formed a large proportion of the motor cyclists available. Here they had learnt to serve the needs of the staff efficiently and mutual confidence had been established between officers and men. A University education and practical work in the field had taught men of naturally high intellectual standard how to use their brains to the best advantage in the particular work on hand.

It would have been difficult to obtain better personnel for the changing conditions forced upon them by the necessity for locating formation and unit headquarters of a rapidly retreating or advancing force, pursued or faced by a highly-trained enemy, and with a fluctuating area of conflict in which contact with the enemy's scouts or patrols was frequent. Such men, also, were more likely than most to possess the linguistic attainments which would permit them to obtain the maximum advantage from free intercourse with the people of the country in which the campaign was being waged, and with the staffs and commanders of the forces of our Allies. A talent for thinking for themselves also enabled them to be of much value in conveying information apart from the despatches they were carrying. No one is in a better position to pick up odd scraps of information about the position of our own and the enemy's forces than the despatch rider who keeps his wits about him. In this way, alone, the use of highly-trained and intellectual men for this purpose was justified, while the insight obtained by them into the conditions of war service and the composition and organization of an army, rendered them eminently fit to join the commissioned ranks of the " New Armies " at a later date.

Riding at all hours and in all weathers ; sleeping when and where they could, at most but a few short hours between swiftly recurring tours of duty ; struggling with imperfectly equipped and unsuitable machines over roads composed of jolting and slippery pavé, or already worn in deep ruts by the passage of the armies ; the motor cyclists of all units surpassed themselves. With imperfect maps and indifferent information as to the positions of billets and staff offices, many journeys would have proved fruitless but for the possession by the particular rider concerned of more than an ordinary share of common sense. They were exposed to all the ordinary perils of the road accentuated by an unorganized traffic compounded of the transport and marching columns of the army and the medley of vehicles of every conceivable description which is an invariable accompaniment of the exodus of a fleeing population. Their work demanded as unfailing a nerve and as staunch a courage as was ever required by any branch of the service in any war. Well did the men as a body rise to the occasion. Personal encounters with the pursuing or retiring enemy were not rare. Every day cases were recorded where motor cyclists failed to return to their units. In some cases the disappearance was more than temporary. The next news of the missing man might then be the information from German sources that he had been taken prisoner, or, possibly, the sight of a cross glimpsed by the victorious troops as they surged back across the Marne driving the retreating Germans before them.

On other occasions, the men, more fortunate, returned after an absence of a few hours only, sometimes with a tale of having overshot the headquarters of the rear or advanced guard unit they had been sent to find and of a brush with Uhlans which had ended in a fortunate escape thanks to a cycle on which an almost affectionate care had been bestowed.

A combination between man and machine such as the despatch rider and his motor cycle, is a delicate mechanism needing peculiar qualities for success when tried to the limit of its powers as on these occasions. The men who came through unscathed and with the plaudits of their officers and of the staff, were those who gave as much care to their machines as to themselves. Without constant and unremitting care no motor cycle of any make whatever could be expected to stand up under the conditions in which these were tested in the autumn of 1914. These days, also, were before the time when repeated test had enabled standardization of motor cycles to be carried out. Cycles of all makes and in all stages of efficiency were included in the motley assemblage which did such yeoman service. All the more honour to the men who rode them, tended them, and coaxed them, through conditions which no reliability trial ever run has equalled.*

* It should not be imagined from the foregoing paragraph that the motor cycles of the British despatch riders were of poor quality. This was not the case. Thanks to the excellent standards maintained by the British motor trade, the machines available were far in advance both of those of our Allies and of the enemy. This was not the case in many other classes of signalling equipment. The absence of standardization and the fact that many of the machines were far from new, did, however, cause much trouble in these early days of the war, as also did the lack of spare parts for such a motley collection of machines.

As the army settled down to its work and the retreat became more of a routine, it followed that the organization of the vital signal communications would improve and take on a more definite aspect. No despatch rider letter service had yet been evolved. This was reserved for later days when the general situation was more stable. Improvements, however, did take place, and of these the most important was the allotment of certain despatch riders to different portions of the formation. This made possible a more rapid and efficient interchange of messages than had before been achieved. Thus, towards the end of the retreat, the normal routine in some divisions was for two despatch riders to be attached to the flank guard, two to the advanced guard, or rearguard as the case might be, and two to the billeting officers. In other divisions, a routine had been evolved which closely approximated to that ultimately adopted throughout the Army, and two despatch riders were already permanently assigned to each brigade. Small changes all of them, but all tending to promote the smooth running of the signal service and therefore worthy of notice in any record of the evolution of signals under modern war conditions.

From the first, it was obvious that the establishment of motor cyclists was barely sufficient for the conditions of mobile warfare. As casualties to men and machines occurred, some divisions were reduced to as few as six or seven motor cyclists, and the work suffered accordingly. Resort had to be had in such cases to cycle, horse, and foot orderlies. Indeed, in all divisions, these means of supplementing the motor cyclist service were freely used.

The four cyclist and eight mounted despatch riders carried on the signal establishment of each Divisional Headquarters* were also the only men trained in visual and this was from the first found to be a great source of trouble. Besides the actual delivery of messages to units, these men were in request as " checks " in the signal office. At the best of times the proportion able to be spared for the divisional visual stations was insufficient. The inadequacy of the establishment was of course much more evident when the men were also required to assist in the delivery of messages to the brigades or to the lateral divisions.

It was perhaps fortunate for the Divisional Signal Company Commander that the headquarters of formations and units were usually selected in low-lying villages or in house-ridden country—spots clearly unsuited to visual signalling. Under such circumstances it was obvious to the staff that for technical reasons it was not possible to establish visual touch. If this had not been so, the problems of the signal officer would have been increased. He must have chosen between a good despatch rider service, and an inferior

* 1915 column. Appendix I.

one reinforced by an equally inadequate visual system ; a division of forces which could hardly have failed to promote inefficiency.

To add to his troubles, horses began to fail from overwork, and government cycles, difficult enough to keep going on the well-made and carefully-tended roads of England, fell to pieces in large numbers under their present rough usage. There was no means of repair at hand. The choice of the officer responsible lay between the possible requisitioning of civilian cycles—most of which had already been removed by their owners—and the slower method of making use of his men as foot orderlies. As time went on, casualties to despatch riders increased and forced a return to the use of the telegraph whenever this was in any way practicable, even for a few hours.

During the day time, on the march, despatch riding alone was possible, but at night circumstances sometimes permitted the use of the permanent routes. In these cases some provision had to be made for the delivery of messages to units in the neighbourhood of each signal office. The signal company could not provide sufficient personnel to carry out this distribution, but in the brigades, where the problem was most urgent, it was solved by instructing each infantry battalion and each battery affiliated to the brigade, to send in two orderlies to Brigade Headquarters each evening. The first duty of these men after their unit had halted for the night was to find the headquarters of the brigade. One then returned to his battalion or battery and the other remained at Brigade Headquarters. When the first batch of messages was sent off to any unit, two brigade despatch riders accompanied the battalion or battery orderly to learn the route, after which a regular system of reliefs could be instituted and every one concerned was able to obtain some rest during the night.

In such ways, organization progressed even in the hurry and turmoil of the retreat ; the demands of the Staff for rapid and reliable communication were met to the greatest possible .extent ; and the improvement in organization went hand in hand with individual increase in efficiency as signallers of every trade settled down to war conditions.

The inevitable fatigue of long-continued and severe exertion was also minimized as routine improved and reliefs were arranged. In the early days, however, shifts of 12 to 16 and even more hours were worked by headquarter operators. Only exceptional devotion to duty enabled work to be efficiently performed during these long periods when every nerve was on the strain and the men on duty could not be changed until fresh operators arrived from some office which had been closed down or from a short spell of well-earned rest.

Nor was the work lessened by the occasional necessary establishment of fighting command posts and report centres. At G.H.Q., especially, the headquarters personnel was taxed to the utmost to keep Rear and Advanced offices in action at the same time. The G.H.Q. signal company was little larger than that of an Army Corps, while a considerably greater volume of work had to be dealt with, since all administrative work of both Corps passed through this one central office. At a later date reorganization relieved the G.H.Q. office of much of the routine work of supply, but this stage had not yet been reached. The volume of traffic in all offices steadily increased as time went on, for the General Staff came to rely more and more on the telegraphed word in preference to verbal instructions. On the 4th of September, the day of the conclusion of the retreat, Advanced G.H.Q. dealt with 230 " A " and " B " forms in one day. This was a total which looks ridiculously small compared even with the work of a Division towards the end of the war. It was, however, a great increase upon the figures of a week earlier and was much more than was expected when the establishment of the company was drawn up. The resources of the signal units generally were severely taxed to keep two offices in full working order. The fact that a considerable measure of efficiency was obtained is the best witness to the quality of both officers and men.

On September 5th the British Army rested in its final positions on a line ten miles south of the Marne. Here a day's well-earned rest was given to the troops before they turned together with their French allies to fight the battle of the Marne which stemmed the tide of invasion and hurled the invader back to the positions on the Aisne from which the utmost efforts failed to drive him for so many months.

Some of the lessons of the retreat as far as signals were concerned have already been referred to in the narrative just completed. Paramount over all had proved to be the necessity for early information of movements and positions. In addition certain features of the training of signal personnel were noted for improvement or for radical change. In particular it was clear that in all mobile warfare a knowledge of map reading and compass work was essential for all ranks of the Signal Service who might be called upon to do duty as despatch carriers. The need for permanent linemen in airline sections had been demonstrated ; the advance was to show that men of like trade were necessary as an essential part of cable sections, also. In later days, when a state of more stationary warfare had set in and revision of establishments became possible, this was reflected both in the addition of permanent linemen to the establishment of the airline sections and in the more general training of signal personnel in permanent line work.

The fuller use of the French telephone system was another lesson learnt by hard experience and from the loss of valuable and at the time irreplaceable cable. As a corollary to the use of the civilian

system, the need for better *liaison* with the French telegraph authorities was brought home. Much trouble would also have been avoided
if good telegraph maps of the country had been available.*

In the future it should be the duty of some signal officer in time of
peace to keep constantly up to date a collection of route maps and
diagrams of the intercommunication system of all countries over
which campaigning may possibly take place. Many of the local
linemen and minor officials were found to have a lamentable ignorance
of the lines not immediately under their control. The higher officers
were not always immediately available and much valuable time
was sometimes lost from the lack of an independent source of information. Finally, as had been expected, it proved impossible with
present establishments and equipment, even with the help of a
friendly permanent line system, to keep good intercommunication
by telegraph within a division during accelerated retreat. The
best results were undoubtedly obtained by the fullest use and most
efficient organization of despatch riders of every description. Visual
was impossible owing to lack of personnel. Even had sufficient
men been available, the staff would have had to change their tactics
and select more suitable sites for their headquarters if this method
of signalling was to be used to any great extent.

Such were the lessons of the great retreat. Once learnt, they
were well-learnt, and errors were seldom repeated. It was, however,
the irony of war that situations also were seldom reproduced. Always
some changing factor entered into the question and required minute
adjustments in policy, organization, or equipment ; the whole
resulting in an evolution which has brought the intercommunication
service to what—in this, the year 1920—it has become.

---

At the close of the retreat to the Marne, a momentary pause in
operations permitted of the replenishment of the stores and cable of
Corps and Divisional signal companies. Although it was not possible
entirely to replace the wastages caused by destruction or abandonment to the enemy, a considerable proportion of the deficiency was
made up and the advance started under fairly favourable conditions.
The Germans, as they retreated, destroyed behind them the permanent
system which had been of so much value during the British retirement, but, in their turn, their retreat was so hastened by our cavalry
and our advanced guards that the work of destruction was far from
thorough.

A policy of exploiting these lines to the greatest possible extent
had been worked out in the last few days and was now put into
practice. A cable detachment accompanied each of the leading

* Good telegraph maps of Belgium were available, but no one had
foreseen the possibility of operations in the neighbourhood of Paris.

Divisions, putting through the wires whenever possible. Where damage was too thorough for this to be done in reasonable time, ground cable was laid or cables were slung on the poles or neighbouring trees. Here, again, the principle of trial and error was in evidence and the valuable lesson was learnt, that, to put through a circuit on a partially destroyed route in the quickest possible time, the top pair should be chosen and its two lines bunched and used as a single conductor. Thus the possibility of other damaged wires falling across the line and causing earthing was avoided and the use of the pair instead of the single wire prevented .the wrong identification of portions of the circuit owing to the frequent crossing of the wires which is a feature of civil telephone construction.

An additional improvement in the organization for utilizing the permanent wires was the use of a motor cyclist officer or N.C.O. who preceded the headquarters with which the detachment was working spying out the routes and indicating the best way in which labour could be saved and a reliable circuit obtained in the shortest possible time. Here, the motor cyclist despatch rider with a small technical knowledge proved exceedingly useful and on this and other occasions during both retreat and advance the value of motor cyclist linemen with Divisional Headquarters and with cable sections was clearly seen. Where such men were not available, this work had frequently to be done by officers who could ill be spared from their sections, and at other times by despatch riders who were urgently required for their own more legitimate work.

Little difficulty was thus experienced by the division in keeping touch with its brigades. Similarly, divisions, corps and G.H.Q, were in uninterrupted communication by telegraph throughout the advance. One pair, previously used by each corps to one of its divisions which was advancing along the main route selected for the general advance, was strengthened by the corps airline section and in turn transferred to G.H.Q. signal maintenance as the corps moved forward. Subsequently, as the G.H.Q. airline sections got to work upon the route, the original single circuit was rebuilt and others added, the permanent line being repaired to a considerable extent and taps taken off to serve R.F.C. headquarters and for other special uses.

Communication with the independent cavalry had been a problem by itself during this extremely mobile warfare, and had been treated and solved along the lines laid down in the pre-war manuals. One motor wireless set and three wagon wireless sets had accompanied the Expeditionary Force to France, and these were intended, and were used, to keep communication between the independent cavalry and G.H.Q.

The history of army wireless telegraphy throughout the war is one of the greatest and most fascinating romances of the Signal

Service. A highly technical subject, " wireless " was looked upon by the General Staff—and, it must be confessed, by many of the officers of the Signal Service itself—with the gravest suspicion. From the tactical point of view its use was indeed open to serious objections. The ubiquitous nature of the signals sent out enabled an enemy equipped with suitable instruments to pick up every letter sent, and enforced the precaution of sending everything of importance in code or cipher. This, again, produced extra work and required a considerable amount of care and intelligence. Carelessly used codes and ciphers give away more than " in clear " messages. An officer of the most ordinary intelligence who has again and again been assured of the danger of the enemy overhearing wireless messages will be careful of what he says in clear English. On the other hand, he has been taught that cipher and code are safe and he uses them accordingly. If, then, any less careful person has given away the cipher or code by misuse, such as the sending of hybrid messages partly in English and partly in cipher, the damage is likely to be far-reaching.

In the early days of the use of wireless telegraphy in the field (in 1914 and 1915) the opponents of this method of signalling were much strengthened both in their dislikes and in their arguments by the almost incalculable harm that resulted from isolated cases of the misuse of wireless—in particular of the sending of important " operation " messages in clear. It was difficult to distinguish between the drawbacks inherent in the system itself and those much more serious failings due to incorrect and careless work. Wireless in consequence fell into disrepute for some months, its use being practically confined to the interception of enemy traffic.

Another serious obstacle to the use of this means of signalling in the early days of the war was the comparative unreliability of the sets in use. Portable army wireless was still in the experimental stage when the war broke out, and, though a fairly satisfactory type of set had been evolved, there were still certain practical difficulties which caused occasional breakdowns under service conditions. A force relying on wireless was likely to be operating—as were the cavalry—at some distance from the main body, and the failure of the sets meant the complete cutting off of communication. One result of this was that, although wireless served the cavalry well during the retreat, and, indeed, until they ceased to take an active part in the normal routine of position warfare, yet occasional failures kept alive the feeling of uncertainty with which it was regarded.

The organization as it existed and was used in the autumn of 1914 is shown in *Plate* II. At G.H.Q., was the motor wireless set which had been the latest pre-war development of army wireless and also three portable wagon sets. The latter had a normal range of 80 miles, and were drawn by six-horsed teams similar to those in use with cable wagons, but of slightly heavier draught.

With the Cavalry Division headquarters were three more wagon sets belonging to the signal squadron, while Cavalry Brigade headquarters were served by a Marconi pack set arranged in a limbered wagon with a range of 30 miles.* By means of these sets satisfactory intercommunication was kept with the major cavalry formations and with R.F.C. H.Q., while individual pack sets even did good work with reconnoitring detachments and patrols. The wireless organizations remained unchanged until the advance from the Marne when the horsed wireless sets with G.H.Q. were replaced by Marconi lorry sets recently arrived from England.

---

During the battle of the Marne which was fought in wooded country, forward intercommunication between division and brigade was by despatch rider by day with, whenever possible, telegraph circuits during the night. For the latter, divisions made use sometimes of permanent line and at other times of cable from their replenished stocks. Brigades, however, having expended the greater portion of their cable, were practically restricted to the use of despatch riders and orderlies,† reinforced, when the situation permitted, by visual.

The country was heavily wooded and somewhat broken up by steepish ridges and valleys and was not normally suited for visual work, but prominent buildings were sometimes used with good effect. In one division, on the first day of the fight, heliograph was worked continuously for four hours from a brigade signal station in St. Cyr to Divisional Headquarters, and it was largely owing to the prompt seizure of all such opportunities by signal officers that an efficient system of intercommunication was kept up.

A method of supplementing the Signal Service in mobile warfare which was much used in the autumn of 1914 was that of *liaison* by mounted officers. This does not actually come within the scope of the Signal Service itself. It is rather a reversion to type due to the desire of the staff for information to supplement the reports sent back by the forward commanders. One of the difficulties which has always reduced the value of the forward signal service has been a shortage of information to deliver. It is not primarily the work of the signal officer to obtain news, and frequently signal offices have been established and well-advertised and yet have not been used.

* Only three sets were available at the outbreak of war for four cavalry brigades and one of these was lost during the retreat. The sets were therefore allotted as circumstances dictated.

† The working of the despatch riders and brigade and battalion orderlies in thickly wooded country was not easy, but free use was made both of the compass and of common sense and no messages went astray.

In the attack or the retreat each commander of a unit in the firing line has rather more work than he can do. He is aware—as he is trained to be—that his superiors and his neighbours require knowledge as to the exact situation on his own front. He knows that if he can find time to send it, there are means available for its delivery. Yet, unless the immediate result of such a message is likely to be succour to himself or to his more immediate neighbours, he finds it difficult to make the opportunity to summarize the situation as he sees it. It is to make up for such lack of information and to provide for the free interchange of authoritative views that the mounted *liaison* officer is useful. It is true that he much relieves the Signal Service and supplements its activities, but of much more importance is the information he can collect. His own personal story of what is going on increases his value threefold if he is an intelligent man. This, his most useful attribute, falls rather outside the scope of Signal Service history.

During the actual fighting against an enemy, stubbornly retreating and contesting every step in fierce rearguard actions, communication by despatch rider was comparatively easy owing to the short distances between division and brigade headquarters. Betweenwhiles, when the enemy's retreat was more hurried, the distances to be traversed were much greater, but, on the other hand, the danger from artillery fire or of overshooting headquarters and running into range of direct machine-gun or rifle fire was much reduced. In either situation, however, the service given by the despatch riders was superb, and though casualties to men and machines were fairly frequent, and the strength of many units was down to a minimum, touch was kept and messages cleared with exemplary promptitude.

The lessons learnt by the Signal Service during the advance which followed the battle of the Marne were much as those of the retreat. Warfare was still mobile and no radical changes in the type of inter-communication took place. The reversal of the direction of movement had only one material effect. The enemy in his retreat had destroyed the telegraph routes more or less thoroughly and this entailed a considerably greater amount of construction on the part of our airline and cable sections. This damage was, however, offset to a great extent by the fact that, in an advance, cable could be expended with more impunity. It might not be possible to pause to recover it, but at any rate it would not have to be abandoned to the enemy. Special parties could be sent out to salve it at leisure when the situation permitted and in the meantime fresh supplies were accumulating. When the line of the Aisne was reached and the situation stiffened, it proved possible to send up supplies and once more complete all signal units to establishment.

The moral effect of the change from retreat to advance cannot of course be overestimated. All ranks had behaved extremely well during the difficult days of late August and early September. On more than one occasion the personnel of signal sections had taken their place beside the infantry in the firing line. Now, however. enthusiasm was unbounded. Long hours had no terrors and the unparalleled exertions of the sections were an immediate and natural result of the uplifted spirits of the men. Many weary months were to pass before the advance would culminate in the march to German territory, but the end of the war seemed quite close in these days of the recoil of the German armies from their great blow at the French capital. It was perhaps as well that victory should immediately precede the fiery trial which the Signal Service in common with the rest of the Expeditionary Force was shortly to undergo at Ypres—Armentières.

By September 12th, 1914, the enemy had succeeded in effecting his retreat to carefully prepared positions on the far bank of the Aisne, positions exceedingly strong and supported by—for those days— a considerable weight of artillery. On the following day, the attempt to force the passage of the Aisne commenced and the rearguard actions stiffened into a considerable battle which was to last, with varying fortune but without decisive result, for many months.

The chief interest in this battle from the signal point of view consists in the first appearance of the more complicated system of signal organization brought about under the conditions of stationary warfare. The original system built up during the early hours of the battle was much as that of previous actions. The presence of the river Aisne was a formidable obstacle to the cable sections, but it was faced by them with resolution and overcome successfully, individual officers, N.C.O.'s and men swimming the river with cables slung round their bodies. The resultant line system on a Brigade front is well illustrated in *Plate* III.

For some few days after a footing had been obtained to the north of the Aisne, the whole of the energies of the divisional signal personnel concerned were devoted to the maintenance of these forward lines under the very heavy and well-aimed artillery fire which was directed upon the new positions. It is an interesting fact and has a distinct bearing upon signal problems, that on the third day of the struggle for the passage of the Aisne the eight-inch siege guns made their first appearance on the British front. These were later to be the most formidable difficulty opposed to the maintenance of uninterrupted communication by means of the six-foot and eight-foot " buries."

By the eighteenth of September, it was evident to the General Staff that the eviction of the Germans from their positions would be a prolonged business and was not likely to be achieved by frontal attacks. Then commenced the marching and countermarching on the northern flank of the line which was to end in the battles round Ypres, Armentières and La Bassée. The immediate outcome of the prolonged nature of the present conflict was, however, seen in the organization of a regular system of relief for the infantry in the trenches. From this again arose constant changes in the signal personnel engaged in the maintenance of particular areas of the signal system.

The first marked result of the hold-up as far as signals was concerned was seen in the duplication of routes from Division forward in the endeavour to render intercommunication more continuous in spite of the heavy artillery fire which was the outstanding feature of the battle. The enemy, who had just retired over the country the British were occupying, had accurately ranged all important points likely to be of use to our men as billets or headquarters and had also paid particular attention to the roads and tracks up which reinforcements and supplies might be expected to come. The weakness of overground cable had already been exposed in the battles of Le Cateau and the Marne—still more was it now evident that a ground cable system would need to be strongly reinforced with alternative lines in all exposed sectors of the front if it was to survive the present iron storm. In every division and brigade, linemen were out day and night on maintenance work and yet the lines could not be kept through.

Various expedients were resorted to. Lines were laid preferably across country and away from roads and buildings ; covered ways were made use of wherever these existed ; ditches and trenches were used as a matter of course even when their use involved considerable deviation from the direct line between two headquarters. In some brigades, where lines to one battalion were run over exposed ground and in consequence were frequently broken, a cable was laid connecting this battalion headquarters to the headquarters of the battalion on its right or left. Thus an alternative route was created and there was possibility of communicating by one route while the linemen were out repairing the other. Incidentally, further light was thrown on the value of lateral intercommunication. Once such a line was available, the battalion staffs used it for regular intercommunication and much valuable information was passed at first hand instead of being circulated through the medium of the Brigade Staff. The value of lateral intercommunication had already been emphasized during the battle of the Marne, particularly in the case of one division which, having established touch with a division on its flank by means of visual, was able to correct the fire of the latter's artillery at a time when the gunners were shooting short and creating much havoc among our own men.

While the dislocation of intercommunication caused by the increase of artillery fire was countered by the construction of alternative and more or less protected circuits, maintenance was facilitated by better

D

organization and—in some divisions—by the use of motor cyclist linemen. Thus, in one brigade at least, a central testpoint was erected in a sheltered position. To this were taken all forward lines passing through exposed country and their condition was here tested at frequent intervals by linemen permanently posted at the station. Similarly, the judicious use of motor cyclists as linemen proved of great avail in reducing the time taken to repair a break. Once the disconnection was found, repair seldom took more than one or two minutes, and the time taken in the search was much diminished when the speed of a lineman was that of a motor cyclist rather than that of a horseman or pedestrian. In this way, the motor cyclist was made use of outside his own sphere in pursuance of a policy of universality which had during the retreat permitted of the loan of mounted linemen at critical moments to act either as despatch riders, or even, on one or two occasions, as mounted patrols.

The growth of the signal system during these few weeks of stationary warfare is shown in *Plate* IV, which presents a graphic picture of the signal communications of the Expeditionary Force on September 28th. The great extent to which permanent line was made use of as far forward as divisions and brigades in rest was a feature of the system, as also was the general absence of visual or other supplementary means in the higher formations. Despatch riders are not shown, although they were in general use, the only exceptions being where, as in the case of the R.F.C., a regular despatch rider letter service was run in the absence of other communication.

The common use of buzzer telephones at battalion and brigade headquarters and the alternative lines over much-shelled country are well indicated, while it is interesting to note that only in one corps and in no division at all, have magneto telephones yet made their appearance. As regards the use of the buzzer telephone, even, it should be said that, although speaking apparatus was available, it was seldom used even by signal personnel. Messages were nearly always buzzed. This was a fact of no small importance when the carrying power of buzzed signals through the earth from faulty lines is considered with regard to the possibility of their being overheard by the enemy. It was perhaps the pressure of work due to the unexpected increase in the demand for line communication that caused attention to be diverted for the time from the serious dangers both of overhearing and of interference between parallel wires using earth returns.

Yet another consequence of the stationary warfare which had now set in was the deterioration of the lines. Frequent breaks and joints, the latter often ill-made under difficult conditions or hastily completed under fire; still more the depreciation of insulation due to wet weather and mud, combined to make line signalling difficult. Circuits were still so few that very little trouble with overhearing was experienced within our own lines, but, as the insulation of the "DI" cable became progressively more imperfect, it became increasingly difficult to hear even buzzer or vibrator over the forward lines. It was soon clear that if they lay in the wet much longer the trouble would be past remedy except by the laying out of an entirely new system.

In order to put an end to this deterioration, it was necessary to raise the lines from the ground. Towards the end of September, therefore, all units were instructed to pole their forward cables, while the corps continued their work on the permanent lines and gradually recovered all cable behind divisional headquarters. The supply of black and white poles which was part of the equipment of airline and cable sections would obviously soon be exhausted if used for the general purpose of poling all forward lines, but to avoid this rough local poles were cut in large quantities. In the next fortnight poled cable made its appearance over the whole of the front where the tactical situation permitted. Where such cables raised to a considerable height off the ground would have been too conspicuous and likely to draw enemy artillery fire, the cable was run either along the sides of trenches or on short stakes at a height of a foot or eighteen inches from the ground. This consolidation of the cable system involved a great deal of heavy labour and the resources of the signal companies and sections were heavily taxed while the work was being carried out. On its completion, however, the advantages of the renovated system over the old ground cable were found to be enormous. Not only was good buzzing and speaking once more possible, but it was soon evident that the constant cutting of lines by traffic which had been so prominent a factor in the maintenance problem would practically cease, while the blast of a shell on loosely slung cable had much less devastating effect than might have been expected from past experience with open wires. For the first time, since the increased enemy fire, divisional linemen were able to cope with the maintenance of their circuits. The despatch rider could at last obtain some remission from his hitherto continuous work, a rest which was particularly necessary in view of the early departure of the Expeditionary Force to the north, where mobile conditions might once more be expected.

It was upon the Aisne that visual signalling first began to fall into disrepute. Certainly, in close proximity to a vigilant enemy, both the flag and the Begbie lamp were unsuitable. The one was too prominent, the other too noisy, to be used with safety. After many casualties had been caused amongst battalion signallers and amongst the infantry generally by the attraction of an undesirable amount of enemy attention through the use of these instruments, they fell into temporary disfavour. During the moving warfare which immediately followed a measure of popularity was regained, but the distaste for visual was destined to return in much greater measure in the following winter with the result that for a time this means of signalling fell into disuse almost entirely. Some battalions went so far as to send their flags back to England.

Always, however, the more far-sighted signal officers appreciated the possible value of visual as an alternative method. From the first, their efforts were directed—not towards its extermination—but towards its reformation and rejuvenation by means of less conspicuous and more efficient implements. The outcome of this policy was later seen in the evolution of the signalling disc and shutter ; the periscope for reading under cover, and the electric signalling lamps which operated silently and had a much greater range and smaller dispersion than the pre-war Begbie lamp.

In the meantime, visual by flag and Begbie lamp had to be used when other methods failed and intercommunication was vitally necessary. This was especially the case with *liaison* between infantry and supporting artillery. By means of carefully worked-out schemes, artillery support was arranged for with the mimimum of signalling and undesirable enemy attention was thus avoided. In one Infantry Brigade, communication from the front line to the artillery was carried out by flag by day and by lamp by night, two letters only being used, " O " meaning " Open fire " and " P " " Cease fire," each being repeated until the signal had produced the desired effect. The system worked with such smoothness that artillery support in the form of rapid fire on certain pre-arranged areas, could be relied upon by day or by night within a period of 20 seconds of the time when the call was first made.

Little has been said so far about artillery signals, but this is for the very good reason that artillery intercommunication up to this time was not the concern of the Signal Service. This was one of the great mistakes of the pre-war organization. It at once became apparent that something was wrong. Artillery, General Staff and Signal Service, all three chafed already under the anomalous condition of affairs that was arising. The Staff, forgetting the delimitation of responsibilities for which their predecessors had themselves been responsible, frequently called signal officers to account for failure to get into touch with artillery units. The artillery, hampered by an inadequate establishment of signallers and telephonists, were already finding themselves unable to deal with the increasing demand for closer *liaison* between the infantry and their supporting guns. The number of artillery units was growing and a separate system of command was inevitable in the near future. Radical changes of organization cannot be made in a moment, however, and the time was not yet ripe for the Signal Service to take over artillery lines. Old conventions die hard, and the artillery were unwilling to give up the semblance of freedom in favour of the concrete gain of increased efficiency. Something had to be done at once and the difficulty was in many cases met by unofficial co-operation between individual artillery and signal officers. In this, the example was set from the top and was soon followed by the majority of the officers concerned. When new artillery units arrived, their initial line system was as often as not constructed or laid by the Signal Service who were naturally ever afterwards entitled to take a proprietary interest in the maintenance and renewal of these circuits. Thus was the way paved for the logical step which followed when, in 1916, Signals were made responsible for the artillery system as far forward as brigade headquarters.

Mention has already been made of the system of relief in trenches which was inaugurated about the middle of September, 1914, and a passing reference should here be made to the result of this, the first suggestion of associating signal systems with a particular area rather than with particular units. During the latter days of September and the beginning of October, the front held by each division was definitely divided into areas or " Sections " as they were then called. At once the advisability of the Signal Service concerning themselves rather with positions than with units or formations sprang into prominence. Before any change of policy could be formulated, however, the relief of the Expeditionary Force by the French took place and any consideration of " Area " signals was relegated to the background by a resumption of mobile or semi-mobile warfare on a new front.

Other points which deserve slight mention before proceeding to study signal practice during the battles of Ypres and Armentières, are two slight but significant innovations which took place for the first time in the Aisne position. Although the armies were not long enough stationary to cause the General Staff greatly to increase their demands on the Signal Service, yet, either by request, or more probably by the exercise of initiative by the signal officers concerned, magneto telephones now first made their debut forward of G.H.Q. One division went so far as to connect up divisional headquarters with reserve brigade by this means.

Undoubtedly, evolution of signal methods was inevitable, and it was well for the Signal Service itself to initiate the changes. The fact remains, however, that this step possessed a significance far beyond any immediately apparent or conceived in the minds of the reformers themselves. The advance in comfort and convenience represented by the introduction of these instruments was immense. The discovery of the magneto telephone by the General Staff was the beginning of endless expansion of signal activity and has probably been responsible for a revolution in Staff methods as great as any that has ever occurred in the history of war. From the date of the general installation of magneto telephones (which was, however, not yet) the resources of the Staff, both for the collation and conveyance of information and for the discussion of policy, were quadrupled, while the time factor in personal conferences was reduced to a minimum.

The days when staff officers took their stand at the signal office table and carried on lengthy, laborious, and highly self-conscious conversations through the medium of interested and often critical operators, were soon destined to pass. A further result of the habit of telephone speech, together with the general adoption of the D, Mark III. pattern of buzzer telephone, was to sweep away the old buzzing convention and permit the above-mentioned instrument to take its rightful place as an effective medium of speech.

----

The final innovation which brings to a close the history of signals during the Aisne period was the introduction of wireless receiving sets for observation purposes in the Heavy Artillery. Until the present War, aeroplane " spotting " for heavy artillery was unknown. Only recently had the development of aeroplane engineering brought such a thing within the realm of practical politics. Now that these machines could remain in the air for a time only limited by their petrol supply or by the attention of enemy planes, some means had to be designed for communication between the observers on the planes and the guns.

For some time experiments were carried out with visual appliances but with indifferent success, owing to certain technical difficulties connected with the constant and rapid movement of the plane.* From the first, however, wireless was hailed as the obvious means of overcoming the difficulty and, on October 1st, 1914, a wireless mast with receiving apparatus was erected at a battery position. An aeroplane with a small Sterling transmitter at once carried out " spotting " tests for the guns with conspicuous success. The new invention quickly showed that it had come to stay, and from this date a great organization was built up for this purpose alone, with ramifications which embraced the Signal Service, the R.F.C., and the Intelligence Branch of the General Staff. Divided authority in this as in all similar cases caused much trouble, but eventually adminis-trative control was vested in the Royal Flying Corps to whom the sets and the men who manned them belonged, while the working of the " Ground sets," as the sets at the guns were called, was technically supervised by the wireless officer of the formation to which the battery belonged.

Much useful work was done by these sets throughout the days of

* Lamp signalling was tiied from aeroplanes near Aire-sur-la-Lys on February, 20th, 1915.

the early development of wireless, small wireless stations in 1914 and early 1915 being confined to the Flying Corps alone. Later, when the attention of the wireless world was fixed more upon the development of small portable wireless sets for command purposes in trench warfare, the R.F.C. sets continued to do good unobtrusive work. They were, however, only a side issue, though an interesting one, in army signals, and the present notice must suffice for them, the more especially as their history will presumably be found in detail in any account of R.F.C. wireless or signal work.

# CHAPTER III.

Soon after the beginning of October, 1914, the British troops were gradually withdrawn from their positions on the Aisne and entrained for the north, division by division, as they were relieved by French troops. By October 19th the move was complete, and the troops deployed on the new front, G.H.Q. being at St. Omer and the Base at Havre.

Touch was first established with the enemy west of La Bassée, where the opposing lines took a north and south direction to the neighbourhood of Estaires. Here the advance was almost at once stopped by the opposition of superior German forces and there commenced the series of attempts on the part of each side to outflank the other with the idea of breaking through and cutting their opponent's communications. The frustration of these attempts is a matter of general knowledge. Their ultimate result was the relative stabilization of the situation by the formation of a nearly rigid line of opposing trenches right across the face of the northern portion of France and the west of Flanders. With the completion of this line, trench warfare set in. The chief characteristic of the First Battle of Ypres was the attempt of the German higher command, by the use of a hitherto undreamt-of concentration of artillery, and with considerably superior forces, to break through the British line at various places between Ypres and La Bassée. The enemy's greatest efforts were made north of Armentières and in the neighbourhood of Ypres. It is on this account that the latter town, where the thin brown line repulsed his fiercest attacks, will always be associated in the British mind with this, one of the most critical battles of the whole war.

With the growing size of the British forces engaged, and a corresponding increase in the number of formations in the Expeditionary Force, it will no longer be desirable, if the evolutionary character of this history is to be maintained, to deal with each separate battle as it took place. What will be aimed at, is a general survey of the situation as regards signals as a whole ; connected so far as possible by the thread of time ; and giving a picture of the Signal Service

struggling with ever fresh developments and responsibilities ; sometimes failing, more often succeeding, and always improving and
learning.

By the study of such a history it should be possible for future gener-
ations of signal officers, plunged into war without previous experience
to guide them (as was the case with so many officers in 1914) to draw
upon the experience of their predecessors—not perhaps for conclusions as to how to deal with any particular situation now long
past—but for lessons of far greater importance.

What were the lessons of the war to the Signal Service ? These
should become apparent as the adaptation of the service through
long years of war is studied. One thing already stands out, however, and cannot be too much emphasized. History may repeat
itself as regards its broader features ; but interwoven in the woof
of life are a multitude of ever-varying threads, constantly changing,
and together making up an infinite gradation of situations never
exactly reproducing themselves. Constant adjustment of ideas and
nimbleness of thought is needed on the part of those who would tackle
these situations efficiently and keep the weapons in their armoury up
to date. The signal officer like the rest of mankind must be ever
on the alert to meet and foil ; if possible, to foresee, the ever-
changing menaces to his intercommunication system. What is well
suited to the needs of this Saturday is hopelessly inefficient by next
Friday. Brains must be kept active ; personnel well trained ;
methods up to date ; and implements of the very latest pattern.
Thus, and thus only, in the next war as in the last, the Signal Service
may live up to its responsibilities. By a study of its failures and
successes in the past, much may be learnt to help its triumph in the
future.

---

The three days' march of the divisions from Railhead to their
positions on the northern front passed without incident and was
carried out in peace-time fashion, units marching by night instead of
by day to avoid the observation of the enemy to the greatest possible
degree. Already the influence of aircraft on war, which was to have
such a decisive effect on signal practice among other things, was
becoming apparent. During the march, communication was normal
—despatch riders keeping touch by day and cable spurs being connected to permanent lines at night. Contact with the enemy brought
about stationary warfare at once in the southern portion of the front,
the only difference being that the country in which the fighting was
waged was flat and covered with mining villages. Artillery support
of our advancing troops was therefore difficult, and visual signalling
almost impossible except over the shortest distances.

Further to the north, the advance continued for some days, cable
touch being kept with brigades by one detachment of the divisional

cable section which was detailed to proceed with, or even ahead of, Brigade headquarters. This detachment with its office on the wagon always in action, also provided a useful means by which the movements of the Brigade could be directed and its advance diverted in this direction or in that as the situation demanded.

Few days elapsed, however, before equilibrium was established in the northern area of operations also. The 7th Division which had been operating towards Antwerp fell back into line with the rest of the Force, while on the left flank French and Belgian armies completed the line to the sea. Then commenced the series of German attacks—first about the neighbourhood of Ypres, Wytschaete, and Messines ; later at Armentières and the line north east of Bethune— which were only withstood with difficulty by virtue of the supreme devotion of an exhausted army.

This last spell of mobile warfare again gave the despatch riders an opportunity of distinguishing themselves, of which they took the fullest advantage. Here at last they were to receive official recognition. In his dispatch of November 20th, 1914, Field-Marshal Lord French writes :—

" I am anxious in this despatch to bring to your notice the splendid work which has been done throughout the campaign by the cyclists of the Signal Corps. Carrying messages at all hours of the day and night in every kind of weather, and often traversing bad roads blocked with transport, they have been conspicuously successful in maintaining an extraordinary degree of efficiency in the service of communications. Many casualties have occurred in their ranks, but no amount of difficulty or danger has ever checked the energy or ardour which has distinguished their Corps throughout the operations."

The building-up of the forward system of communications in these battles took a normal course. On the La Bassée line in the first day of the fight, despatch riders alone were relied upon. Later, as the situation stabilized, cable was laid from Divisional headquarters to brigades. As time went on, lines to battalions once more made their appearance and these and all the divisional lines were poled, improved and reinforced by alternative routes to minimize the risk of interruption of intercommunication through shelling.

It was here that the linking-up of flank divisions by cable was attempted for the first time as a general policy. Already, on the Aisne, individual divisions, pioneering—as occurred in the case of most innovations—had laid out flank lines to particular neighbouring formations with which their staff required reliable and rapid intercommunication. From now on, these flank lines became recognized as part of the normal signal system of Divisions, Brigades, and even of battalions. Gradually, also, the convention arose that these lines should normally be laid from right to left. In this, however, throughout the war, the Division next to the French was faced by a special problem. Not only did our Allies generally despise lateral lines, but they did not possess operators with the necessary skill to work to British telegraphists. All along, the French Signal Service had relied upon the telephone in preference to the telegraph and their personnel was not trained to fast buzzer working. This difficulty was overcome for the present by the loan of instruments and operators from the British Division. Later this trouble disappeared, magneto telephones being introduced into those British formations which required touch with their French neighbours.

Forward of Brigade headquarters, trouble was experienced with maintenance of lines to a much greater extent even than on the Aisne., No intricate system of communication trenches yet existed. Maintenance by day in forward areas was sometimes impossible and at other times was only achieved at the expense of the lives of many brave men. Artillery activity continually increased, especially immediately preceding and during the constant attacks which were hurled on one portion after another of the British lines. Just at the time when good intercommunication was essential, lines would be broken right and left and the attempt to keep them through resulted only in the loss of valuable lives. The necessity for *liaison* between artillery and the troops they supported already pointed to the advisability of extending the telephone system forward to the front-line trenches, but for some time this proved impossible. With every desire to help, the Signal Service was unable to undertake such an extension of its responsibilities with the means at its command.

As the trench system in front became more perfect, however, conditions of maintenance improved and towards the end of November the buzzer telephone was firmly established in important front-line posts. A typical divisional system of line communication at this period is shown in *Plate* V. Considerable extra work was caused by this extension of signal communication, and the bulk fell upon the already overworked personnel of the Brigade Signal Sections.

The pre-war establishment of all units which required a considerable amount of internal signal communications, included a certain number of men trained as signallers in semaphore and Morse. The strength of these signalling detachments is given in *Table* III. Small as the numbers originally were, a large proportion even of these men were not now available for the special duty for which they had been trained.

Before the war, battalion signallers were trained in visual signalling only. As conditions of warfare changed and visual signalling became more and more unpopular, a larger and larger proportion of the battalion signallers were absorbed into the firing line, and the internal communications of many battalions decreased in efficiency accordingly. Taking place as it did just at the time when stationary warfare was setting in, this much increased the perplexities of the

TABLE III.

| Unit. | Establishment N.C.O.'s | Men. | Remarks. |
|---|---|---|---|
| *Cavalry*— | | | |
| Cavalry Regiment, H.Q. ... | 1 | 5 | |
| „ each squadron ... | 1 | 2 | |
| Cavalry Squadron (Div. Cav.) ... | 1 | 2 | |
| Squadron of Irish Horse with Army Troops ... | 1 | 5 | Despatch riders. |
| *Artillery*— | | | |
| H.Q., R.H.A. Bde. ... | 1 | 8 | Telephone detachment ; all trained signallers. |
| Battery, R.H.A. ... | 1 | 6 | Trained as semaphore men and signallers. |
| Ammunition Column ... | 1 | 2 | S. and C.S. and two gunners, trained in semaphore. |
| R.F.A. Bde. H.Q. ... | 1 | 11 | Trained signallers and telephonists. |
| R.F.A. Battery ... | 1 | 6 | Trained signallers and telephonists. |
| Ammunition Column ... | 3 | 2 | Three bombardiers and two gunners, trained in semaphore signalling. |
| R.F.A., Howitzer Brigade ... | | | As R.F.A.Bde. but Ammun. Col. one bombardier and two gunners only. |
| Heavy Artillery Battery ... | | 7 | Trained in semaphore signalling and telephony. |
| Divisional Artillery Column ... | | 6 | Mounted bombardiers trained in semaphore signalling. |
| Siege Artillery Bde. (Medium) ... | 1 | 11 | Trained observers and telephonists. |
| Siege Artillery Bde. (Heavy) ... | 1 | 12 | Trained telephonists. |
| *Engineers*— | | | |
| Field Squadron, each Troop ... | 1 | 2 | |
| Field Company, each Section ... | 1 | 2 | |
| *Infantry*— | | | |
| Infantry Battn., H.Q. ... | 2 | 15 | Trained in semaphore only. |
| „ each Company ... | | 8 | |
| *R.A.M.C.*— | | | |
| Cavalry Field Ambulance ... | 2 | 2 | Trained in semaphore only. |
| Field Ambulance ... | 2 | 2 | Trained in semaphore only. |

NOTE.—Unless otherwise stated, men are trained in Morse signalling with heliograph, lamp, and flag (blue and white, large and small) and in semaphore.

divisional signal officer, who, although not officially responsible for battalion communications, was more and more being asked to extend his activities towards the firing line. Out of this situation two corollaries eventually arose which later changed the whole position as regards signals in the forward area.

It became quite clear that visual signalling with flag, heliograph, and lamp, must be allowed to become of very secondary importance until leisure would permit of further experiment and the improvisation of apparatus to suit the changed situation. As communication to the firing line was more essential than ever, some substitute for visual signalling must be arrived at. The result of this position was the forward extension of the "D3" telephone and this carried with it the necessity for training battalion and other unit signallers in the care and manipulation of these instruments and the laying of simple lines. As things settled down for the winter, the training of such signallers became one of the main preoccupations of the Divisional signal company commander. The logical outcome was the formation, first of classes under Brigade arrangements, and later, as the advantages of centralization became evident, of Divisional Signal Schools. The second axiom which for the same reason now became part of the future policy of the Signal Service, was the necessity for the control of forward signals by the technically trained signal officer. The care and proper use of instruments ; the repair and maintenance of lines ; the training of the personnel, all needed expert supervision. The attainment of this ideal was long in coming, but it was speeded up to some extent by the fact that the absorption of battalion signallers into the firing line at a time when the proportion of casualties was very high, soon caused a shortage which could not be immediately made up Mobilization had absorbed back into their regiments the instructional staff of the schools in England whose duty in peace time was the training of the battalion signaller as well as other specialists, and the result of this policy was now being severely felt. The training of men in the field to replace those who had fallen was at best a slow business. It could not even be attempted until the German attacks had lessened in their intensity and the winter lull gave the exhausted troops time to recover from the fatigue of long-sustained fighting. Far less was it possible to attempt to initiate the few remaining signallers into the mysteries of laying and maintaining the line system now considered essential.

The line system aimed at for battalion intercommunication in January, 1915, consisted of the following circuits :—

(a) From battalion headquarters to each company headquarters.

(b) From battalion headquarters to the headquarters of lateral battalions.

(c) Between neighbouring fire trenches.

When the question of laying the lines came to be considered, it was found that battalion signallers were far too few to carry out the work. This was especially the case since the absence of a battalion signalling officer deprived the section to a certain extent of that co-ordination and supervision which is necessary to enable the greatest amount of work to be obtained from the minimum of personnel. Frequently, therefore, the Brigade signal officer was compelled to complete the system right up to the fire trenches. In this way, the divisional signal company obtained a footing in the supervision of battalion signals which—although not recognized formally for some time—was never lost, and which much increased the efficiency of the signal communications of the army as a whole, while it also improved the relations between the Signal Service and battalion commanders and their officers.*

---

Some consideration must now be given to the development of the command system in Signals and to the building-up of an efficient and all-embracing rear organization for the supply of stores and reinforcements and for dealing with the ever-increasing demands of the administrative services. Battles are won as much by good organization on the lines of communication as by stout fighting and efficient leadership in the forward areas. The Signal Service with the original Expeditionary Force, adapted as the latter was for a short sharp trial of strength, made no provision for any great increase in the size of the Force or in the amount of material required to supply it with satisfactory intercommunication.

Two of the problems confronting the Director of Signals and his Staff, which were never to lose their significance, were the supply of reinforcements to the various types of signal units in the field, and the provision of the technical instruments and stores required to keep these units in an efficient state. Each of these two questions was to grow until it required a department to itself, but we are at present concerned with the creation of the first rudiments of an organization out of such personnel as could be spared from G.H.Q. and

* This question of signal service absorption of regimental signallers remained a matter of controversy throughout the war. The final decision arrived at was that the policy of control by unit commanders should be retained and the arguments in favour of this decision are summarised shortly on page 158, Chapter, IX of this history. A great measure of control over regimental lines by the Signal Corps is, however, necessary, and this has been achieved by the extension of the powers and responsibilities of the Divisional signal officer exercised through his lieutenant the Brigade signal officer. The efficacy of this supervision is much increased by a system which recruits many of the junior officers of the Corps of Signals from the roster of battalion signal officers.

" L " Signal Company, with the addition of a few stray men from the signal units with the Army Corps.

Perhaps the most pressing problem of all was the question of reinforcements. The pre-war organization made provision for the automatic supply of reinforcements up to a certain percentage of the original strength of all units in the field. Under this scheme the signal personnel of all trades was sent to the Royal Engineer reinforcement depôt.

In view, however, of the technical complexity which had already served to differentiate the Signal Service from the remaining branches of the Engineers, it was not to be expected that the men of the different signal trades would necessarily be drafted from the Depôt to the units where they could be utilized to the best advantage. Besides, under the continually changing conditions of the war, the proportion of trades required by a particular unit was not always a constant factor. As an outstanding example, the demand for permanent linemen in cable and airline sections might be cited, but there were many lesser occasions when a unit could find great use for a tradesman to whom they were not normally entitled.

The remedy for the situation was soon seen and the Director of Signals applied for permission to concentrate all signal reinforcements at a Signal Depôt whence they could be distributed to units as required, and where their training could be continued in the interval between their arrival in the country and their posting to units. It was suggested that this Depôt should be formed at the Advanced Base and the numbers required were estimated on a percentage basis which throws an interesting sidelight on the proportion of signal casualties during the autumn of 1914. The figures were :—

10 per cent. of all trades in signal squadrons, signal troops and divisional signal companies.
5 per cent. of trades of the rest of the Signal Service.
20 per cent. of motor cyclist despatch riders.

Worked out for the whole Signal Service in France, the total number of men to be administered at the new Depôt would be 250 and a request was put forward for the approval of an establishment based upon this number.* Casualties were to be reported by units as usual through the Deputy Adjutant General, 3rd Echelon, who would ask the Signal Depôt to make good with men of the proper trades.

It was some time before formal authority for the new establishment was obtained, but in the meantime much was achieved (with the tacit approval of the General Staff) by the withdrawal of a few N.C.O.'s from forward units and by means of the gradual absorption

* The actual figures were :—One captain, one subaltern, one C.S.M., one C.Q.M.S., four serjeants and N.C.O.'s in proportion.

of trained men who had either been invalided home or to the Base and for whose return to the Signal Depôt when fit, arrangements were made. Gradually, as the new organization took hold, a useful amount of training was done. From one source and another, much equipment was collected and, in December, 1914, the establishment was approved and a nucleus of training equipment was also allotted to the Depôt.

A few days afterwards, the Signal Depôt moved to Abbeville, and from that time onwards grew steadily under the direction of the Deputy Director of Signals (Lines of Communications), until it had become an integral and very important part of the Signal Service in France and a type on which similar depôts in other Expeditionary Forces were later modelled.

Throughout the war, its original functions—the final equipment of reinforcements for active service, and their allotment to best advantage according to the quality of the individual—continued to be its main work.* Officers commanding signal companies would apply officially through the D.A.G. for the men they required, but, simultaneously, an unofficial letter would pass to the O.C. Signal Depôt, always with satisfactory results, if the general situation as regards reinforcements permitted the exercise of any latitude at all. Men were thus allotted to the best advantage, while the efficiency of the service and good relations between officers and men were particularly well fostered by a policy which permitted N.C.O.'s and men to be returned by their own wish to the unit with which they had served before they became casualties. Always in the hands of men who had the interests of the Signal Service at heart, the Signal Depôt at Abbeville and the policy of which it was the expression did perhaps more than any other single thing to promote *esprit de corps* within the service in France, together with a feeling of comradeship which helped much towards the alleviation of the discomforts and privations of war.

* In practice a considerable amount of training was actually carried out at the Signal Depôt. Reinforcements were exercised in their duties from the time of their arrival in the country until they were drafted to units. These exercises were supervised by N.C.O.'s and officers with experience in the field and the efficiency of those men who spent some weeks at the Depôt was greatly increased during their stay. A feature which was developed to a high degree of efficiency in 1918 was a school for Signal Service N.C.O.'s. These men were withdrawn from their units for a month, were formed into squads and taken in hand by instructors specially chosen as best fitted to impart the maximum amount of instruction and infuse the maximum amount of discipline into their classes in the short time available. The results were extraordinarily good, and N.C.O.'s thus stiffened up and with their technical knowledge brought up to date were well calculated to raise the general efficiency and *morale* of the units to which they belonged.

Less important, only, than the question of reinforcements, was that of the supply of stores. The policy adopted in this respect was an amplification of that already foreshadowed in the *Manual of Army Signal Service—War*, which was under revision in July, 1914, shortly before the war broke out. In this textbook the principle was laid down that on the outbreak of war special depôts for the supply of signal equipment should be formed. Such Depôts were to be administered by the Deputy Director of Army Signals, who was responsible for all intercommunication along the L. of C., and whose post was at the headquarters of the Inspector General of Communications. Immediately the landing in France was completed, steps were taken to evolve a workable system on these principles. On August 18th, a working agreement with the Ordnance authorities was made, whereby all items contained in Sections 28*b* and 29*a* of the priced Vocabulary of Stores,* together with certain items in other sections, should be collected in such a depôt to which the name of Signal Park was given. As soon afterwards as possible the Signal Park was opened at the Advanced Base†, and all the above items were collected there together with a number of telephones which had been obtained from the Post Office.

On the evacuation of Amiens on the 29th August, the stores were removed to the new Advanced Base at Le Mans, where they remained to the end of the year, when they were moved to Havre. Later in the war, a second Signal Park was formed on a second Line of Communication at Calais. These two Signal Parks served the whole of the Signal Service in France throughout the war, delivering direct to units in the earlier stages, and, later, when decentralization set in, to similar signal stores which were set up at the various Army headquarters.

In this way Signal Service control over technical stores was firmly established at the outset of the war. A system was now required whereby the authorities concerned with their distribution could be reasonably certain that they reached the units who most required them and that they were issued in strict proportion to the needs of the armies in the field. For the achievement of this purpose strict supervision was essential. It was only to be expected that the commander of each signal unit should be convinced of the paramount urgency of his own needs. If demands were not carefully scrutinized by officers familiar with the conditions on the spot and yet in a position to take a broader view of the situation, it was likely that the percentage of stores supplied would depend largely on the vehemence with which the particular applicant expressed his views either verb-

---

* The above sections include all technical signal equipment except certain stores not in the vocabulary but usually obtained by direct *liaison* with the General Post Office Stores Department

† Amiens.

E

ally or in writing. This would not necessarily be in strict proportion to the validity of his case, but might be expected rather to depend on his personality, or on his powers of rhetoric or composition.

In the first few months of the war, when the Expeditionary Force was small, normal demands for all stores were passed direct to the Signal Parks. Special demands or demands on an unusually large scale were referred back to the Director of Signals for countersignature before they were passed for supply. When passed, supply was made direct to units. This routine worked very well until the Force outgrew it. At first the demands of the Staff for intercommunication were limited, and the supply of stores was therefore equal or nearly equal to the demand. Later, in the middle of 1915, as the telegraph and telephone service grew in extent, a modification of the existing arrangements became advisable and a very happily conceived scheme was inaugurated.

A certain number of items, which experience showed were required in such quantities that supply was not equal to demand, were selected for this special treatment. From time to time lists of such " controlled " stores, as they were called—which comprised chiefly the different kinds of cable, airline and telephones—were issued to all concerned. All demands for the items named in these lists had to be sent through the usual channels to the Director of Signals. At each step in the chain of command these demands were scrutinized, co-ordinated, and modified if necessary. They were then passed forward. Finally, in the office of the Director of Signals, they were compared with the lists periodically submitted by the Signal Parks of the total quantity available for issue. Considerable diminution in demands was usually necessary at this stage. These were reduced, not necessarily in strict proportion to the amounts asked for, but in accordance more with the present state of the unit and the general tactical situation.

If an offensive was imminent on the front of a particular Army, or if an attack by the enemy was likely to take place on a particular Corps front and it was considered that the Defence Intercommunication System of that Corps required reinforcing, the particular signal units concerned would receive priority of supply.

Thus the meagre supplies available were apportioned to the immediate needs of the moment, while, as a by-product of the same policy, a reserve of cable was carefully built up both at Corps and Army against the possibility of a future emergency. By means of this far-sighted policy, though the supply of cable was always considerably in arrears, absolutely essential needs were met. As the months passed, the increased output of factories and improvements in the organization at home which dealt with the design, production and distribution of technical stores of all kinds, brought about a great increase in the available supplies. The forward cable system was thus enabled to expand in direct proportion to the two factors which most affected it ; namely, the increase in size of the British forces, and, secondly, the greater demands for telephone communication due to the education of all officers in the convenience and ease of this method of intercourse.

In a general summary such as the present, it is impossible to deal adequately with every step in the growth of the great signal organization which gradually grew up in the rear of Army headquarters. The chief points of development to date are, however, well seen in *Plate VI** which gives a comprehensive view of the whole Signal Service of the Expeditionary Force on December 12th, 1914.

One feature which early began to exercise the ingenuity of the L. of C. Signal Service was the necessity for the organization of some regular service to deal with the increasingly heavy routine traffic which could not be accommodated by the telegraph. Many bulky returns and administrative orders and circulars had to be given a secondary place in the consideration of the Signal Service. As time went on and the requirements of the staff increased, the tendency was for the telegraph to be reserved more exclusively for command purposes, the single exception being the telegraphing of Ordnance indents and summaries which continued until a late stage of the war. The rise of the telephone did not ease matters to a great extent, for this instrument was reserved almost entirely for conversation between officers, which, while it often accelerated action by enabling written orders to be anticipated, could not replace the latter.

At the outset of the campaign the only method of transmission of such letters and parcels was by train. This was, however, of necessity an uncertain and irregular method. The despatch riders of all units were already working to full capacity and were dealing with a considerable quantity of the more urgent traffic, but all packets carried by them were treated as " specials." It was clear that if the maximum use was to be made of the small number of motor cyclists available, a regular despatch rider letter service must be organized.

On September 25th, 1914, orders were given by the I.G.C. for the establishment of a regular D.R.L.S., and on October 29th, after some experiment, the first routine orders were issued and the new service commenced running to a recognized time table between the bases, depôts, and G.H.Q. The number of despatch riders on the strength of " L " Signal Company was not sufficient to man the new service,

* This appears to have been the last general diagram prepared. The quick growth of the signal system after the introduction of the telephone, which is described in the next chapter, made it necessary that diagrams in future, to avoid unwieldy size, should be confined to the particular signal system for which the signal officer of the formation issuing the diagram was personally responsible.

but they were reinforced by 50 men and machines taken over from G.H.Q.

From the first, reliability was aimed at rather than speed. The service rapidly gained in popularity, increasing its scope so quickly that, when, much later in the War, the telegraph system became heavily overburdened, practically the whole of the surplus routine traffic had been transferred to the D.R.L.S. and so a dangerous situation was relieved.*

Simultaneously with the inception of the L. of C., D.R.L.S., a similar service was commenced by G.H.Q. and Corps headquarters. Indeed, the honour of organizing the first regular D.R.L.S. in the Expeditionary Force rested with Corps Signals. Early in October, 1914, a regular service was initiated with success between 2nd Corps headquarters at Château Murette, its Divisions, and G.H.Q.

A radical change in the organization of the Expeditionary Force as a whole which directly affected the Signal Service, was the formation of the Armies in December, 1914. The growth of the Force to five Corps had made central control from G.H.Q. without an intermediary step very difficult, and in this month a reorganization involving a certain amount of decentralization and short circuiting took place.

The effect on the Signal Service communications is well shown by the comparative diagrams of *Plate* VII. These show (a) the scheme of communication as it existed at the date of the change; and (b) the new proposed system for enabling each Army to deal direct with the Lines of Communication and the Bases as regards many questions of supply. The net result was to eliminate the two Report Centres of G.H.Q., the personnel and instruments of which were absorbed to form the nucleus of the new Army headquarters signal companies. In addition, work at G.H.Q. was reduced by the establishment of direct communication between the Armies, the I.G.C. and the L. of C. generally. A certain proportion of personnel could therefore be released from G.H.Q. Signal Company to help to complete the new signal units. A considerable number of reinforcements were, however, required and these were obtained by special demands on the Post Office and on the Territorial Army Troops signal companies who were training at home. For tactical work the Army headquarter's signal company was obliged to be ready to find personnel for an advanced headquarters, so that in the aggregate a considerable increase was involved.

Simultaneously with the greater reorganizations in the Signal

* Until the last year of the war the practice still was for Ordnance indents to be telegraphed. Towards the end of 1917, however, the D.O.S. was persuaded to give the D.R.L.S. a trial. Such good time was kept, and such good results given, by this service that the practice of telegraphing indents was never reverted to.

Service, certain lesser changes occurred which are worthy of notice. The horsed airline and cable sections had done good work during the retreat and advance, but various defects had been shown up in both. In particular, it was soon realized that for units such as airline sections working in rear areas where the roads were good, horsed transport was vastly inferior to motor transport.

The change from horsed to motor vehicles had gradually been setting in throughout the army in the years before the war, and the Signal Service, though naturally taking a secondary place to the supply services, had shared to a certain extent in the revolution. The first motor wireless station has already been mentioned, and the 1914 war establishments allotted both to G.H.Q. and to Army Corps signal companies their due proportion of mechanical transport.

The winter of 1914–1915 was the first opportunity for reorganization. Now, for the first time, things had settled down and there was no great change, and little prospect of great change, in the situation from day to day. Staffs had time to look about them and to co-ordinate and draw conclusions from the rough notes, mental or written, made during the strenuous days of the summer and early autumn campaign. The main results, so far as the Signal Service was concerned, were instructions that, in future, airline sections should be issued with motor transport; an increase of personnel to the Divisional signal company, including extra motor cyclists and a one-ton motor lorry; and the determination to supply a proportion of future wireless sections with motor transport.*

Yet another small reform which foreshadowed the formation of a new branch of signal activity occurred during the winter of 1914. Less significant, even, than the " cloud of the size of a man's hand," the introduction of the use of pigeons by the Intelligence Corps was regarded by the heads of the Signal Service as a matter of general interest only. On the 11th September, 1914, 15 pigeons were handed over to the British " Intelligence " by the French. These birds were used for intelligence purposes only, but from this small beginning was destined to grow a great branch of the Signal Service which in 1918 numbered 20,000 birds with a personnel of 380 experts. No less than 90,000 men in battalions and other units had been trained to care for and fly pigeons.

The significance of the use of pigeons for intercommunication purposes in intensive warfare is better dealt with when recounting the lessons learnt from the battles of 1915. For some time after the period with which we are at present dealing—the early winter of 1914–1915—pigeons continued to be controlled by the Intelligence Corps and were primarily used for intelligence purposes. Even so,

* The original regular army horsed airline sections retained their horses, but were transferred to one or other of the eastern theatres of war.

the service grew continually, for circumstances were all in its favour The district round St. Omer, to which place British G.H.Q. moved for the operations round Ypres and Armentières, was famed for the keenness of its pigeon fanciers. Lofts were requisitioned one after another ; and control over all flying of pigeons in the area occupied by the British armies was obtained as a matter of safeguard against espionage. The nucleus of what was to become a very important branch of the army expanded rapidly, and was taken over later by the Signal Service in a state of efficiency, and applied by that Service to its special needs.

It was through the medium of the Intelligence Corps, also, that army wireless telegraphy found its most useful function in the early days of stationary warfare. During the mobile warfare in the autumn, wireless had been the main means of communication with the independent cavalry. Cable was used by the latter to a subordinate extent only. Visual was limited, sometimes by the country traversed, sometimes by the early morning mists, sometimes by a lack of trained signallers owing to casualties in the already sparse ranks of the signal troops.

With the settling down of the opposing armies to the grim and moveless struggle of position warfare, cavalry ceased entirely to play their original part. Dismounted cavalry in the trenches contented themselves with a normal line system, and wireless therefore lost much of the interest and importance it once had.

The rise of the use of small receiving sets with heavy batteries for observing purposes was such a specialized branch and had so little general interest, that it attracted little attention, the more especially as it was controlled by the Royal Flying Corps who had no particular reason to advertise its doings.

Thus wireless sank to a very third-rate position, not only in the eyes of the army generally, but even in those of many signal officers not personally connected with it. Good work was being done, however, in an unobtrusive way in the interception of enemy messages. These were dispatched to the Intelligence Corps, by whom valuable deductions were made as to the enemy's dispositions and movements. In the meantime, the officers more intimately connected with wireless both at home and abroad were working with intelligence and zeal towards the rehabilitation of this method of signalling in the public estimation. No subject in army signals has rivalled wireless telegraphy in its power of arousing enthusiasm in, and making devotees of, the men whose duty it has been to advance its interests. Much thought was expended on the problem of overcoming the drawbacks under which army wireless laboured and the reward of the men who toiled long on thankless work was to come later in the war.

Meanwhile, intelligence wireless was daily gaining ground and in October was reinforced by the arrival of the first wireless " compass " station in France.* This set was designed to give the accurate direction of any enemy station whose working it intercepted. The use of the device is obvious. If two or more bearings could be obtained on any enemy station within reasonable distance, the position of the latter could be accurately plotted.

A line of compass stations established well behind the front and out of reach of any hostile action ensured an accurate knowledge of the position of every enemy wireless station heard. It was already realized from previous interception that certain wireless stations were associated in the German army with certain definite formations. Carry the argument a step or two farther and it will be quite clear that the Intelligence Branch of the General Staff had by this innovation gained a weapon of incalculable value. From this time, wireless intelligence never looked back. Increasing steadily in size and scope as apparatus and organization improved, it became of progressively greater importance and contributed in no small degree to the efficiency of the British Intelligence Service.

* The set was a Bellini Tosi pattern modified by the Marconi Company. Its outstanding features were the exceedingly sensitive valve receiver, a specially designed directional aerial, and revolving inductances by means of which the strength of the signals received from the distant station could be varied.

# CHAPTER IV.

THE factor which perhaps more than any other brought about great changes in type in the signal communication system of position warfare was the growth of artillery. Both on our own side and on that of the enemy, the tendency was for the armies to dig themselves into the ground in the attempt to find shelter from an artillery fire of ever-growing intensity.

At first this increase in artillery fire was confined to the German side, the conditions of manufacture and supply in England preventing any possibility of retaliation on a large scale for some months. Both guns and shells were limited in number, and the fighting troops and, incidentally, signal communications, suffered from the enemy's overwhelming superiority in this respect. As the months wore on, however, the situation commenced to improve. Month after month saw a steady increase in the number and weight of our own guns and in the supply of ammunition for their use. The first batteries of 60-pounders and 4·7 guns reached France in early October, 1914, and, through 1915, the British guns in action grew steadily in number. At the same time, reserve batteries of field guns and 4·5 howitzers were being accumulated and it soon became clear that the organization of artillery would have to be radically changed and a central command system built up for this arm.

The situation was faced with decision, and Heavy Artillery and Field Artillery were both, in early 1915, organized in groups each acting under the orders of a Lieutenant-Colonel. These groups in turn were organized at a later stage into yet higher formations under General Officers commanding Royal Artillery.

The first feature of particular interest to signals was the constructive effect on signal organization of the increase in importance of our own artillery formations. In 1914 each individual battery carried out its own somewhat primitive system of intercommunication. Battery telephonists, not too highly trained, connected their guns to the necessary observation posts and to the affiliated infantry. With a few batteries only engaged and with a small degree of *liaison* only expected, this system worked comparatively successfully for the two or three months of mobile warfare. Where the system broke down, a generous measure of help was forthcoming from the local signal officers. For some time all went—if not well—at least sufficiently smoothly to allow the artillery to build up a well-deserved reputation for efficiency in action.

With the coming of position warfare and the simultaneous increase in artillery, however, the situation underwent a decided change. The early trench system, without a good network of communication trenches, was difficult to organize. The principle of defence in depth was not yet adopted ; all the available forces were concentrated in the front line trenches ; and close artillery support was essential to the holding of these positions. Failure of the artillery at the critical moment might lead to irretrievable disaster. A more intricate system of *liaison* between artillery and infantry was vital to the scheme of defence and must be provided. In this connection, also, must be considered the fact that lines forward of Division were becoming more and more difficult to maintain.

Thus,. towards the end of 1914, it became increasingly evident that reform in the relations between artillery communication personnel and the Signal Service was urgent, and action was taken in the next few months to relieve the situation. In December, 1914, increases in establishment were allowed to the Divisional Signal Company to enable it to carry out divisional artillery communications as far forward as artillery brigades. This addition took the form of the addition of another cable detachment and a few N.C.O.'s and men to man a signal office at the R.A. headquarters of the Division. From the time of the arrival of these men—about April, 1915—No. 1 Section of the Divisional Signal Company was organized in two halves, each consisting of two cable detachments. One detachment was then placed definitely at the disposal of a subaltern of the company who was detailed to take over charge of artillery signal communication. It was some considerable time before an officer was officially allowed for this purpose, but the practice became general in the course of the year.

To summarize the state of affairs as regards artillery signals in the summer of 1915, by which time position warfare had persisted sufficiently long for evolution of methods to have taken place to a considerable extent, the main facts were as follows. The old divided control of artillery signal communications had gone. No longer was the battery intercommunication officer responsible for lines from O.P.'s to the guns, and the brigade officer for lines from batteries to brigades. Orders had been issued giving to the artillery brigade signal officer control over the whole system of his formation. He, in his turn, was expected to keep close *liaison*—in the case of the heavy artillery—with the the Divisional Signal Company commander, in the case of Field Artillery—with the infantry brigade signal officer. To the latter, the O.C. Divisional Signal Company had meanwhile delegated his supreme responsibility for all lines in the Brigade area. An officer had also been definitely appointed to supervise the divisional artillery communications. The corps organization had not, however, at this time progressed so far ; indeed, in different armies opinion was not yet standardized as to whether control over heavy artillery should be exercised by Army or by Corps.

As to the amount of signal communication expected, this is intimately bound up with the next subject to be considered, the general growth of the telephone system. It was, however, laid down as a principle that, for effective *liaison* between infantry and artillery, there must be good artillery and infantry telephone systems, independent but cross-connected at both ends. That is, direct lines were required, both between the infantry in the trenches and supporting batteries, and between the C.R.A. and the Divisional Commander. In most, if not all formations, this was also reinforced by a line between artillery and infantry brigades. In principle, the system as thus amended remained in force, unmodified as to its main features, throughout the whole period of position warfare.

The revolution in ideas as to the tactical use of artillery was no mean factor in modifying and complicating the Signal Service and in particular the telephone system of the Force. Pre-war signal establishments practically ignored the use of the telephone except for artillery observation. Trained telephonists were unheard of except in artillery units and in the higher formations such as Army Corps and G.H.Q. The trade " Telephonist, switchboard operator," had yet to be created. At the time of the landing of the Expeditionary Force in France, very few telephone exchanges or telephones were in the possession of its signal units. Forward of G.H.Q. (with the exception of the hand sets of the vibrators, which were exclusively reserved for signal use, and the few " D1 " and " D2 " telephones already alluded to), some Stevens phones issued for trial, a few others possessed privately by battalions, and the meagre equipment of artillery units, were the only instruments available.

The use of the civil telephone system during concentration and during the battles of the autumn of 1914 might have awakened the Staff to the convenience of the adoption of the magneto telephone on a large scale, but for two very relevant points. The first was that on the afternoon of the battle of Mons it was discovered that it was possible to speak to many towns far within the German lines. In addition, our own buzzer signals, and therefore a general *résumé* of the intentions and actions of the British General Staff, could be heard by anyone on any of the telephone wires in the neighbourhood of the battle area.

The significance of this was obvious, and though precautionary measures were at once taken and routes were thoroughly destroyed forward of battalion headquarters, a feeling of uncertainty resulted which must have confirmed the Staff in a distrust for telephone communication on any scale but a minimum.

The second consideration that militated against the immediate adoption of the magneto telephone throughout all formations was the highly trained character of the General Staff and other officers of the original Expeditionary Force. Trained from their youth up in dealing with similar but theoretical situations by means of message book and personal interview, these officers did not feel the need for frequent telephone conversations.

All had been taught to frame explicit orders and to act upon such orders when received. The use of Staff cars; mounted *liaison* officers; and despatch riders, provided a nucleus of communication which seemed for the present to satisfy all requirements. The dislike to the introduction of an innovation during the full tide of battle, so often a conservative element retarding evolution in war, was supported by many weighty considerations. Indeed, who shall say that an extensive use of the telephone in this mobile warfare waged under the direction of a very efficient Corps of officers would have been justifiable even if it had been possible?

With the removal to the north and the setting in of position warfare an entirely different problem presented itself. As casualties occurred, the carefully trained officers of the Regular Army were replaced by temporary officers with little or no experience. In time, inroads were made into the General Staff itself. Messages and orders increased apace and were less carefully worded. On the Aisne, the magneto telephone had already made its appearance in isolated cases at Corps, Division, and even at Brigade headquarters. Where it was adopted it was a marked success. In the Ypres-Armentières and Bethune districts, alike, the British army was operating in a country where a complicated and very complete civilian telephone system had been developed to meet the needs of industry. Every evacuated town and village had its quota of abandoned telephones. What was more natural than that signal officers, desirous of meeting the wishes of their staff, should take into use increasing numbers of these telephones and so, for the sake of immediate relief, project their harassed companies and sections into innumerable new difficulties. This was what actually happened. Kleptomania as regards telephones, telephone exchanges, and telephone and telegraph accessories of every description, became a confirmed habit. Journey after journey was made into devastated towns in search of instruments. Where the owners or lessees could be traced, receipts were given and in some cases local payments were made. In any case, the net result was the issue of yet more telephones to branches of the Staff and to units. By the late spring of 1915, an informal military telephone system was in full swing.*

There was a very real need for some method of intercommunica-

* The first metallic circuit trunk (between St. Omer and Bailleul) was built by G.H.Q. Signal Company in November, 1914.

tion to replace the telegraph. Very few trained signallers now remained in the lower formations and the telegraph had become both a slower and a more uncertain method of passing orders and messages. The deterioration in the qualifications of the Staff and of officers generally and the consequent multiplicity of messages has already been referred to. Traffic had increased to such an extent that, during operations in March, 1915, one Army Headquarters dealt with over 3000 messages in one day, while in May one Division refers to dealing with 758 messages by wire alone. These totals should be compared with the figure 230 given by G.H.Q. as an exceptional number in September, 1914. In addition to the above considerations, trench warfare had made rapid intercommunication between artillery and infantry, and between troops in the line and reserves comparatively far back, an urgent tactical necessity. To cope with the situation the telephone was the only apparent remedy and yet its use was not to be without considerable drawbacks.

The few direct telephone communications established in the first battle of Ypres and at La Bassée between the staffs of higher formations presented little difficulty. With a few lines only in existence, induction troubles had not yet arisen to any great extent and the direct telephone without the intervention of an exchange was at once hailed as an unmitigated boon. With the more general adoption of the magneto telephone further forward, however, the number of officers with equal or nearly equal claims to consideration were so many that complications at once arose. The demand far exceeded the supply both of telephones and exchanges, and the illegitimate means resorted to by resourceful signal officers only partially enabled the more urgent cases to be met.

One great difficulty was the unsuitability of civil telephone instruments to active service conditions. Everywhere on the Flanders front, dirt, wet, and mud were in the ascendant. It was impossible to keep signal offices or instruments dry. As the forward Staffs were forced further into the ground to gain protection from the enemy artillery, the conditions of their offices became more unsuited to the use of delicate telephones intended for well-constructed, damp-proof houses.

The situation did not improve, and it was soon evident that suitable apparatus must be devised to meet the emergency. This work was at once put in hand, but in the meantime the best had to be made of what was available. A very indifferent telephone system resulted, though even this was better suited to the new conditions than the old telegraphy.

The increase in the number of local telephone circuits which followed immediately upon the introduction of the magneto telephone at once made it out of the question for signal officers to run direct lines between the various subscribers of their system. This difficulty was met by the introduction of the telephone exchange, but here the Signal Service was again faced with two difficulties—one material and one moral.

The material obstacle was, of course, the question of supply. Civil exchanges, far more even than civil patterns of telephones, were delicate pieces of apparatus quite unsuited to the rough work of army life. They were suitable for use at Corps and Army headquarter offices, but they soon proved unfitted for use in Brigade offices and for the forward artillery formations and units. Various types of home-made switching arrangements were therefore designed and these were adopted by the signal units most concerned. They proved to be extremely useful and in most cases served the purpose for which they were intended very well, but they were not, of course, standardized and their general use gave rise to a special set of difficulties which will be mentioned later.

The introduction of telephone exchanges was not viewed favourably by the General Staff. In the early days of the telephone the cry for " direct " lines was universal. The great advantage of the instrument was the personal nature of the intercommunication it provided. Immediately this was realized, all users of the telephone became more and more impatient of the least delay in establishing communication. In the case of the " Operations " branch of the Staff concessions were made and a certain number of direct lines was provided, but it was soon evident that this tendency was adding another burden to the already overwhelming load sustained with difficulty by the signal personnel of all formations. Direct lines had to be suppressed as far as possible. This could only be done by placing all subscribers upon Corps, Divisional and Brigade exchanges which could be manipulated from the central signal office of the formation. This reform was carried out and at once complaints arose concerning the shortcomings of the exchange operators which increased steadily both in volume and virulence until subscribers had been thoroughly educated in the use and the limitations of the new instruments. It might have been anticipated that the telephone exchange operators provided would have been inefficient, for no men of this trade were carried on army signal establishments. This was not usually the case, however, for many men in all signal units were employees of the General Post Office.

Amongst these there was normally a proportion of men trained in switchboard operating in a civil capacity at home. Thus, except in the lowest formations, there was at once available a sufficiency of trained men to meet the initial demand. At a later date, shortages were to occur, but these were met by a special system of training and by the enlistment of further qualified men from the G.P.O. to fill the needs as they arose, while the creation of the army trade " Switchboard operator," finally regularized the situation.

At the time of the introduction of the telephone switchboard, however, complaints were rife and from such complaints grew the necessity of a campaign of education among telephone subscribers. Typical of such complaints and of the way they were dealt with are the two following cases which illustrate both the necessity for educational propaganda and also the difficulties which beset signal officers in these days of the installation of the magneto and buzzer telephone system.

In a certain Territorial Division, the appearance of a small home-made buzzer switchboard at the R.A. headquarters was viewed with suspicion. The C.R.A. at once sent for the Divisional Signal Officer for his explanation. Why was there need for an exchange and what exactly were its functions ? The O.C. Signal Company explained at length but without convincing the R.A. staff. The chief difficulty seemed to be that the operator could not attend to more than one person at a time. Suppose the C.R.A. and his Brigade Major wanted to call up officers of two brigades simultaneously. It was suggested that a second line to the exchange would solve the difficulty, but this was without avail. Finally, the signal officer wisely decided to point out the advantages of the new system by emphasizing the troubles inherent in the old. New local telephones for the rest of the R.A. Staff were insisted upon, but they must be fixed up without an exchange. " Signals " said they would do their best. Four or five " D3 " telephones were brought in and arranged in a row on a convenient grand piano. The arrangement was approved of, but it lasted two days only. Two or three officers tried to speak at once and the result can be better imagined than described. The Divisional Signal Officer was again called in ; the home-made exchange was installed ; and peace and efficiency reigned supreme once more.

The second case, which is typical of another type of complaint, is concerned with the relations between the subscribers of the military telephone system and the exchange operators. In the higher formations, these men were highly skilled and did devoted and arduous work throughout the last three years of the war without intermission. Working long hours at a monotonous but nerve-testing operation, their skill, tact, and patience cannot be too highly praised. Remarks which would have been sufficient to cancel any civil telephone contract were often levelled at their heads and received by them with the utmost sang-froid. Indeed, on more than one occasion, impatient officers have invaded the signal office itself and have even gone so far as to place the telephone operator under arrest. In such a case the signal officer concerned had of course no option but to request the officer to permit him to manage the internal economy of his own unit and to make his complaint through the proper channels. Complaints through these channels, also, would frequently not bear investigation and thereby hangs the second illustration.

In one Division, during operations, an infuriated senior officer burst into the office of the O.C. Signal Company to complain of unparalleled insolence from an exchange operator. The case was stated with vehemence and appeared to be unpardonable. Scarcely had the complainant departed, satisfied with a promise of immediate inquiry and redress, when the telephone bell rang loud and long. The speaker proved to be the G.S.O.1. of a neighbouring division with a precisely similar complaint, the incident having occurred at exactly the same time. Putting two and two together, a visit to the signal office was the result, when it transpired that the two officers had originated urgent calls from either end of a telephone circuit at one and the same time. Each being eager to speak kept his telephone receiver to his ear. The operator at either end, plugging through, made the connection and each staff officer, disdaining formalities, commenced with his own particular urgent business. Each, thinking he was speaking to the exchange operator at the distant office, chose his words and tone accordingly, and the double complaint was the ultimate result. A statement of the case despatched to each complainant was a useful lever to secure a minimum of trouble from these particular officers in future, but often similar cases, less susceptible of explanation, made the signal officer's billet anything but a bed of roses.

The latter incident shows well how difficult the education of non-technical officers and men was and illustrates some of the troubles of the Signal Service   Much could be done and was done by organizing visits of staff officers to signal offices where they were given first-hand evidence of the difficulties under which the much-maligned exchange operator worked. Cards or papers of instruction were issued to all subscribers ; exchange operators themselves had the primary importance of courtesy and tact continually impressed upon them and any proved cases of impertinence were punished by drastic disciplinary action. Gradually, initial difficulties of this kind were overcome. Typical of the better spirit that arose was the visit of a Divisional Commander to his signal office after a great and most important battle. He walked round the office, shook hands with the principal members of the staff, and—admitting pleasantly that he himself sometimes lost his temper, and often forgot to " ring off "—thanked them in a few well-chosen words for their devotion to duty and their services in the recent action. Such incidents cheered the office staff and immensely improved the *morale* on which their efficiency so much depended.

So the magneto telephone and the magneto and buzzer exchanges gradually won their way in public estimation. The earlier telephones, obtained in this way and in that, varied in number within formations according to the initiative and good fortune of the signal units concerned. Gradually, it became clear that the telephone had come to stay, in spite of all its drawbacks. It was impossible to prevent its use becoming general, and, indeed, it would have been undesirable to do so, for the very sufficient reason that nothing else existed to replace it. It was much better to acquiesce and to legalize its adoption by granting an establishment of telephone equipment to each formation.*

Even after the recognition of the magneto telephone had taken place, the question of supply had still to be solved. The Post Office authorities had long ago been approached with the request to make up suitable magneto telephones in their workshops from the standard parts already available in their stores. Similarly the Army workshops themselves, while concentrating on the production of " D3 " telephones for forward work, experimented with various types of magneto phone for position warfare purposes. The early types produced were unsatisfactory, but after many experiments a good trench telephone—the Telephone " 100 "—was designed and was approved as a standard type.

Long before the question of supply had been overcome, the rapid growth of the telephone system had raised other very serious difficulties. Telephones were useless without lines, and lines were becoming more and more difficult to maintain. In early 1915, there was no single co-ordinating authority responsible for the supervision of the forward signal system. These two facts produced a state of affairs which bade fair to wreck the whole intercommunication service. One thing to be particularly noticed about the first half of 1915 was the fact that there was an inclination to rely upon the telephone system to the exclusion of every other means of signalling. The understaffed signal companies had their whole personnel engaged in laying, maintaining, or improving lines ; in installing telephones ; in building signal dugouts, etc. Their whole resources were concentrated upon this new hobby of the Staff. No one could work without a telephone ; no one appeared to foresee conditions when forward telephone communication would be impossible over lines laid haphazard without adequate supervision by some central controlling authority.

During this period there was great danger of all supplementary methods of intercommunication being ignored, and reliance placed entirely on what was becoming an inefficient telephone service. Fortunately, one of the lessons driven home by the autumn offensive in 1915 was that telephone communication must be augmented by other means. In the meantime, however, visual was in abeyance,

* This was the line followed by the Director of Signals and, on January 5th, 1916, an establishment of one 20-line and one 10-line exchange and 20 magneto telephones per division was approved. In December of the same year the issue of magneto telephones and exchanges to R.A. and Infantry Brigades was also authorised.

wireless was not yet sufficiently developed to be of any practical use, and pigeons were used only by the Intelligence Corps. In fact, if warfare became much more intensive, it appeared quite likely that the Signal Service might be unable to shoulder its responsibilities.

The matter of the multiplicity of lines was itself the greatest danger. At the time which is at present under consideration, March to December, 1915, the number of lines in the forward area was increasing daily. Not only did the growth of the system keep pace with the increase in the number of subscribers, but lines multiplied without any true relation to the number of circuits in use. Difficulties of maintenance were many and increasing; trained signallers were steadily decreasing in number and—in the forward units—in standard of efficiency. The battalion signaller knew just enough to lay a line along an existing track where it was most likely to be cut or trodden under foot. When the original line was damaged, the general custom in forward units was to lay another line in replacement and leave the damaged one to rot where it was. The tangle of lines which littered the forward areas thus became more and more complicated.

The sides and bottoms of all trenches—communication, support, and fire trenches alike—were covered with festoons of wire. Frequently wires leapt across a trench from side to side either at top or bottom. In either case the result was disastrous and likely to bring the Signal Service into disrepute. Free movement in the trenches, especially by night, was impossible; movement of any sort was difficult; and all the time, lines—especially artillery lines—increased in number. At one small artillery headquarters, apparently deserted, a signal officer found no less than 76 lines. Examination disclosed the fact that only six of these were in use. Yet, as the officer left the building, another party of artillery signallers led in yet another line.

Indeed, the artillery were by far the worst offenders. A good story, of which the accuracy is not guaranteed but of which the moral is very apt, is current throughout the Signal Service. " A brigade signal officer was watching his linemen carefully stapling a line to the side of a communication trench. Satisfied with the way his men were doing their work, he turned away and strolled back along the trench examining his line as he went. To his annoyance, a bare quarter of a mile away, he came across a party of battery signallers, themselves laying a line and carefully securing it to the battens arranged at intervals along the trench with staples extracted from the line his own party were engaged in laying. His own line meanwhile was allowed to fall upon the duckboards of the trench, where its ultimate fate could not be in doubt. He soon put matters right and set the party to work reconstructing his own circuit at the expense of their own, but the equanimity of his temper was not reduced to normal until, continuing his way along the trench, he

F

came across yet another artillery party engaged in reeling up the line their comrades were as busily laying in front. They had tapped in on the circuit with a buzzer, had received no answer to their calls, and had immediately proceeded to ' make ' a little badly-needed cable." When things were approaching this stage and— whether the particular story is true or false, it is a good example of the actual state of affairs—drastic remedy of some sort was sorely needed to prevent a *débâcle* which would for ever discredit the telephone.

The evils of the situation were fully realized by the Signal Service, but with inadequate personnel and improvised equipment and, particularly, with only a shadow of control over forward signals, little could be done. Long before affairs had reached this pass, however, the number of lines running along all forward routes, and lying indiscriminately all over the forward area, had given rise to yet another trouble which affected telephone subscribers themselves more immediately. It was impossible to speak without being over-heard by all and sundry ; conversely it was exceedingly difficult to pick out from the medley of sound, the conversation of the officer to whom one was speaking. At first this caused friction between the Staff and signals, since all intercommunication troubles were at once ascribed to the latter. By continual reiteration, however, it proved possible to convince the Staff that the Signal Service could not take responsibility for this or any other shortcoming of the telephone system unless complete power of supervision over all forward lines—artillery and infantry—was given to them.

Once this principle was accepted as a necessary postulate, orders were issued throughout the Armies that in future the O.C. Divisional Signal Company should exercise complete control over all lines throughout the area controlled by his Division. This was a great step in the direction of reform and, despite difficulties, the order was gradually enforced. The task, which seemed almost impossible on the top of the duties already carried out by the signal sections, was eased to a certain extent by the collection of lines into " routes," which was brought about partly as a matter of policy and partly as a natural result of the introduction of buried cable.

In Divisions, the responsibility for lines in Brigade areas was delegated to the Brigade section officer and the instructions issued were framed so that, in theory, no line could be laid without the consent of these officers. In practice, a certain amount of latitude was always allowed to artillery intercommunication officers, while commanding officers of battalions also acted arbitrarily sometimes so far as their own battalion lines were concerned. A considerable measure of control was, however, soon achieved with good results which became more evident as time went on.

In this manner, the greatest difficulty in the way of an efficient telephone service was removed, and at the same time improvements in apparatus and methods of construction made possible still further advances in the same direction. In addition, confusion was rendered much less widespread by the adoption of a standard system of labelling lines, and by insistence upon its use. This, in its turn, led to individual lines being more easily traced—and so repaired—instead of being disconnected and new lines laid to replace them. Orders were also given that all lines not in use were to be reeled in and, though the overworked state of the companies at first made these instructions somewhat of a dead letter, yet the threat itself was salutary and a warning of impending action was usually enough to make the unit in question make an attempt to set its house in order. In the autumn and winter of 1915, great strides were made towards the improvement of the system, and in this advance the standardization of methods of construction helped very much.

In the days of reliance on the telegraph, new construction was naturally a small part of the work of the Signal Service. Lines were few in number and, towards the rear, the requirements of the Army could be accommodated without difficulty upon the permanent lines of the civilian telegraph and telephone system. Little trouble was experienced by the cable sections in keeping level with the demands for new telegraph lines in the forward areas. The winter of 1914 found the army well content with a moderate network of lines : permanent lines in rear of Division ; ground cable, poled cable, cable slung on trees, permanent poles, or short stakes, forward of Brigades. Between Brigades and Divisions—the limit of the zone of frequent hostile shelling—a hybrid line, part permanent line and part cable, was the usual type in existence.

Two factors were to change the system radically. The growth of the telephone service made necessary the provision of some dozens more circuits on the rear main routes. As in the forward zone, once the telephone habit was acquired, it spread like an epidemic through all departments. This demand for telephones could not be accommodated without considerable construction and the original L. of C. signal service was not designed for the building of permanent routes on a large scale.

Airline sections could in an emergency restore or erect permanent and semi-permanent routes, but they had neither the stores nor the trained personnel to do this on the large scale now required. A unit of an entirely different type was required and, early in 1915, the Director of Signals put forward proposals for the formation of Telegraph Construction Detachments on the Lines of Communication to deal with the new problem. At the same time, Railway Telegraph Detachments were formed to deal with the construction of a special system along the railways which were being built forward in the rear of each army.

These proposals were approved, and with the co-operation of the Post Office large dumps of permanent stores were formed and construction was soon in full swing. This reform involved the addition of 20 officers and 370 men to the Signal Service of the Expeditionary Force. Most of the personnel required was drawn from the Engineering and Maintenance Staffs of the G.P.O. and the British Railway Companies. As the years passed, and the British armies increased in size, the Lines of Communication signal service continued to grow until it finally reached a total of 100 officers and 3358 men. All these officers and men were fully employed in meeting the needs of the L. of C. services and in assisting the Army signal companies in the construction of the large routes which were then necessary, even in Army areas, to deal with a telephone service swollen to very great dimensions.

In the forward areas, where, until December, 1914, poled, ground and trench cable reigned supreme, two factors were soon to exercise a decisive effect. The first—the shortage of cable—already foreshadowed in the autumn of 1914, and now a very important fact, brought about the erection of the bare wire routes to which the name " Comic Airline " was given. The second—the growing intensity of the enemy's artillery fire—gave rise to the buried cable system which was to be the main feature of forward line communication in 1916 and 1917.

When making use of the telephones and exchanges of the civilian system in the evacuated villages of the Ypres-Armentières district, many signal officers had their attention drawn to other accessories of the system. Once improvisation commences and who can tell where it will end ! The shortage of cable was being felt more in all Divisions and Corps as day succeeded day and ever demands for more circuits were received. No more permanent line stores were available than were required for the construction of the rear routes. In any case, the personnel of the forward sections could not have built permanent routes and, even if built, they would not have been suitable for close proximity to the shelled zone. Small inconspicuous routes of a few wires each were required.

Poles were to be had for the cutting, and it occurred to zealous officers that an ample supply of iron and wire bobbin insulators could be salved from the towns and villages of the evacuated zones. This was no sooner thought of than carried out. Before the end of December, construction was in full swing in several Corps and in the early months of 1915 this improvised airline had assumed a definite importance in the area between Corps and Brigade headquarters. A certain unprofessional appearance was characteristic of the routes when compared with the neat black and white poles and service insulators of their more official predecessors. The word " comic " was irresistible in its application to the queer erections that appeared as each individual officer worked into his routes his own peculiar idiosyncrasies. " Comic " airline entered the signal vocabulary at any rate for the duration of the war, and probably until airline is replaced entirely in the far future, possibly by wireless, possibly by some means of communication as yet undreamt of.

Coincident with the development of comic airline occurred the invention of various more pretentious semi-permanent routes. Of these, perhaps the most interesting was the " trestle " route, afterwards generally adopted and standardized by our French allies. *Plate* VIII. gives a good idea of typical poles on such trestle routes, the great advantage being the large number of wires which could be run along each route compared with other types of semi-permanent routes. Maintenance also was very easy, the wires on each pole being readily accessible without the aid of climbers.*

Forward of Brigades, since the beginning of the war, poled cable and airline had both been at a discount. Both were too conspicuous and therefore too liable to draw fire, while the effect of the blast of a shell many yards away was sufficient to put the latter out of action. Cable suspended on short stakes stuck in the ground at intervals of a few yards was, however, more immune from observation and therefore from deliberately aimed fire. These " staked " routes, as they were called, although more conspicuous and more liable to damage from shell fire, were preferred to ground cable for many reasons. The insulation of the lines was less liable to be destroyed by the almost universal layer of mud and they were also more easily seen by our own men and so less likely to be damaged by traffic. Finally, they were easier to maintain, being easily traced and not mixed up with the tangle of lines which was the drawback to every forward area. For all these reasons, staked routes were fairly popular both with signal officers and linemen and are therefore worthy of notice.

Where these staked routes were not possible and ground cable for many reasons was not liked, trench cable was the last resort of the forward signal officer. Practically all lines forward of battalion headquarters were laid in trenches wherever trenches were available. The evil of indiscriminate laying of lines in what were the only safe channels of communication was soon forced on the attention of every-

* The latter consideration was one, indeed, which always limited the size of routes which had to be regularly patrolled by the personnel of forward signal units. To overcome the difficulty to a certain extent, four permanent linemen were added to the establishment of each divisional signal company, while an issue of " climbers, pole " to brigade sections was intended for the same purpose. A comparatively small proportion of field linemen were, however, capable of working on the larger routes. The issue of these stores is of interest as showing a marked difference between the volume and range of enemy shell fire in these days and two years later, but the climbers themselves were seldom used except when the brigades were in " rest."

one concerned. It reacted both ways. Infantry officers and men censured the Signal Service as they stumbled about the trenches by day and by night, falling over wires stretched knee-high across the bottom of a trench, or recoiling from breast-high or neck-high obstructions of a similar nature. Signal officers equally heartily blamed the infantry when lines went " dis " and examination proved either that they had been torn down, deprived of insulation by fires lighted in the bottom of the trench, or maliciously cut. Both condemned the artillery for their share in creating the spider's web that tried the patience of all alike from General down to Private or Pioneer.

As time went on, improvement set in. On the one side it took the form of a slowly-deepening sense of the value of intercommunication as evidenced by rapid artillery support, or even by the punctual arrival of rations, accurately apportioned according to the ration strength telephoned each afternoon from company headquarters. From the Signal Service side, the improvement was manifested in the evolution of better methods of laying trench lines and the co-ordination of forward signals. Various methods of tidying up trench cable were invented and insisted upon. Frequent inspections by angry General Staff officers gave a fillip to the task. Wooden battens with nicks in which to lay the lines were a great improvement. As these gained in popularity as firewood, inventive Signal Service talent again triumphed over the new difficulty, and they were replaced by more indestructible wire supports. In some cases, lines were pinned along the " berm " of the trench, in others they were placed beneath the duckboards, where they were very safe from traffic but were correspondingly more difficult to maintain. Each and every method was given its fair trial and always advance was made in the direction of an orderly trench line system. These reforms did not take place in a week, a month, or even in a year. The changes were the result of constant adaptation of method, carried out by an exhaustive policy of trial and error, and the evolution of a satisfactory system took a considerable time. At the same time, improvements in supervision became operative and, as artillery and infantry came into line, the old induction and obstruction troubles ceased to occupy so prominent a place in the preoccupations of the signal officer.

While these improvements were taking place in the battle zone, ease of maintenance was being facilitated further back by the collection of the circuits into routes with central testpoints. This policy was persisted in until fresh conditions forced a modification in the autumn of 1917. A well-controlled system was gradually built up and, as conditions improved, the telephone gained in popularity day by day. In early 1916, its use was universal ; the official issue of magneto telephones to Divisions and Brigades was imminent, and " D3's " were being turned out in large quantities each month to complete battalions and batteries to scale. Artillery observation posts, each with its own telephone, increased in number daily. This method of signalling was nearing the climax of its popularity with the infantry and the introduction of buried cable had long ago indicated a way in which maintenance troubles could be minimized and still greater expansion carried out.

The future prospect of the telephone would have been rosy in the extreme, but already experiment had proved the existence of a danger which was to strike it to the heart as far as forward areas were concerned. The question of enemy overhearing had arisen in the summer of 1915.* Experiment, deduction, Intelligence reports, all combined to prove that the leakage of information to the enemy which had long been noted was intimately connected with the extension of the telephone to the front line trenches. It would indeed have been surprising, in view of later experiments, if he had not been overhearing, for the practice had arisen in many portions of the front line of running the lines connecting the forward posts along the edge of the barbed wire zone. The impossibility of the survival of lines in and behind the fire trenches was the reason, and on the face of things, a good reason, for this ; but the result must have far outweighed in gravity any advantages we gained from the safety of these lines. The question of overhearing generally is, however, a large and all-embracing one. Intimately wrapped up with it are many incidents which happened in 1916 and 1917. Although first recognized as a menace in 1915 and guarded against that year by many primitive precautions, its main development and result are alike found in later history. Detailed consideration of it will therefore be left until after the description of the first buried cable systems and the discussion of the lessons learnt from the battles of 1915.

In the present section of the History an attempt has been made to indicate the main lines of development of the early telephone service. The concentration of attention on this burning question to the exclusion of everything else has been emphasized. The chief obstacles in the way of efficient telephone communication have been dealt with as they arose, and the methods by which they were overcome have been indicated. By constant alertness, by education both of its own personnel, of telephone subscribers, and of the main mass of the army in France, the Signal Service extricated itself just in time from an awkward situation. Frequent failures of the telephone once more directed attention to supplementary methods of communication. The evolution of trench wireless and the formation of the pigeon service were part of the results of the lessons learnt during

* On June 12th, 1915, enemy messages were reported to be passing over railway metals near Beauvray and Serre in First Army area. Investigation failed to confirm this report, but messages from our own lines were overheard quite plainly.

this memorable period when the Signal Service was nearer to break-down than it ever came before or since.

The need for radical reorganization and a great accession of personnel to deal with the special problems of stationary warfare was clearly indicated. Already it formed one of the principal subjects of debate at frequent conferences of signal officers. It was to find expression in the first great reorganization of signals in 1916.

The conferences themselves were the outward and visible sign of the co-operation which had been forced upon signal officers of all ranks and of all kinds of units by the circumstances which pressed so hardly on them and on their men. This co-operation was to have results of increasing importance as time passed. The Signal Service was in a fair way to become a "Corps" in all essentials. With the specialization of the Service and the closing up of signal ranks to find mutual support we see the cause of the birth of an *esprit de corps* which is now a very valued fact. The times of trial made possible many things in the more successful future. Tactful and zealous advocacy at General Headquarters and at the headquarters of the higher formations, generally, had convinced the Staff that the Signal Service had its rights as well as its responsibilities. The signal officer of a formation must be treated rather as a technical adviser to the Staff than as an executive officer. The first fruits of this was the order giving the Signal Service control over all line communications. The question was to be emphasized yet more during the Battle of the Somme ; to emerge from that battle as an established principle.

Already it was accepted as such by the heads of the Signal Service itself and all future reorganization was aimed, and aimed successfully, at relieving the senior signal officer of each formation of his executive duties and establishing him as a member of the Head-quarters Staff, in fact, if not in name.

# Chapter V.

ALTHOUGH the main feature of Signal Service evolution during 1915 was undoubtedly the rise in the popularity of the telephone, numerous other lessons were learnt from the battles of this year.

On the front held by the British Force, the comparative peace of stationary warfare was interrupted by three main actions. Two of them—Neuve Chapelle in March, and Loos in September—were offensive operations on the part of the British Army, and at Loos the Cavalry Corps was massed behind our lines ready to exploit success should any considerable measure be achieved. In both cases, however, little advance was made and the position remained substantially unchanged. In the other battle which needs special consideration—the Second Battle of Ypres—the Germans once more concentrated their reserves in a sustained attempt to break through the British lines at the Ypres salient. Thanks to the employment of poison gas they were very nearly successful. Whole battalions of front line troops and supports were horribly asphyxiated and, but for the tenacity shown by the survivors, this second attack on Ypres might well have ended trench warfare in a *sauve qui peut* towards the coast.

This was not to be, however, and in the self-sacrificing stand without means of defence against this new and terrible weapon, the Signal Service played its part. All honour should be given to the runners who, despite the waves of suffocating gas, delivered the messages calling for reserves or artillery support to save a desperate situation. Equally splendid was the work of battalion and battery signallers and of the linemen and despatch riders of Brigades and Divisions. Until strength was exhausted and breathing no longer possible, they persevered at their tasks, only then to crawl away and die in agony, or, at the best, to be taken to the nearest Casualty Clearing Station and evacuated to the Base, there to cough and gasp away their lives with nothing but a consciousness of duty well done to sustain them in their agony.

No history of Signals nor of any other branch of the Army could be considered complete without some tribute paid to these men who, regardless of personal safety, stood fast at this most critical time.

73

Later months brought with them various measures, more and more efficient as time went on, combating this and all other gases the enemy could bring into use. Almost at once the first " tube helmets " gave comparative immunity, but in these first days nothing saved the situation but sheer heroism displayed by infantry, artillery, and all other arms alike.

Before dealing in detail with the lessons learnt by the Signal Service in the battles of 1915, a short general discussion will not be out of place. In the story of the rise of the telephone system and its adaptation and improvement until efficiency was obtained, it was pointed out that the predisposing cause of this increase was the corresponding growth of the artillery. Throughout the year, as through succeeding years, war was becoming more intensive. Never before had armies had to face anything like the amount of shell fire which was now a daily feature of the enemy's prosecution of the war. Our own guns with their daily ration of a dozen shells or so could not compete. During battle, and notably during the actions mentioned earlier in the chapter, this normally heavy fire increased to an, as yet, unparalleled extent. It was not to be expected that the slender unprotected cables stretched across miles of country which were the frail connecting links between infantry and artillery, between front line and supports, between headquarters of units and formations, could survive the tornado to which they were exposed.

Multiplication of lines might give temporary immunity ; the heroic work of devoted linemen might secure intermittent inter-communication ; but one great lesson of position warfare was that line communication without an adequate and increasing amount of protection was unreliable in the extreme. More, it was too costly, for linemen's lives are not cheap and the skilled men necessary to deal with a system of increasing complexity cannot be replaced at will. This lesson was taken to heart at once. After a little time attempts were made to solve the problem. The Buried Cable System of 1916 was the final answer which with various small modifications outlasted the war.

This lesson had, however, an important corollary. There was no prospect of a shell-proof system being built immediately. Indeed, a good system must take weeks to evolve and months to build. In the meantime something must be done to supplement line communication at once. Here was an intricate problem for solution. Visual was already discredited ; Army Wireless was in its infancy ; the runner, though reliable, was slow and far too costly. Where was the answer to be found ? The problem was only solved by the development of all these methods to suit new conditions, and by the formation of a Carrier Pigeon Service. Thus the second great lesson of the battles of 1915 was the development of supplementary means of communication. No longer would the Signal Service carry all its eggs in one basket. During 1915 itself, and during the early months of 1916—until the Battles of the Somme gave opportunity of putting all these means into practice in a great offensive—every effort was devoted towards the evolution of practical systems of trench wireless, trench visual, and, last but not least, an efficient carrier pigeon service for forward work. This year may be characterized as the year of evolution of new methods of signalling ; next year was to see the co-ordination of the various means in centrally-controlled and well-advertised schemes.

The culmination of this particular branch of Signal Service activity may be seen in the formulation of a general policy of forward signal work which was finally crystallized and set down in " S.S. 148." The publication of this manual marked a great step forward in Signal Service progress and will be further considered in its place.

Finally, the trying times through which the Signal Service was now passing were, as already indicated, not without result of another kind. Co-operation was first imposed on Signal units by the mushroom-like growth of the telephone system. The comparative failures of Signals in 1915 forced signal officers in self-defence to combine to make the most of their very limited resources. The vagaries of particular formation staffs gave birth to a need for sympathy and for knowledge of what was happening in the adjacent formations. Similarly, the hope of help from above made the O. i/c Signals of the lower formation more inclined to look for assistance to his colleague at the Corps or Army behind him. All these things combined together for good, and out of the many difficulties and distresses of the present arose the future organization which gave to the signal officers of rear formations senior rank and a greater power of supervising, guiding and formulating forward signals. All this was to the benefit of the Signal Service.

A general summary of the lessons learned from the 1915 fighting thus shows three main ways in which the evolution of signal practice and organization was most marked. It is now time to consider them one by one and review their history in detail.

From the beginning of the war the vulnerability of airline and field cable to intensive shell fire was forced upon the attention of everyone concerned. Various methods were tried to overcome this very serious difficulty in the way of maintaining line communication, but for some time with little success. The first step following the exposure of the relative vulnerability of open wire routes was a considerable extension of the use of cable in the forward areas. It was then discovered that cable slung lightly on poles was much less vulnerable than ground cable to high explosive shells bursting on impact. The former was, therefore, substituted for the latter wherever possible. The next improvement was the adoption of " trench " cable and this at once caused certain modifications in the use made of the various types of cable in the forward area. The enamelled wire and "D1" issued to infantry and forward artillery units served well enough for short periods of time over dry ground or slung on hedges. Their insulation was not, however, intended for trench work, and gradually, as the wet weather set in, both were almost entirely replaced by "D5" even in the front line trenches. This meant, of course, the issue to infantry of lengths of "D5" cable to carry out repairs to the lines which were in their maintenance areas, and the use of the lighter cables fell into abeyance to a certain extent. It is, indeed, interesting to note that enamelled wire never regained any measure of popularity. When broken, it was just as difficult to mend as "D1" or "D2" cable. It was easily damaged by traffic and was particularly liable to such breaks owing to its comparative invisibility. Once the break had occurred, also, the stiff wire ends sprang away and were only retrieved with difficulty, and sometimes after long search.

The next improvement in the line system was the duplication or triplication of lines with the idea of obtaining alternative circuits. In the case of some Brigades operating over heavily-shelled country, as many as six different lines were laid between Brigade and battalion headquarters. These were bunched where they entered the shelter of the trenches and bunched again in the more sheltered areas further to the rear, but spread out by different routes where they passed the more exposed intermediate zone. This policy was attended with a certain measure of success, but was only a palliative. It was also exceedingly wasteful of cable at a time when the supply of cable was very scarce and its economical use all-important.

By the early spring of 1915, however, experiments were already being made with buried "D5" cable, and in this connection it is interesting to note that the first efforts recorded were directed against damage to the lines by traffic rather than shell-fire. This was a natural sequence to the use of buried cable at gate-crossings and gaps of all kinds where traffic was likely to cross the line, which had long been an established feature of the cable wagon drill. The first extension of the use of such local buried crossings was the burying of cable routes along the edges of aerodromes in Flanders.

As early as the month of January, 1915, a further extension of the use of buried cable occurred between a Brigade headquarters and the Keep at Givenchy which was held by one of its battalions. This strong point was expected to be able to hold out for some considerable time, even if the surrounding trench system was overrun by the enemy and it was considered advisable to have a secret means of communication with the garrison. Experiments with trench wireless were yet to begin. Visual as then practised could not by any stretch of imagination be considered secret. There remained the possibility of constructing a line which could be securely hidden. With this in view a " D5 " cable was buried between the two headquarters in a trench 18 ins. deep. About the same time, the laying of traffic-, splinter-, and shrapnel-proof cable in trenches up to 30 ins. deep was tried in several British Divisions. The advantages of the new system at once became so obvious that this method of protecting lines was persisted in in face of the labour difficulties which were always its greatest enemy. No special labour could be allotted for the purpose. At first, the work was carried out by the Signal Company personnel themselves, but it soon became quite clear that these men, already overworked, could not deal with a buried system on anything like the scale required. The next advance was the employment of small parties of 10 or 20 general duty pioneers from the Engineers. In some Corps, even, small labour parties of Belgian civilians were recruited and these men were paid contract prices, the adults receiving three francs for a working day of ten hours and boys from two to 1½ francs according to their strength.

By this means and that, it proved possible to dig the first few experimental cable trenches, but the conspicuous success attending them soon caused the desire for buried cable to become universal. The use of shrapnel was much more general in those days than high explosive. The new trenched cable was not immune from a direct hit by a high explosive shell, but shrapnel, traffic, and even shell splinters, were powerless against it. Time after time, a few minutes after operations had commenced, the one or two "D5" cables in filled-in trenches were the only survivals of a complicated system.

Buried cable had established its right to existence even at some inconvenience and at the cost of considerable labour. Somehow this labour must be forthcoming. The problem was finally solved by the system—exceedingly unpopular with the victims—of employing large parties of infantry in rest to dig and fill in the various trenches required. Before the end of the summer of 1915, the dangerous zone between the rearmost communication trenches and the advanced Brigade headquarters was usually bridged by one or more cables buried to a depth of 2ft. 6in., and on many occasions these buried cables remained through when all other line communication had long been shot away and could not be replaced.

From the first, one of the main problems presented by the new method of using cable was the water-logged condition of the ground where buried cable was first brought into use. In particular, the district around Ypres, where shell-fire during the Second Battle of Ypres first caused the general use of buried cable as a system, was very wet, and only the best "D5" cable could be used with safety. The latter cable, however, did yeoman service under the new conditions for which it was never intended. Month after month, circuits which were not blown to pieces by direct hits kept through, and in some cases these early buried lines remained in working order well into the next year. In the wet and muddy soil near Ypres they were buried a good 3ft. before they could be considered even moderately safe from shells. It was indeed surprising how well the insulation of the lines lasted under the most severe conditions of test. Perhaps the greatest innovation took place when similar "D5" cable was laid through the water of Zillebeke Lake. Prophecies of its immediate failure were many, but all were falsified. The great difficulty proved to be—not the loss of insulation—but the many breakages which took place near the edge of the lake, where the depth of water was not sufficient to protect the cable either from shrapnel or from splinters. It was here cut again and again and the submerged end could only be recovered after long search with improvised grapnels. This finally caused the diversion of this portion of the cable round the edge of the lake, but the experience of the resistant nature of the insulation of "D5" was very reassuring and led to its more general use in similar situations.*

Many methods of guarding the cable against the wet and at the same time of giving it additional protection from mechanical strain were tried, but were not usually found worth while. Rubber tubing was used with fair success at ditch and stream crossings ; many lengths of cable were laid in gas piping to prevent direct contact between the cable and the soil ; in yet other cases iron piping of 1 in. bore was used. In the long run, however, it was found advisable to rely on the "D5" cable, carefully laid in a trench with a level bottom, and to use this until its insulation failed, or until it had been shattered and repaired so often that it was necessary to relay the whole or portions of the line.

Towards the end of the year various improvements had been tried and the systems generally had been more or less standardized. The main features were, however, still the 2ft. 6in. buries between the rearward limit of the zone of frequent shelling and the nearest communication trenches or battalion headquarters. Routes had become more common and many Brigades and Divisions holding particularly exposed fronts such as those in the Salient had duplicated or even triplicated their main buries. In one or two formations, a four-horsed plough had been used successfully as a labour-saving device and this led to exhaustive experiments which will be referred to later in describing the 1916 Buried System. Already several lines were being laid in the same bury, as the policy of concentration of lines was steadily carried out. There was, however, a limit to this

---

* It is a fact that constant unchanging conditions—whether wet or dry—exert a much less injurious influence upon the insulation of a cable than constant alternation from one to the other. The test referred to above was therefore perhaps of most value as providing a useful example of a law, well-known, but likely to be overlooked.

concentration. Earthed lines were still in general use and induction troubles were very marked on the early multiple buried routes. Some times during operations one line only in each bury could be used. If more were employed, over-hearing and consequent irritation and inefficiency far outweighed the advantage of being able to carry on two conversations at once. The use of twisted pairs was indicated and was already a matter of general discussion. For the present, however, the shortage of cable was too acute to allow this solution of the difficulty to be adopted. It was reserved for the more serious question of enemy overhearing to sweep away the prejudice against metallic circuits. In individual cases signal officers took the matter into their own hands, and twisted " D3," sometimes, even, improvised twisted " D5," was laid and buried, but as a general rule earthed lines were persisted in, in spite of induction troubles.

A special variety of buried cable which should receive passing notice was that laid in the forward trenches. Even these did not give sufficient protection against shrapnel, bullets and splinters, and especially against traffic. Buried cable soon spread beyond its original forward limit and many lines were buried 6ins. below the bottom corner of the trenches. This custom did not gain general popularity, however. It is true the lines were safer, but the difficulty of maintenance was also much increased. Trench cables such as those described in the last chapter were much preferred and buried cable in trenches was never universally adopted.*

Before finally leaving this description of the earlier buried cables, mention should be made of the first proposal for the introduction of armoured cables. This was made in the autumn of 1915. The use of these cables did not actually become general until the following year and they are better considered in detail when describing the evolution of the " deep " bury. They first sprang into prominence, however, in this autumn, when at a conference of signal officers of one of the armies they were referred to as the " only possible solution of the present complicated forward trench system." In isolated cases they had been used in buried cable routes before the year was out and it soon became evident that the only obstacle to their general adoption was that of supply.

Not the least of the problems raised by the general adoption of the shallow bury was that of the identification of the routes. Trampled upon by traffic of every description, used as a guide by

* In late September, 1916, a method was tried of combining buried cable with a communication trench. A trench eight feet deep was dug, cable laid therein and then two feet filled in. There were possibilities in the idea but it proved a failure. (a) the task was too great for a single night and the depth was not obtained ; (b) the bottom of the trench became too muddy and was impassable in places ; (c) the organization and execution of the work was defective.

all ranks returning to and from the trenches, the neat rounded mound which marked the site of the newly-buried cable was soon levelled with the surrounding country and reduced to the semblance of the numerous tracks that covered the war-worn country in an intricate network. Time after time, the earlier buries were lost to all intents and purposes and it was soon evident that some means of marking buried cable routes clearly and definitely was urgently required. Here, as in many similar cases, unexpected difficulties arose. The neat stakes or standards with their carefully-painted blue and white squares were trampled under foot or torn up and burnt by cold and hungry soldiers. The final solution of the difficulty came with the introduction at a later date of special metal buried cable " markers," but a temporary remedy was early found in at least one Corps in the Ypres district. Despairing of the ordinary stake marker which was erected only to be used by the private soldier for his own illegitimate purposes, an ingenious subaltern hit upon the idea of marking his buries with a series of wooden crosses with the inscription R.I.P. He had chosen the one emblem the British soldier will respect himself and will not allow any other man to abuse. From the date of the erection of the new emblems, his lines were labelled for the duration of their usefulness, and the incident is a striking example of the ingenuity necessary to keep ahead of circumstances. Much of the thought expended by officers and men of the Signal Service during the war was devoted to over-coming the obstacles put in their way by the mass of the soldiery whose needs they were serving. This is a factor which will recur in future wars, unless a campaign of education is carried on among the rank and file of the troops—both Regular and Territorial—in time of peace. Instances will arise in this History again and again of special efforts directed towards the education of the rank and file in the uses and limitations of signalling in war, or of special organiza-tion or devices to combat the results of an ignorance which was as dangerous as it was universal. The blame for this in the past cannot, perhaps, be accurately apportioned. It is for the Signal Service of the future, with its vastly greater powers and responsibilities, to see that efficient propaganda is carried on and that the situation does not recur. Had the energy expended on policing circuits, on tracing routes lost through the wanton removal of the means of identification, and on repeating work wilfully destroyed, been available for improve-ment of the existing system, better results cannot but have been obtained.

A special aspect of the protection of the line system against enemy artillery fire was that which arose in the very forward and exposed areas where the trench system was incomplete or even entirely want-ing. This was particularly the case after an advance or a reverse. In either case the infantry, having left their original defence system which had been made good by many months' work, were compelled to dig themselves hastily into little unconnected strips of trench or into individual rifle pits. Some system of signal communication between the principal posts and headquarters had to be devised, and this difficulty was overcome to some extent by the use of " laddered " cable. Two lines were laid from front to rear with an interval of the order of 60 yards between them. These were then cross-connected by a number of lateral lines, the resulting network resembling the uprights and rungs of a ladder. Such a device minimized the likelihood of a complete disconnection, although individual breaks were more difficult to locate. Laddered cable was very useful during and immediately after an advance or a retreat, and became at one time very generally used. The main drawback to its use was the necessity for constant overhaul of the whole network in order to ensure efficiency. If this was not done systematically, weak places would accumulate, until a final break might render the line useless.

A local variant used in some formations was rabbit netting. This was often experimented with, its value being that it was more difficult to cut than cable. Lengths were laid with six inch overlapping joints, connected by copper wire, but not soldered. The netting was tried both suspended on stakes and lying on the ground, and good buzzer signals were obtained over distances up to 1000 yards. It was very cumbersome, however, and by no means immune from the effects of high explosive shells. Although frequently employed near heavily-shelled spots such as cross-roads, it never gained a prominent place in the scheme of forward communication.

-----

It is now necessary to consider the second great lesson of the battles of 1915—the necessity for supplementary means of communication to reinforce the telephone system. This need was driven home—also by the German artillery—both in attack and defence. Did the enemy attack, then his attack was preceded and accompanied by such a barrage of shells that all line communication became uncertain and, in many cases, the life of the forward lines could be measured in minutes. Did the attack come from the British lines, it was invariably countered by heavy enemy shelling on the whole forward area, both that occupied before, and that captured during the battle. In all cases, the persistence of line communication as far forward as battalion headquarters was the exception rather than the rule.

Late in the year, the general adoption of the splinter-proof bury eased the situation, but even that was not infallible and when broken took some time to mend. In the meantime the great need was for some means of communication which depended for its safety and usefulness on some other factor than the continued maintenance of an uninterrupted thread between headquarters. Good work was being

G

done in battle by the lines to the rear of Division, and also between Division and Brigade. In the Ypres fighting, telegraphed messages between Army and Division averaged 15 minutes, while exceptionally good times ranging between six and eight minutes were not uncommon ; D.R.'s over the same distance taking from $\frac{1}{2}$ to $1\frac{1}{4}$ hours.

It was in the forward area—in the zone of frequent shelling—where the disconnections were most common and continuous, and it was here that supplementary means of signal communication were most needed. Whether the matter in hand was the relief of our own hard-pressed troops, reeling back before the waves of German gas and battered beneath a hail of shells ; or whether the problem was to bridge the gaps between our own advancing troops and battalion and Brigade headquarters, signal touch could not be maintained with lines. Constantly shifting their targets as the situation changed, the German artillery thrashed the contested area continuously with an iron storm. Lines laid before the attack were blown to pieces before they could be used. Further attempts to establish line communication resulted in casualty and failure. Again and again would front line troops be isolated for hours, and sometimes even for days. Driven by sheer necessity, battalion commanders and Brigade signal officers alike began to have recourse again to visual. Flags were sometimes used from sheltered sites in buildings and copses without attracting the enemy's attention. Discs and shutters, as inconspicuous and small as could be usefully employed over the distances involved, were designed and manufactured in large numbers, issued to front line troops, and used by them on occasion with great success. Exposure of the receiving station was minimized by the introduction of the trench periscope ; its safety was catered for by the building of heavily-concreted emplacements or the use of specially strengthened buildings. In this respect, evolution was parallel with that which was taking place in the line system simultaneously with the introduction of buried cable. Central test stations and central visual stations were planned on similar lines, though usually the same building or shelter was not used for both purposes. This could not well be, for one of the first principles of the new school of thought as regards line routes was that they should avoid all prominent features of the landscape. Test stations in particular were to be as inconspicuous as possible, reliance being placed rather upon freedom from enemy observation than on protection once attention had been attracted. Fortification as applied to trench warfare was yet in its infancy and the occupants of the new central visual observing posts were in no enviable position. Few shelters yet existed which would stand the direct hit of any but the smallest types of high explosive shell. Visual stations were necessarily in exposed positions, though in the worst cases attraction of undesirable attention was minimized by the adoption of D.D.D.D. working. Any prominent point was, however, a natural target for artillery, and many casualties testified to the devotion shown by the Divisional, Brigade, and battalion signallers whose efforts made possible the rejuvenation of visual.

A modification of the use of the disc was afforded by the issue of discs on long poles intended for use from the comparative shelter of forward trenches. These were, however, not an unqualified success. They were a considerable encumbrance to the regimental signaller, laden as he already was with his full infantry equipment, and in many cases they did not reach their destination. In later types this difficulty was overcome to some extent by adapting the disc to fit on to the signaller's rifle. Always, the powers of endurance of the men had to be taken into consideration. So often the various new devices for forward signalling in an attack—excellent as many of them were —proved to be the proverbial last straw to break the camel's back. At the ordinary steady pace of an advance, the signaller could just stagger along with all his various *impedimenta*. If, however, anything out of the ordinary happened, if special haste were required of him, or if he became involved in the vagaries of a bursting shell there was the chance that his signalling apparatus would be the first thing to be dropped. Not once nor twice, but many times, signalling parties arrived at their destination only to find themselves useless owing to the loss of some essential piece of apparatus. Discs and shutters are only a case in point. Later, with the introduction of more complicated means of forward signalling, this factor assumed a more important aspect. For the present it may be noted as the most prominent cause of the failure of the long-handled signalling discs from which much was expected by their sponsors.

The rise of the signalling disc in popularity was admittedly the feature of the new visual telegraphy by day. Semaphore with the necessary exposure of the person was still unpopular save under exceptionally favourable circumstances. Morse on the flag was also relegated to a subordinate position. The daylight lamp was yet a thing of the future, though the germ of the idea was already forming in minds ever searching after new expedients. For night work, the old Begbie lamp had proved itself hopeless. Both by sight and by sound, even—so said some signallers—by smell, its presence betrayed itself to all enemy posts in its immediate neighbourhood. Its place was now definitely taken by the much more portable and much more silent electric signalling lamp, the first pattern generally adopted being that used in the French Army.

The large degree of dispersion of the rays of this lamp was still a decided drawback in the eyes of forward signal personnel. Still more was this so in the eyes of their neighbours, who, without a personal interest in the signalling lamps, were exposed to the full effects of the storm of shot and shell so frequently brought down upon the vicinity of visual stations by their too incautious employment.

This matter was also taken in hand in 1915 with good effect, however, and excellent results were obtained over distances up to half or three quarters of a mile by the use of tubes 1in. or 2ins. in diameter, which reduced the dispersion of the signalling beam. With the rays directed and controlled in this manner, two-way working was possible, even with one station within a hundred yards or less of the front line. Horizontal and vertical dispersion were both reduced to a very few yards over the distances covered. To make assurance doubly sure it was only necessary to see that the lamp at the rear station was aligned so that its rays projected slightly downwards. There was then no likelihood of a distant German station picking up its light. This artifice proved successful and was very generally adopted in forward stations both for one-way and for two-way working. The use of these tubes demanded considerable skill and care both in the original alignment of the station and in the subsequent working, but keen men soon reduced the setting-up and working of the new visual stations to a routine.

Once more the front at night was starred with minute winking flashes of light·as the Morse messages passed to and fro, the only difference being that from now on each station had its own particular star jealously screened from all alien observers. Indiscretion or bad management had an altogether disproportionate penalty. A lapse, no matter how slight, might result in summary extinction. At the least it was likely to be visited on the head of the offender in the form of the wrath of the nearest Brigadier. Many a signaller would have found it difficult to say at short notice which he would have preferred. In both cases, the result was the same. Slips were seldom made and gradually visual regained a certain usefulness and popularity.

Thus, in one way, the yawning gap between front line and artillery and supports, and between advancing troops and directing Staff, was bridged without the intervention of lines. The weakness of visual was that it was never of universal application. Beyond every other method of signalling, it is dependent on favourable weather conditions. The mists of early dawn—the usual hour for attack on either side—were fatal to its use. The " fog of war " was another obstacle which was inseparable from the conditions under which supplementary signal communications were most essential. The smoke and dust of bombardment were fated time and again to cause the entry in the reports of signal officers of the words " Visual impossible." It was quite clear that visual schemes, useful as they sometimes were, could only be a partial solution of the problem of replacing an unreliable line system.

Some other means was required—if possible one independent of weather conditions. The problem was to do away with wires. One inevitable answer was " Use wireless telegraphy," but in the path of the adoption of this solution stood many obstacles. Wireless telegraphy was yet in its infancy and many months of experiment would be required before decisive results could be hoped for. In no army had wireless yet been adapted for trench work. Use could not be made of work already carried out by our allies ; deductions could not be drawn from progress made by our foes. Our own Intelligence informed us that in neither army were small wireless sets in use for tactical purposes. The nearest approach to what was wanted existed in the British Flying Corps and it was along the lines of these sets that the first experiments were carried out.

In the summer of 1915 the problem was tackled in earnest, and officers were definitely appointed to carry out experiments in trench wireless. Thus the first step was taken in the programme that was destined to rejuvenate wireless, converting it in time from a temporarily obsolescent type of intercommunication, into one of the mainstays of the signal system, as it became during the advance in 1918 and on the Rhine in 1919. This result was not achieved in a day. The struggles of forward wireless for recognition—first as a possible means of intercommunication in emergency, then as a regular means of supplementing line communication, and finally as an efficient means, under certain circumstances, of replacing lines—form no mean part of the history of the Signal Service from this time onwards.

It was at once evident that it was worth while to endeavour to produce stations suitable for work as far back as Corps headquarters. Already the range of the enemy's guns was encroaching upon the hitherto inviolate territory behind Divisional headquarters. In this year Bethune was shelled with 15-inch shells and soon afterwards these projectiles became a recognized feature of back area shelling. It did not need much prescience to foresee a considerable rearward extension in the immediate future of the zone affected by enemy shelling. An additional argument in favour of Corps stations was the necessity for control which would at once spring up with the general adoption of small range wireless sets. Behind Corps head-quarters, the sets already in existence, with perhaps slight modification, would suffice. The Marconi $\frac{1}{2}$ kw.*pack set might even conceivably be of use forward of Corps headquarters, but the ranges for which this set was intended were considerably greater than the distances over which it would have to work under the new conditions. Excess of power was to be deprecated for several reasons. For one thing, universal jamming † might be expected to result ; for another, any undue use of power would assist enemy wireless stations in their work of intercepting our messages.

For both these reasons the pack wireless set was ruled out for

* Kilowatt.    † Wireless interference.

general forward work, though used for the early experiments. The men engaged in building up the new system were given the task of designing two suitable sets ; one for use near the front line or at Brigade or Divisional headquarters, the other slightly more powerful, for use as a directing station with the Corps.

Meanwhile the first experiments in the line were actually commenced with Stirling transmitters and short wave receivers borrowed from the R.F.C. On June 15th to 17th, 1915, four of these sets were erected at the headquarters of two divisions, one brigade, and one battalion of the V Corps. A series of exhaustive tests were carried out and the value of the new short range wireless as an emergency method of communication was at once demonstrated. In these early experiments the directing station was a lorry set specially adapted for short wave working, but it was from the first obvious that this must be only a temporary expedient and that as soon as possible it must be replaced by a more portable and less conspicuous set. A rough sketch of the position of the sets and of the type of aerial employed with the set at Ypres is shewn in *Plate* IX. Although not on this occasion used for messages of tactical importance, touch was successfully maintained under adverse conditions and the possibilities of the new application of wireless were fully demonstrated.

The experiments were continued and obstacles to progress were steadily overcome. At the same time a fresh use for wireless was suggested—that of direct wireless communication between observation posts and the headquarters of batteries or brigades of heavy artillery. This problem was a similar one in its essential features and its solution was attempted along the same lines. R.E. personnel could not be spared, but Signal Service instructors and some small sets were provided for the brigade chosen for the experiment, and N.C.O.'s and men of the artillery were collected in a class and trained in the principles of wireless telegraphy and in the use of the small portable wireless sets. This experiment was even more successful than the former one and from the first the sets were used for observation purposes. Their value was demonstrated almost the first day of their arrival when enemy shelling destroyed six out of the seven cables running to one of the observation posts, and four men were wounded or killed in carrying out the necessary repairs to the lines. The small wireless aerial did not escape attention. It was shot away again and again, but was easily replaced in the lulls of firing, and was maintained throughout the " shoot " without loss of effectives.

By the middle of August a design had been drawn out for a suitable wireless set for forward work. It was sent home together with an experienced technical officer who had been personally engaged on the problem, and the building of 100 sets to this design was ordered.

It was this set slightly modified which finally took its place, as the B.F. set, in the standard equipment of all Divisional signal companies. The cryptic letters of the name round which much speculation on the part of the uninitiated has centred, refer essentially to the main purpose for which the set was intended. It was designed for use by hurriedly trained operators and was therefore to be as nearly as possible "fool-proof." Hence, by the Army generally, with its tendency to provide nicknames for everything and everybody, the letters B.F., given as an appropriate title to the set by its designer, were acclaimed as being an ideal appellation. The new instrument was known as the B.F. set to all within whose range of experience it came, and the title by which one was accustomed to refer to it when describing it to Generals at official inspections— the British Field Set—was in part devised to cast the mantle of respectability over the original meaning of the letters. Well-conceived for the work for which it was intended, the station could be successfully worked by the most inexperienced wireless operator, and with its general adoption much later in the war the early troubles of forward wireless were much reduced.

In the early days of experiment the set was not produced in sufficient numbers to stand alone. Many others shared the field for some time and chief among these was the Stirling transmitter and the R.F.C. type of short wave receiver.

These latter, however, uncombined as they were, required a party of five men to transport them. The bigger the party required, the less likely was it that the whole of it would arrive at its destination, while there was also a greater waste of personnel for a given amount of result achieved. The new British field set was a combined receiver and transmitter, stoutly built and designed to stand the conditions of forward work, and it soon outdistanced all rivals.

While the development of a suitable wireless set for forward work was being made the subject of experiment, search was being made for a set of slightly greater power, and yet with as high a degree of portability as possible, for use as a directing station at or about Corps headquarters. This was very quickly solved by the discovery of the possibilities of the Wilson wireless transmitter combined with the Mark III service short wave receiver. With a mast 30 ft. high— quite a possible height under the circumstances in which the set would be used—good signals were obtained both ways between this set and the new B.F. set at a range of 10 miles.* The Wilson set possessed a very musical note and a satisfactory degree of simplicity and strength, and was probably the most successful of all the spark wireless sets produced during the war. It at once replaced the pack

* This figure was a normal range in the most suitable country. On the Somme it was often necessary to push Wilson sets forward to limit the range to 6,000 yards.

set as a directing station and, with the B.F. set, was destined to become the standard apparatus for forward wireless working in the area between Corps and Brigade headquarters for the duration of the war.

During the first experiments much trouble was experienced with the R.F.C. wireless sets working to the artillery. The latter possessed an almost complete monopoly of wireless working on short wave lengths during the early months of this year, and, not unnaturally, were jealous of any infringement of their rights. In the first trench wireless experiments their own type of sets was in use and complaints of jamming were numerous from both sides. The tactical significance of trench wireless was not yet quite clear and at first the new stations laboured under considerable disadvantages, their working being suspended on several occasions while special shoots and reconnaissances were carried out. Both sides were, however, amenable to reason and a compromise was soon effected, the R.F.C. retaining complete control over wave lengths up to 300 metres and the new army wireless sets being standardized on 350, 450 and 550 metres. From this time, jamming troubles with our own sets were less acute, though the situation was soon to be complicated by the arrival on the scene of action of German trench sets of much greater power than our own, and by the enemy's employment of special jamming stations.

It was at the Battle of Loos in September, 1915, that the tactical employment of the short range wireless stations was first justified in action. For this operation a wireless section consisting of two lorry sets, two pack sets, and six short range sets was attached to First Army under a specially-qualified senior officer. Previous to the battle, one pack set was installed in a dug-out on the Bethune-Lens road near Vermelles, and the short range sets—to man which a considerable proportion of the personnel of the motor lorry section was absorbed—were arranged to provide emergency communication between each of four divisions and one of their brigades in the line. The dispositions of the sets were altered from time to time during the battle and one set in particular was erected in Loos after its capture and did most excellent work in spite of heavy shelling by shrapnel and high explosive shells. In a general summary like the present, it is not possible to go into the details of the action, but on three critical occasions wireless messages were got through when all other means of communication had failed. On one occasion, the cavalry would have been ordered forward under the impression that the enemy's line was pierced and must infallibly have suffered heavy casualties but for a message from the small wireless set in Loos. On a second, the troops in Loos were hard-pressed and wished to withdraw. They would have done so, and Loos would have been lost, had not a wireless message been received advising the immediate advent of support. In the third case, casualties were occurring among our own troops from our own artillery fire. All means of signal communication had failed except wireless, but by this means the error was corrected and the fire of the guns directed on to enemy targets.

Many minor administrative difficulties were betrayed by this operation and the correction of these was put in hand at once. A far greater obstacle to the use of trench wireless was, however, not so susceptible of immediate improvement. There was a general disinclination to use it even though it had already proved its value. Commanding officers considered that wireless was likely to give their positions away ; Staffs thought the code that had been arranged for the occasion inadequate and cipher troublesome ; Signal Officers themselves had little faith in the value of the new method of signalling. Once again the Signal Service, and in particular the officers detailed to promote the use of wireless, were faced with difficulties which could only be surmounted by a campaign of education and propaganda. This was at once commenced. The history of trench wireless during the following year is largely the attempt to popularize this means of signalling both within the Signal Service itself, and amongst the Staffs and Commanders who would have to use it as a means of transmitting orders and information. It was a long uphill struggle and was complicated by the occurrence of the many technical failures which are inseparable from the building up of a complicated organization and the use of delicate instruments under war conditions. It was not until 1918 that forward wireless really came into its own, though both in 1916 and 1917 individual cases occurred when wireless proved the only survival of a shattered intercommunication system. Such cases properly advertised converted many officers from hostility to warm partisanship. The education of the Signal Service itself was carried out by means of classes of junior and senior officers, held first at the wireless headquarters at Campagne les Hesdin and later at the Wireless School at Abbeville. Every wireless officer was an enthusiastic teacher, preacher, and prophet. As we go on to consider other phases of the growth of Signals, we can leave the wireless service carrying on with its experiments, its schemes, and its educational programme. The organization through which this new branch of signal activity was controlled and manned will be reviewed in some detail in a later chapter.

---

The natural rival to visual and wireless for bridging the forward zone where wires were difficult or impossible to maintain was the pigeon. In a previous chapter the use of pigeons by the Intelligence Corps in the early months of the war has been referred to. It was in the spring of 1915 that the attention of Corps and Divisions was first attracted to the possibilities of this method of conveying messages. In May, during the enemy attack at Ypres, pigeons were successfully used to bring back situation reports and requests for assistance and artillery support, and it was as the result of these operations that the first Corps Pigeon Service was organized in the Second Corps in that month.

From this date the growth of the forward Carrier Pigeon Service organization was rapid. The obstacles in its way were considerably less than those which hindered the advance of trench wireless. The carrier pigeon had long been recognized as a trustworthy and speedy means of conveying messages over distances far greater than those involved in the new experiment. The birds had no great objection to shell fire ; they were much less susceptible to the effects of poison gas than human beings. The chance of their being hit whilst on the wing was very small, and if hit while in the trenches they were much more easily replaced than the runners instead of whom they were being used. One disadvantage of their use was the fact that the lofts had to be kept well back out of sight of the enemy and out of range of his guns. This meant of course the abandonment of the ordinary channels of communication, and pigeon messages went straight from battalion headquarters or from pigeon posts in the trenches to Division or Corps headquarters. As the majority of the messages were intended for the Brigade to which the battalion belonged, a certain amount of delay was inevitable. It was, however, reduced to a minimum by connecting up the lofts to the nearest signal offices of the formation which the birds served. Messages were treated as priority and were given preference over all less important telephone traffic. Thus a message from the trenches could be relied upon to reach Brigade headquarters in 10, 15 or 20 minutes, according to the distance flown by the birds. In addition, the barraged zone was traversed in minimum time with minimum loss of life, and as a result pigeons increased rapidly in popularity amongst the front line troops.

One trouble which had, of course, to be faced from the outset was the human element in the problem. Men were carefully trained in pigeon duties. Stringent regulations were made as to the feeding and watering and the general care of the birds, but here again careful education was necessary to avoid wastage both of birds and of opportunities to use them.

It was very difficult at first to prevent the infantry making pets of their birds, feeding them at odd times and on forbidden food, and in other ways making them disinclined to leave their baskets in the trenches. The limitations of the pigeon were also not at first understood, and many messages were rendered of no avail through birds being liberated in the dark or too late to enable them to reach home before darkness fell. Similarly, if cocks and hens were liberated together, the result, while it might ultimately increase the numerical strength of the pigeon service, was not liable to improve the time of the individual message concerned. Pigeon nature altogether is not unlike human nature, and the natural habits and desires of the birds had to be taken into account so far as was possible. As more and more men were trained as brigade and battalion pigeoneers, a greater degree of efficiency was attained. Pigeons were properly handled, properly fed, protected against the rats, which were their natural enemies in the trenches, and against wet and mud. The care of pigeons became as natural to the men entrusted with them as horse-mastership is to the men of a mounted unit. Whenever possible, men with previous experience of the birds were chosen, but whether this was so or not there was no difficulty in obtaining a sufficiency of enthusiastic volunteers. As the service became more efficient, a greater proportion of birds homed successfully and in better time and, by the autumn of 1915, the carrier pigeon had become a usual and most valuable supplementary method of communication.

The organization of the first Corps service included the allotment of certain lofts to the Corps and the formation of a pigeon station for each Brigade sector of the front. At each Brigade station was a basket containing four pigeons in charge of a specially trained man. Two copies of the same message were usually sent off by different birds to avoid possibility of miscarriage and the time of flight from all stations averaged about 15 minutes. At the loft, an ingenious arrangement was contrived, by which the pigeon landing in the trap automatically rang an electric bell which served the purpose of notifying the loft attendant of the bird's return and in some cases of calling up the local signal office. On receipt of this warning, a D.R. at once proceeded to the loft and brought back the message. This was then handed in at Corps headquarters, a copy being wired simultaneously to the Division and Brigade concerned.

The extension of the Carrier Pigeon Service for general signal purposes was very quick and widespread in the summer of 1915, and G.H.Q. Intelligence at once realized the danger and inconvenience of divided control. In June of this year the proposal was definitely made that the Director of Signals should assume complete control over a remodelled service and without any further delay the reorganization took place. It is impossible here to go into the detail of this reorganization, but in principle it provided for a Carrier Pigeon Service centrally controlled from G.H.Q. and catering for the establishment of ten pigeon stations with each army and a similar number with the Cavalry Corps. A considerable number of extra men was required to man the new service and the enlistment of 60 specialists was sanctioned. The question of the immediate supervision of the service was overcome by transferring to the Signal Service the officer who had organized the Carrier Pigeon Service for the Intelligence Corps. He was now made responsible to the Director of Signals for the efficiency of the new Signal Carrier Pigeon Service. The original estimate of ten carrier pigeon stations per Army was soon exceeded and First Army organization towards the end of 1915 is seen in *Plate* X.

During the battle of Loos when trench wireless first underwent extensive trial, pigeons were also employed, and to a more considerable extent. During the fortnight that followed the commencement of the offensive many urgent messages were transmitted by pigeons. Casualties were few, 14 birds in all being lost, and times were very good. A slight reform which had good results was the invention of a smoke bag to protect pigeons from gas while in their baskets. This was made on the same principle as the smoke helmet and was very successful, birds being kept in gassed areas for as much as six hours without bad results.

---

So far, in the present chapter, the protection of cable routes in forward areas and their reinforcement by other means of signalling have been considered. An equally important step forward in the evolution of the Signal Service is seen in the general consolidation of its policy and its members and the building up of an *esprit de corps* under pressure of circumstances. The original signal units which landed in France in 1914 were unco-ordinated. No senior officer commanding a company owed allegiance to anyone except his Staff and—in very much less degree—to the Director of Signals at G.H.Q. Attempts of the signal officers of higher formations to assume control over the Signals of lower formations would have been resented and co-operation generally was at a minimum. As time passed and the pressure of circumstances increased, the first result was a certain interdependence between units. With formations constantly shifting about in the line, Os.C. Signal Companies were constantly coming into contact with one another, exchanging ideas, and modifying points of view based merely on their own experience. Systems admirably adapted for one part of the front were not suitable for another. The open routes of sheltered and undulating country could not survive the conditions which the shallow bury supported with difficulty on the flatter front in Flanders. Gradually a spirit of co-operation began to pervade all ranks of the Signal Service. The blue and white armband became a badge of comradeship. Everyone was out to help defeat the conditions which bade fair to strangle an over-burdened service. The result was manifested in many ways. Control of the wires in the forward area, with the greater responsibility and authority conferred thereby, improved the position of the Divisional signal officer, while at the same time it prepared him for a logical extension of the same principle which should in time make him subordinate to his immediate superior at the Corps. In the same way, the appoint--

ment of senior officers as O. i/c Signals at Army headquarters gave birth to a new power of co-ordination throughout the whole of each Army. It did not need much farther thought along the same lines to complete the chain of command in Signals by the creation of two posts which practically made the senior signal officer at Corps and Army a Signal Adviser to the Staff of his formation. Early in 1916, the O.C. Signals, Army, was released from his executive duties and appointed Deputy Director of Signals to the Army Commander with the rank of Colonel and with general supervision over the whole of the signal communications of the Army. A little later, a similar administrative reform took place at the Corps and for the first time the chain of command in the Signal Service was complete. These reforms were the direct outcome of the gradual but definite extension of Signal responsibilities, of which the first fruits had been the acceptance of responsibility for signals in the higher artillery formations and the general control of forward lines. They immensely strengthened the position of the Signal Service.

Elaborate signal communications had become essential to the success of modern warfare. It had long been recognized in theory that the signal officer must be consulted beforehand, if operations were to be carried through according to programme. This principle, too often ignored by Staff officers, had now become an uncontrovertible fact. It was no longer to be a question of saying : " such and such are my dispositions ; such and such signal communication must be forthcoming." Future operations must be modified by considerations of intercommunication problems in the same way that signal systems are dependent upon operations. The need for some such reform had already been well shown in the battles of 1915, particularly in the case of lower formations. Divisions and Brigades had commenced to split up into front and rear headquarters. In one particular case, a Divisional headquarters split up into three portions, while at the same time the Divisional artillery also divided into two, and each Brigade established an advanced and rear office. The result might have been foreseen. The Signal Company, already strained to its utmost capacity to deal with a normal number of signal offices, was quite unable to lay and maintain all the circuits required. At one time all the linemen were out on the lines at once. The artillery had to be left to run their own intercommunication as regards operators, and little could be done for them as regards lines. The visual signallers of the company were all employed on the telephone system and additional cyclist orderlies had to be borrowed. A gallant attempt was made to maintain touch, but it not unnaturally failed.

At one time this splitting up of headquarters and the still more aggravating constant moves of headquarters, because the Staff did not like their billets or because of enemy attention, became the rule rather than the exception. Gradually, however, the representations of signal officers, reinforced as they were by frequent failures of intercommunication that could be traced directly to the changes, began to have effect. The division into advanced and rear head-quarters became a normal procedure, but it was recognized that the main responsibilities of the Signal Company consisted in maintaining communication between the fighting headquarters. Rear headquarters were connected, it is true, but they became of secondary importance during operations.

Another question intimately connected with the movements of formation headquarters was that of reliefs. The lower the formation and, therefore, the nearer the fighting line, the more frequently the troops became worn out and had to be relieved. This meant, of course, that the responsibility for signal communication in the same sector was constantly changing. Here, also, as time passed and experience was gained, improvements in organization took place. In the first few months of trench warfare, signal units moved out with their formations, carrying off with them every inch of cable or wire and every instrument and terminal. The incoming unit had to reconstruct the whole system of communications, often at the expense of several casualties, always with unnecessary expenditure of labour and stores. The disadvantages of this system were soon seen and individual officers handing over to men they could trust, left their lines in position, taking over in exchange an equivalent amount of wire or cable. Gradually, as such reliefs became a part of the normal routine of every unit, this practice became universal and the exaction of the *quid pro quo* in the form of line stores fell into disuse.

The same could not be said about instruments, however, and in the earlier days when the personnel of units was trained to work with improvised and unstandardized instruments, this dislike of exchanging to instruments probably of a quite different type was understandable. The disadvantages of the relief procedure in existence were certainly obvious, though acquiesced in by everyone concerned. In Brigades, particularly, and in Divisions to a great extent, moves were frequent, and the instrument repairers spent a considerable portion of their time in the signal office either installing, improving, or taking down the instruments on completion of a relief which had just taken place, or in preparation for a relief to come. Work thus proceeded under disadvantages, yet the custom persisted. Even in 1918, it was the exception rather than the rule for a Division to hand over its instruments in position to the incoming Division, though this was often done with test-panels, and, less commonly, with telephone exchanges. Perhaps the motive at the root of this policy of constant change was a low opinion of human nature ; perhaps an affection for instruments that had been in use for many months. Whatever was the cause, it was one which might well receive the attention of future signal officers. If a complete system of office relief can be evolved and insisted upon, much will be achieved in the direction of greater efficiency and incidentally a policy of faith in one's fellow men will be inculcated with good effects.

One difficulty which was first experienced in this year to a serious extent was the lack of continuity of signal responsibility in areas. Every few days in the case of Brigades, every few weeks in the case of Divisions, every two or three months in the case of Corps, a move took place and the whole of the signal system of the areas concerned was either replaced altogether or changed hands. There was no continuity of policy or of acquaintance with the system or the area. Even the habit of handing over line systems complete had its drawbacks from this point of view. Records were seldom exhaustive in detail or up to date. The new company or section had to grope their way through the system of their predecessors step by step ; a proceeding nearly as difficult in some cases as re-laying the whole. Some co-ordinating authority was required, who would have a general and continuous responsibility over the area, who could insist on a standard system of records, and who could provide a nucleus of personnel who would remain in the area independent of reliefs. These directions of reform were indicated from the first and formed a prominent subject of discussion in the many Army and Corps signal conferences that were held during the year.

Out of these conferences arose a policy which differed in different Armies and Corps, but followed the same general lines. In one Army a cable detachment was attached from the Corps to each Division in the Corps. The personnel of this detachment was given general charge of the working of all forward lines, manning of test-points, keeping of records, etc. This personnel belonged still to the Corps Signal Company and did not move with Division. In Second Army area, on the other hand, properly constituted area parties consisting of one officer and eight men were formed—also from the personnel of the cable sections—and one such party was told off to each area to control the maintenance of all lines not in use. The original proposal, which contained the germ of the whole future official policy of the Signal Service, was as follows :—

" Before laying cable or wire the new officer taking over should refer to the officer in charge of the permanent party. Once taken over maintenance to be by unit. Officers to keep a complete record of all wires in their area. These permanent parties to be attached to each Infantry Brigade Section."

In putting forward this proposal, it is interesting to note that an analogy was drawn from the German system already in use, where one officer and forty men looked after, and were responsible for, area signals.

To carry any regional policy into effect, a careful delimitation of areas was necessary and, in November, 1915, the Director of Signals ruled that signal areas should be allotted by Armies to Corps, by Corps to Divisions and by Divisions to Brigades. About the same time, the O.C. Corps Signals was made generally responsible for the signal communication in the Corps area generally, and in order to ensure continuity of policy it was decided that the Corps Signal Company should not move with the Corps, but should remain in the area when the new Corps headquarters took over.* This, of course, separated the Corps Signal Company in many cases from its Corps and led to some confusion and difficulty of identification. This position of affairs was permitted to persist for some time, but was finally set right by the allotment of letters to the Corps Signal Company, the original First Corps Signal Company becoming " A " Corps Signal Company, and so on throughout the alphabet as far as necessary.

At the same time as the reforms referred to above, it was represented to the Staff that signal efficiency could not be reckoned upon unless the frequent changes of headquarters so common in 1915 were reduced to a minimum. This was a fact that was rapidly becoming self-evident. Changes of headquarters, other than those taking place at reliefs, were invariably followed by a certain dislocation of traffic which was quite clearly unavoidable with the present complicated line system. Still more so did this become the case when buried cable became general. Buried routes could not be moved and the rebuilding of a buried system took many nights of the labour of large parties of men. New spurs, even, could not be dug in a few hours. Either the Staff must learn to stay in one place between reliefs or they must be satisfied with indifferent signal communication for some days after each move. The problem was solved partly by the appreciation by the Staff of the quite unnecessary difficulties they were putting in the way of their own signal companies, partly by the improvement in the methods of fortification of headquarters that was rapidly taking place.

Some of the past moves of headquarters had been capricious. Far more had been made to avoid enemy shelling or to find better protection. As headquarters were more thoroughly protected against direct hits, and as the Staff came to realize the difficulties under which the Signal Service was working, moves of headquarters were reduced to a minimum. Moves between reliefs became less common except in the event of advance or retreat. A greater victory still was gained for signals when it became an established custom for incoming headquarters almost invariably to take over the headquarters of the formation or unit they were relieving. This, again,

* This particular reform was not popular either with Corps Staffs or A.D. Signals. It was given a fair trial in the late winter of 1916, but was soon dropped.

was in the main due to the necessity for fortification on an ever increasing scale. Suitable headquarters were very few. Those that existed were constantly being improved both from the point of view of convenience and of safety. Soon there was no temptation for an incoming Staff to go elsewhere than where their predecessors had lived.

Thus 1915 and the early months of 1916 saw the crystallization of the comparatively rigid signal system necessary to cope with the conditions of stationary warfare. The main features of the new system were :—

(1) The general introduction of the telephone.

(2) The protection of forward lines.

(3) The devising of supplementary means of bridging the zone between the front line and the limit of hostile shelling.

(4) The extension of Signal Service responsibility forward to the front line, and to artillery and infantry communications.

(5) The allotment of areas of signal responsibility and the consequent attainment of a continuity of policy in such areas.

(6) The evolution of a good system of signal relief generally.

(7) The recognition of the necessity for a Chain of Command within the Signal Service.

(8) The commencement of the recognition by the Staff of the importance of the Signal Service. While still quite properly regarded as the servant of the Staff, the signal officer was in process of being raised to the status of a Confidential Adviser.

On these lines advancement continued throughout 1916. The latter year was one of great re-organizations. Before, however, it is possible to proceed to deal with the principal features of this— perhaps the most interesting year of trench warfare as regards signals—it is necessary to consider in some detail the weakness which caused the death of the forward telephone system, or rather its paralysis and atrophy.

H

# Chapter VI.

AN outstanding feature of all great catastrophes which shake the fabric of society to its deepest foundations and by which the faith of mankind in the durability of the established order of things is rudely disturbed, is the fear of the unknown. This invariably shows itself in one manner or another.

In the particular instance of a great war—perhaps the most earth-shaking of all social phenomena—this is usually manifested in the ever-recurring " spy " mania. The present war was no exception to the rule. From the day of its outbreak the wildest rumours were bandied about from mouth to mouth.

Certainly, very clever espionage was taking place, and—to deal only with instances affecting the British Signal Service—numerous cases both of malicious cutting and tapping of our lines, were reported during the early months of the war. Officers returning home at dusk would report strange wires joined on to our system at points where no headquarters existed. Unfortunately, it seldom appeared to the original observer to be within the scope of his duty to follow up the wire at the time of his discovery. On report being made to the local signal officer, a party would be sent out, usually only to discover that the supposed line was non-existent or that it had been laid for some legitimate purpose by our own signallers. In every surge backwards and forwards of the tide of war cases undoubtedly did occur of German agents being left behind with orders to secure information and transmit it by any means possible to the new German line. By far the greater number of cases, however, existed only in the imagination of the officers and men concerned ; the cutting of lines by unfriendly peasants and by straggling parties of the enemy only needing exception from this statement.

As the situation settled down and everyone became more used to service conditions, so the rumours decreased in volume, until in the summer of 1915 the enemy did suddenly appear to be extra-ordinarily well informed of all that was going on behind our lines. This was manifested in many ways. Carefully planned raids and minor attacks were met by hostile fire, exactly directed, and timed to the minute of the attack. Trenches where a relief was taking place were heavily shelled at the very time of the relief, when they were naturally filled with double their complement of men. This occurred too often to be a mere coincidence. The arrival of a new gun, the establishment of a new machine-gun post, the installation of a new trench mortar—were all signalized by immediate and accurate fire before ever the new weapon had advertised its presence by its own activity. Lastly, when relief was taking place in a quiet sector, the relieving troops on the following morning would be greeted by shouts of welcome from the opposing trenches. The greeting was usually more pointed than refined, but was intimately and accurately associated with some salient feature, perhaps of the history of the battalion or regiment, perhaps of its nationality. On some occasions boards were displayed with suitable inscriptions ; sometimes with the name of the regiment on them ; sometimes the number of the battalion, and usually with a cordial invitation to " come over " and a promise of a hot reception. One day, even, a well-known Scotch battalion took over its new front to the strains of its regimental march, exceedingly well played upon a German cornet.

That leakage of information was taking place was sufficiently clear, and at first this was put down to the activities of spies within our lines. The search for and precautions against these unbidden and unwelcome guests were redoubled. In spite of the greatest efforts, however, no signs of espionage sufficient to account for even a small proportion of the leakage could be detected. Innumerable false scents were taken up and abandoned after thorough investigation.

One such trail which led to nothing but some amusement, and a certain amount of suspicion of the *bona fides* of certain civilians, was connected with an estaminet just within the British lines. Listening in at Divisional Headquarters on a line which had already been reported as subject to strange voices breaking in upon conversation, the O.C. Signal Company heard on the line what was obviously the noise from an estaminet. It was just what one might have heard when passing the door of the estaminet. A melodion was playing ; men were singing " Keep the Home Fires Burning ; " a woman was chaffering with the men about money for drinks, etc. The noise was traced down stage by stage through various exchange operators who had heard it and who, by pulling out their plugs, ascertained on which line it was heard, down to the line from a battery exchange to the battery horse lines. Investigation followed and it was ascertained that in all likelihood the disturbance proceeded from a small estaminet which this line passed. In this estaminet were pigeons confined in a basket and other suspicious signs. Nothing tangible could be proved, however. The noise may possibly have been due to a spy working in a room adjoining the estaminet and accidentally pressing the speaking switch of his telephone. Whether this is so or not, the story has more interest in the present connection as an illustration of the extent to which overhearing may inadvertently take place. Here was a circuit on which, undoubtedly, conversation between Division and Brigade headquarters must have been plainly audible at least to within a few hundred yards of the front line.

At the time that the leakage of information appeared to be most widespread, that is about June, 1915, the trouble with induction and overhearing over the jumble of lines immediately behind our front was causing serious anxiety and demanding the closest attention both of the Signal Service and the Staff. It is no exaggeration to say that at this time it was possible to speak from any given signal office on the British front to almost any other. In fact no one knew when he picked up a telephone, to whom he would be speaking or whether he would be able to pick out from the *mêlée* of sounds the words of his own *vis-à-vis*.

It was a step in a logical argument to the further conclusion that the universal overhearing which was rapidly ageing both Staff and signal officers might be affording interest from a different point of view to the enemy and in the same month orders were issued that experiments should be carried out to test this theory. It was pointed out that, even if overhearing could not take place without some friendly conductor, yet there were railways, pipelines, and water channels, leading straight from our own to the enemy's lines, which might be affording him an opportunity of overhearing conversations and messages not meant for his ears. Certain experiments at home as to the possibilities of earth induction telegraphy also made everyone concerned feel very certain that overhearing might take place even without the presence of a better conductor than the earth itself.

At about this time, the French Signal Service reported a deliberate attempt on the part of the Germans to tap French artillery wires. The enemy had run a wire along the bed of a stream across the front of a French post and through the French barbed wire entanglement. The attempt was discovered, almost by accident, and amongst other things a pole was found sawn through lengthwise and with a length of telephone wire inserted, evidently with the intention of substituting it for one of the French poles at a favourable opportunity. Through this and through the frustration of other similar attempts, the attention of the Allied signal services was kept on the alert. The result of the experiments was to direct their thoughts into slightly different channels, for they confirmed the suspicion that the presence of specific good conductors was not essential to regional overhearing.

In the first primitive experiments on overhearing in First Army area in June and July, 1915, very simple apparatus was used. A wireless receiving set with repeating coils in a ratio of 1 to 16 was employed, but even with this comparatively insensitive apparatus speech could be overheard at a distance of 100 yards and buzzer

4

signals up to at least treble that distance. It was an epoch-making discovery from either of two points of view. Its most interesting possibilities seemed at first sight to lie in the direction of overhearing enemy conversation and messages. Far more important, really, was its relation to the leakage of information that was already taking place from the British lines. Here was an explanation sufficient to account for all the knowledge the enemy had obtained in the past ; equally staggering was it to contemplate what he was overhearing every moment in the present, and what he might overhear in the future unless precautions were promptly taken.

No wonder he was well-advised as to our movements, our plans and our dispositions. With a Staff who trusted almost entirely to messages buzzed over the forward lines, often to the most advanced posts ; with an inexperienced soldiery, unused to the exercise of discretion in their every day conversation over the telephone, there was no end to the devastating possibilities presented by this newly-exposed factor in the situation.

The consequences of overhearing were so far-reaching that it seemed impossible to devise adequate means of protection against them, and meanwhile, day by day, fresh and more convincing evidence came to light. At the beginning of August, 1915, information was received through a *liaison* officer that our Allies, whose attention had been early directed to the same problem, had a station established well forward in their own lines and were overhearing scraps of German conversation. Nothing useful had yet been obtained, but on the 7th of August the O.C. Signals, First Army, visited the French post and examined the installation. The product of the fertile brain of a French infantry private who had been an electrician by profession, this fore-runner of the listening set is of great interest and a general idea of the installation is given in *Plate* XI.

Advantage had been taken of a series of saps and mine galleries that had been tunnelled towards the German lines. Wires had been run along these saps and tunnels, and to the end of each cable a number of 75 mm. shell-cases were attached as earths. These were buried in charcoal to prevent oxidation, and the earth was rammed down over them to make a good earth connection. A width of about 350 yards of front was covered, and in this area, as can be seen from the diagram, there were no less than four separate series of earths, the furthest advanced of which were believed to be within a few metres of the German trenches. Indeed, the installation compared favourably both in thoroughness of conception and of execution with many which were devised much later in the war.

The only weak point was the overhearing apparatus itself. It was before the days of the application of the three-electrode valve to this work, and the only instruments available were a pair of ordinary low resistance telephone receivers of the French Post Office pattern. In

charge of the listening post was the French private to whose genius
the idea was due and two interpreters patiently awaited opportunities
of sorting out intelligible German conversation from the disconnected
phrases which were overheard from time to time. Such was the first
primitive listening post from which was destined to grow a large and
complicated intelligence organization.

Important as it was to make use of the new discovery to overhear
the intentions of the enemy, yet the policing and improving of the
British telephone system was a still more urgent matter. The
measures taken were of two kinds, technical and general. All signal
officers were at once instructed to improve the insulation of their
circuits in every way possible. Earths were to be brought back at
least 100 yards from the front trenches. At the same time memoranda, detailing subjects that were in future not to be referred to forward of battalion headquarters, were circulated to all telephone
subscribers. The principal of these tabooed subjects were :—

(a) Names of units or unit calls.
(b) Times of relief.
(c) Movements of units.
(d) Information regarding result of artillery fire.
(e) Location of guns.

A glance at the list will give a very good idea of the value of the
information the enemy must have been receiving prior to the issue
of the order. Indeed, for a year or more after the first discovery
of the fact of enemy overhearing, it can be seen from the reports of
our own listening sets that an almost incredible ignorance or obstinacy
pervaded all the units concerned. As late as October, 1916, the
main obstacle in the path of the men who were endeavouring to overhear German conversation was the never-ceasing conversation on our
own forward lines. Officers could not be made to understand that
half their own worries and a considerable proportion of the casualties
suffered by their units were due to their own indiscreet use of the
forward telephones. Order after order was issued ; precaution after
precaution was insisted upon ; still the leakage continued in slightly
less degree only. It was not until disciplinary action was taken and
carelessness made the subject of a court-martial charge, that forward
telephones were used with any degree of care. Probably more was
given away in 1916 than even in 1915 ; it was certainly to the later
year that the classic example of stupidity in this respect belongs.

When discretion did at last set in, it took the form that might have
been expected. In all forward units there sprang up a dislike for
and distrust in the telephone. The system was still installed, but
was less used, and this gradual atrophy of the telephone habit was
of great importance in view of the change in the conditions of warfare
which marked the closing phases of the war. Overhearing, which

was the direct cause of thousands of casualties in 1915 and 1916, had dwindled to small proportions in 1917, By 1918 its result had been to wean the forward officer from his dependence on the telephone which could no longer be provided for him.

There were several main lines along which improvement might be hoped for. The retirement of the earths of earthed circuits was the first precaution taken. (*Plate* XII). As experiments continued and apparatus improved, the distance to which these earths were carried back increased. From the first trifling distance of 100 yards, the figure leapt rapidly in 1915 to 250, 500, and 1000 yards, and at the beginning of 1916, at the time of the introduction of the first valve listening set, to 1,500 yards, at which figure it remained for some time. At the same time, experiment proved that it was not sufficient to duplicate the line anyhow, but that the second cable must be carried back close alongside the original circuit. Careful test next demonstrated that to obtain a good metallic circuit the two cables were best twisted together.

The next step was the adoption of twisted cable for all circuits in the forward area, but this reform was long delayed by difficulty of supply. Not only was twisted " D5 " cable not an article of normal supply, but single " D5 " cable sufficient to duplicate all circuits in the forward area was not available in France. It was calculated that no less than 50 miles of cable would be required to convert the forward lines of a single Division into metallic circuits. Armies and G.H.Q. were faced with another great problem, but steps were at once taken to solve the difficulty. A supply of twisted cable was placed on order, and in the meantime Army and Corps Signal Companies, with their usual fertility of resource, devised rough and ready machines for twisting cable for issue to the Divisions in their areas. Thousands of miles of cable were twisted, the machines working day and night for weeks at a time during periods of stress. Perhaps no single incident better displays the inventive genius shown by personnel of the Signal Service than the variety of the cable-twisting machines which sprang into existence during 1916. Twisted metallic circuits were not unknown in 1915, indeed they were much used in at least one Army for local telephone circuits early in the summer of that year. Their use was, however, in those days, the exception rather than the rule. The majority of the metallic circuits in the early buries were made of two lengths of "D5" cable laid alongside each other and seized together at frequent intervals with spun yarn. Now, with the new universal demand, suitable machines were designed everywhere, the principal ingredients used in their construction being lorries, wheels of limbered wagons, airline barrows, wire stays, and odds and ends of ropes. Nor was the work carried out in a slipshod manner. The early twisted cables produced with these cable twisters would bear comparison with the products of the best-fitted workshops and they were subjected to severe test before they were accepted as satisfactory. In the Fourth Army, for example, lengths of a mile long were reeled on drums; laid at a canter from an ordinary cable wagon, and reeled up at the same pace. Had there been any sign of wear and tear greater than the normal, or had there been any kinking or unevenness of winding, the cable would have been rejected. The machine was, however, well-designed and carefully tended and the cable produced was satisfactory in every way.

The issue of twisted cable from England did not take place in large quantities until the end of 1916, but long before that time practically all circuits in the forward area were made metallic, and while the likelihood of enemy overhearing was diminished it was found that other difficulties had been surmounted at the same time. The great problem which required solution before the concentration of forward circuits into certain main buried routes could be thoroughly carried out was the induction between the various lines which rendered all of no value if used simultaneously. This difficulty disappeared entirely with the general adoption of twisted cable, and as many circuits as were required could be laid in the forward buries practically without danger of mutual interference. Once again two great obstacles to the efficiency of the Service had been overcome by the same remedy and a great step forward in signal practice had been achieved.

Further precautions against enemy overhearing were particularly necessary during the transition period when the duplication of circuits was taking place surely but very slowly. Throughout the early part of 1916, although earthed circuits in the forward area were gradually disappearing, the number in existence was still considerable. Even when the metallic system was theoretically complete, information might still be given away through badly insulated and otherwise defective circuits. In particular, it was soon found that the earth plate in the "D3" telephone was a source of leakage, and orders were issued that "D3s" were to be kept in their cases while in use and that future issues should have the earth-plate disconnected as a precaution. Another danger always present was the possibility of leakage to earth through the operators themselves. Yet another source of considerable anxiety were the large numbers of disused cables, half or wholly forgotten, which were lying about all over the forward area.

Attempts had already been made to clear up the mess in order to simplify the forward system and reduce induction troubles. These attempts were now redoubled and Corps and Divisional Signal Companies and forward signallers of artillery and infantry, alike, worked day and night on this essential duty. Trenches leading forward towards the enemy lines were deepened for at least two feet in the endeavour to trace and cut lost cables buried underfoot in the mud;

every effort in fact was made to clear the ground. All this work could not fail to have good results and by degrees the congestion of wires in the forward area was relieved and quantities of salved cable were sent back to be destroyed or to be renovated at the Signal Depôt where a plant had been erected for this purpose.

While all this was going on, however, it was necessary to make sure that the quantity of information of value to the enemy which was passing over the forward wires should be reduced to the greatest possible extent. Carefully-framed orders and circulars pointing out the dangers of overhearing were printed and these were issued to everyone in possession of a telephone. Disciplinary action was threatened if orders were ignored or disobeyed, and more rigid restrictions as to the use of the telephone and buzzer were promulgated and enforced.

Once again considerable difficulty was experienced in overcoming the inertia which opposed all change and inprovement of method throughout the Army. Obsessed with matters of life and death on their own account, officers in the forward area had no inclination to be careful of what appeared to them unimportant details of the particular form of their conversation over the telephone. Immediate necessity frequently overbore the general instructions for discretion, and the most momentous affairs were still discussed in detail with a candour which was as naïve as it was dangerous.

Our earliest authenticated positive information that the enemy really were overhearing matters of importance had come from a British civilian who had been interned at Ruhleben Camp. He had heard the medical orderlies at the camp hospital discussing with German visitors and sightseers the fact of their possession of an apparatus which was securing them valuable information in this manner. " They were so pleased with the new invention that they could not keep quiet about it," and it was obvious that the matter was of the very highest importance. In this respect, as in many others at this period of the war, the Germans were well ahead of us. It is impossible to overestimate the importance of what they must have overheard in 1915 before the necessity for precaution had been realized. As the months went on, prisoners captured from the German Signal Service admitted under examination that results of tremendous importance were still being obtained in the same way.

The classical example of obstinate stupidity was brought to light, when, on the Somme in the autumn of 1916, after thousands of casualties had been suffered in earlier attempts to capture the village, Ovillers-la-Boisselle was taken from the Germans and our troops, swarming over the German defences, billetted themselves in enemy dug-outs and converted cellars. In one of these was found a complete copy of a former operation order issued by one of the British Corps for a previous operation. This had been overheard by enemy interpreters, taken down from beginning to end, and issued to the German commanders concerned in good time to enable them to take measures to defeat the attack. Who can wonder that the battalions, debouching from their trenches at zero hour, had been decimated before ever they had crossed " No Man's Land " and reached the enemy trenches. Inquiries were made and it transpired that the order had been repeated in full over the telephone by a Brigade Major to one of the battalions of his Brigade. He, knowing the danger, had protested, but had been over-ruled by his Brigadier. Hundreds of brave men perished, hundreds more were maimed for life as the result of this one act of incredible foolishness, persisted in in the face of informed opposition. The occurrence is a stigma on the fair fame of the British Army, but it should be recorded as an example of the appalling results which may follow from a single failure to adopt precautions ordered by a specialist branch of the Service. It was not until this tale and many others had gone the rounds that officers commenced to realize that discretion was not only desirable but was a duty second in importance to no other. As the year wore on, this fact was gradually driven home and it was assisted by many reforms in procedure and by the organization of an efficient system of policing, by which indiscretions could be brought home to the offenders and bad cases punished with the severity they deserved.

Perhaps the most efficient of these reforms was the introduction of code names and position calls for units and for signal offices respectively. By the use of code names instead of the stereotyped unit calls, the identity of units was hidden until some indiscretion or the piecing together of odd scraps of information enabled the enemy intelligence personnel to pierce the veil thrown over the whole front by the general adoption of the system. This temporary security from identification was made almost permanent by a constant change of names. Every few days fresh lists were issued and their use was carefully insisted upon. Until officers and signallers grew accustomed to the use of the new pseudonyms, there was always the risk of the indiscriminate use of the old and new code name and the unit's permanent call on one and the same day. Familiarity soon decreased the danger, however, and after 1916 cases of the use of unit names or permanent calls seldom occurred.

At the same time the adoption of the position call for signal offices further assisted to prevent the detection of reliefs. No longer were the call signs of the various signal offices associated definitely with the particular unit which manned them. The whole of the front was divided into numerous areas. These again were sub-divided into sub-areas. Each area and sub-area was given a letter. The combination of the two letters was the position call of the signal office in any particular sub-area. If more than one such office existed they could be distinguished by a number. The position call remained the same, irrespective of the formation which occupied the area, until it was considered advisable to change the whole series. Orders were then issued from Army Headquarters and the change in denomination took place simultaneously over the whole Army front, care being taken that the date of the change did not by chance synchronize with any alteration in the tactical disposition of the major formations of the Army.

It is now necessary to give some account of the growth of our own listening set organization and its use both for policing the telephone system and for the overhearing of enemy conversation and messages. Little progress was made in this direction until, in February 1916, the French Signal Service introduced a new listening set involving the use of three three-electrode valves used in cascade, for the purpose of amplifying the alternating currents which were induced in the loops or leads laid out as part of the listening installation.

The three-electrode valve had already been introduced into France in the first wireless compass. The development of this type of valve and its application to Army work is a subject in itself, but it has been fully treated in the various technical manuals and is far too involved to be dealt with in detail here. At the request of the Army wireless officers, experiments had been carried out by the wireless section of the Officers' Training Corps at Cambridge, who were also responsible for the production of a small portable wireless set carried on bicycles and capable of operating over a distance of 6 to 10 miles with a mast 20 feet high. This work, begun in peace time, was continued at Cambridge after the war had broken out, and resulted in the design of the " White " valve which owes its main interest—not to its lasting success, for it was early superseded by the more robust " French " type—but to the fact that it was the first wireless valve designed by and for the Army and used with Army sets.

The French three-valve listening set—better known to the British Army as the I.T. set—at once revolutionized the current ideas of overhearing.* Its possibilities were so enormous that in a few months the depth of the danger zone† was increased, in spite of the adoption of metallic circuits, from 1000 to 3000 yards. The telephone, as a normal means of unrestricted conversation, was forced back to Brigade headquarters and the need of some safe method of replacing the buzzer and vibrator was rendered of greater importance than ever. No circuit appeared to be safe from the eavesdropping capabilities of the new apparatus unless it was twisted and " perfectly " insulated. The perfect circuit could not, of course, exist under the

---

* The first two of these sets used by the British Signal Service were installed at Vermelles in January, 1916. Three loops were laid down opposite the Hohenzollern Redoubt.

† That is, the area in which conversation was first restricted and later banned altogether.

conditions prevailing in the fighting zone. As the range of enemy guns increased, circuits forward of Brigade headquarters could under no circumstances be considered safe. Once broken or even grazed, and the possibilities of earth leakage were greatly increased. More and more did it become evident that freedom from enemy overhearing must be dependent more on discipline than on technical improvements to lines or instruments.

With the introduction of the metallic circuit and the deep bury, these latter methods had been carried as far as possible. It now remained for the listening set organization which was created in 1916 to ensure that all indiscretions should be reported and visited on the heads of the people responsible. Naturally the service was unpopular. The appearance of an I.T. set was always viewed with suspicion. Definite orders backed by high authority were necessary to secure accommodation and rations for instrument and personnel. The life led by the unfortunate operators, linemen, and interpreters who manned these sets, was never an enviable one. In the early days it was made as uncomfortable as possible both by the enemy and by our own forward troops.

These detachments were intended for two purposes : one, the policing of our own telephone system ; the other, the overhearing of enemy conversation. Both reasons for their existence demanded that they should be as far forward as possible and occasionally sets were installed in disused trenches or saps in " No Man's Land " or in our advanced posts in a most uncomfortable position.

For the efficient use of these listening sets some organization was necessary. This was gradually made more efficient, until in the winter of 1916 (the period of their maximum usefulness) a service had been built up consisting of from 20 to 30 sets controlled by an officer at general headquarters with the title of Inspector of Listening Sets. Some of these sets were used for policing purposes only, and some both for this and for overhearing enemy conversation. Success in the former rôle was never in doubt. Month by month reports were sent in giving detailed conversations, some indiscreet, some frivolous, some only superfluous. All bad cases were taken up, and little by little the amount of dangerous matter passing over our wires decreased. The improvement was very slow, however. The front of all Divisions could not be policed at once. Once the removal of a listening set was generally known, indiscretions were liable to recur. Typical fragments of conversation overheard as late as October, 1916, are given below :—

". . . went up there but there was nobody there except about 25 majors, 17 colonels, one 2nd lieutenant and a lance-corporal. Tell old Cooper not to laugh so loud, the Germans will hear him."

" You know that at ' C ' Co. headquarters in the support trenches two new 18-pounder guns have been placed behind the hedge—they are to fire at Gommecourt during the attack."

The first is merely frivolous and needed no action except a little satire. The second is a good example of dangerous conversation and led to the postponement of the attack for a month. If our own listening set picked this up the chances were that the Germans had also done so. In September, 1916, one single set heard between 30 and 40 units mentioned by name, including one Army and several Divisions. Movements of troops were referred to. Infantry operations were discussed. Whole operation orders were quoted. Positions behind the line were mentioned. One unit even reported 50 casualties from our own Stokes mortars, information likely to cheer the whole German Army. All this in one month, within a semicircle with a radius of 3000 yards. It would not have been surprising if the German Intelligence Service had been able to reconstruct from its listening set reports practically the whole constitution of the British Army as it existed at that time, and to anticipate the most jealously-guarded intentions of the Staff. If they were unable to do so, his Intelligence Corps must have been far less efficient than our own. The policing sets began to take effect in November, 1916, and from that time indiscreet use of the telephone decreased considerably. In March, 1917, the post of Inspector of Listening Sets was abolished and the detachments—already technically controlled by Corps— were entirely administered from Corps headquarters, the results obtained being co-ordinated and acted upon by " Intelligence " at headquarters of Armies. The stations continued in use for policing purposes until the close of stationary warfare. By this time their presence was well known to the whole of the British Army, and the cabalistic letters " I.T. " represented to many of its victims the outward symbol of an almost uncanny power.

From the point of view just considered, the listening set had indeed proved its value. In its other function—the overhearing of the enemy, it had been almost equally useful, though perhaps less conspicuously successful. Many reasons prevented such outstanding results from the attempts to spy upon the German telephone system. The methods used by the German General Staff and commanders differed fundamentally from our own. These differences were probably accentuated by the fact that the very success which had attended the early efforts of this branch of the German Intelligence Service had placed the enemy on guard against similar indiscretion on the part of his own telephone subscribers.

As early as September, 1915, German prisoners had betrayed the fact that the enemy was very nervous, indeed, lest we should overhear his plans and dispositions. Stringent orders had been issued by the German General Staff long before reforms were initiated on the British side of the line. To this early-roused suspicion must be added the possession of a more highly-trained Staff, the stricter signal discipline of a conscript army, the better material available for the making of linemen and operators in a nation long trained in bulk for war, and, lastly, the more workmanlike system of trenches in which his lines were laid. It is not surprising, therefore, that, at the first attempts, little German conversation was overheard. His circuits were fewer and better controlled.* His signal discipline was good both in his Signal Service and the rank and file of other arms. An efficient trench system, organized in depth, enabled a good and comparatively safe line system to be carried well to the rear of the danger zone. One example of the trouble faced by the British Signal Service in overcoming the overhearing menace even when it was fully realized, is seen in the equivocal position of the Divisional signal officer. Armed though he was with a general authority over all lines within his area, if he desired to make his control effective, he was continually obliged to make complaints to senior officers. The latter, too often, only recognized him as a regimental officer and not as the representative of the Staff. Battalion commanders frequently took no notice whatever of his advice. If lines were bad he was expected to mend them or re-lay them himself. Backed up by an energetic General Staff he was all-powerful, but if left to his own resources as he sometimes was, he could do little to enforce his own regulations.

It was not until the French listening set appeared, with its great advance in efficiency over the earlier primitive circuits, that much German conversation was overheard. Even then the results were very patchy.† In one sector nothing at all would be heard. In another a listening set would continually record a good quantity of useful enemy conversation. Specific cases when such information proved of immediate use were many, and the information obtained was always of assistance to the Intelligence Service at Army and Corps headquarters.

The general use of the listening set for overhearing enemy conversation led to the creation of an entirely new Army trade—that of interpreter operator. With each listening post, special interpreters were employed to record the fragments of German conversation heard. At first these men were collected from here, there, and everywhere amongst the infantry, but after this source of supply gave out, specially qualified men were enlisted. In either case the first step in their training was to teach them enough knowledge of Morse to enable them to pick up enemy call signs and signals buzzed by the compara-

* The British telephone service was used to a much greater extent than the German. In consequence, British listening sets not only heard little German, but were prevented from reading what they heard. On the other hand, it should be recorded that the British telephones were of more use for the purpose for which they were installed, namely, facility of intercommunication.

† Results depended largely upon the nature of the soil.

tively slow regimental signaller. A curious instance of the alteration in detail which was constantly exercising the minds of the Signal Service is afforded by the fact that, when the use of power buzzers by the Germans became general in 1917, these interpreter operators had to be withdrawn for further training or even replaced by men of better qualifications as Morse operators. They were quite incapable of reading the Morse messages sent by the experienced wireless operators who were manning the German power buzzers which had become at that time the main source of information obtainable by means of listening sets.

A special use of the listening set took place in the Fifth Army in December, 1916. A set was made as mobile as possible, and was taken forward immediately behind attacking troops. The object was to connect the instrument to the enemy's abandoned line system and endeavour to overhear his plans and his new dispositions. The idea had its possibilities, but was not successful in practice. Our attacks were so thoroughly prepared by the artillery that the German line system had been completely shattered by our shells before ever the assault took place. Fragments were sometimes overheard, but nothing of sufficient importance to justify the general adoption of the new scheme which was therefore abandoned.

Two important developments directly dependent on the question of overhearing were the invention and introduction of the fullerphone and the screening buzzer.* The power buzzer was another innovation attributable to the same cause, but the introduction of this instrument as a means of forward signalling belongs mainly to the 1917-1918 period of stationary warfare and is better left to a later chapter. The abolition of the vibrator and the restrictions placed upon the use of the buzzer in forward areas at once very much reduced the resources of forward signal officers. This was felt the more in 1916, because the introduction of the deep bury had just indicated a way by which line communication might be made very much more reliable and continuous, as least as far forward as battalion headquarters.

The properties possessed in common by the vibrator and the buzzer which were the cause of the overhearing and induction set up by them, were the comparatively high potential and the rapid alternations of the currents sent out along the line. These set up similar currents in the adjacent circuits either by induction or by earth leakage and this was a difficulty which could not be overcome without radical alteration in the circuits used.

No time was lost in endeavouring to provide a substitute for these instruments and the genesis of the experiments which resulted in

* Suggested in 1915 but not adopted as a precautionary measure until two years later.

the invention of the fullerphone* is interesting. As early as August, 1915, the Director of Signals asked the Signal Service Training Centre to experiment on methods of communication without wires. Earth induction telegraphy proved suitable for this purpose, and this was an independent reason for the attraction of attention to the subject of overhearing. In the late summer, the officer conducting the experiments was struck with the idea of substituting for the alternating line current sent out by buzzer and vibrator an infinitesimally small direct current which should be broken up in the receiving instrument itself in order to make it audible. The idea was a far-reaching one. Once it was adopted, the evolution of the fullerphone was a matter of mechanical and electrical detail and was soon accomplished. The direct current in the line caused no induction worth speaking of, and the danger of overhearing was reduced at once beyond the limit of practicability under service conditions. The current in the receiver of the fullerphone was broken several hundred times a second by an electrically-driven interruptor. By means of this, the current passing from line to instrument was alternately driven into the condensers and through the telephone receivers, the alternations taking place at an audible frequency. The dots and dashes of the Morse code sent on the key at the sending end were, therefore, reproduced in the receiver without varying the steady line current. Induction was almost eliminated and with it the possibility of overhearing.

The general adoption of the fullerphone was delayed for some months by the exhaustive tests carried out with the earlier instruments, and by the inevitable delays of manufacture. The first instruments were tried in France towards the end of 1915 on a line run from Reninghelst *via* Goldfish Château to Ypres and back to Reninghelst by another route. This trial was successful and their adoption was recommended. In 1916, supply commenced on a large scale and signal officers were delighted with the new instrument which was, however, at first to add considerably to their work. The earlier patterns required delicate adjustment ; in particular the earlier type of interruptor was not very good. Battalion signallers, while quite able to operate the instrument once it was adjusted, were quite incapable of adjusting it themselves. Compared with the robust telephone, D3, the fullerphone was a delicate mechanism and at every move the Brigade signal officer had to go round to all offices and personally attend to its adjustment. Classes in fullerphone operating were at once started, and Divisional signal schools did good work both in popularizing the instrument and in familiarizing the operators with its vagaries. Towards the end of 1916, the fullerphone was firmly established ; in 1917 it was in use at Brigade headquarters

* Named after its inventor.

also, and, in 1918, many Divisions had adopted it for all their forward circuits. As time went on special types of trench fullerphone were devised which were better suited to the needs of position warfare. One type, which was not, however, the most successful, was made by adaptation of the ubiquitous D3 telephone. The scale of issue steadily increased until June 1918. When semi-mobile warfare again set in, the fullerphone was no longer required for its original purpose. It could, however, be superimposed easily on a telephone circuit and never lost its popularity in some Divisions.

By means of this instrument messages could be sent right up to company headquarters with immunity. Always, however, one thing had to be borne in mind, and prevented the new instrument from being absolutely safe. Most types of fullerphone were fitted for emergency use with a telephone hand-set, and speech on this was, of course, still liable to be overheard. The " call " on the fullerphone was also an ordinary buzzer call. It was, therefore, necessary to prohibit the use of this call, under threat of heavy penalties, for any purpose but that for which it was intended. The danger of the hand-set being used indiscreetly was overcome in some types of instrument by making it detachable. It was then carried in the pocket of a responsible officer and could not be used without his knowledge and express permission.

Of considerably less importance was the invention of the screening buzzer. It was natural—in view of the prevalence of wireless jamming—that one line along which solution was sought, should be the evolution of an instrument which should " drown " the noise of the induced currents in the overhearing circuits. The experiments already made in earth induction telegraphy pointed out a way in which this might be accomplished. Slightly more powerful buzzers and specially arranged earths were all that was necessary, and these were soon devised. Early in 1916 their general use along the entire front was suggested by the Director of Signals to the General Staff at General Headquarters, but the proposal was over-ruled on account of the importance of overhearing enemy conversation. In June of the same year the Assistant Director of Fortifications and Works at the War Office once more raised the same question, his proposal being based on experiments carried out at home. This time it was decided to give the new instrument a trial and, in August 1916, the " screening " buzzers were first provided on a scale of 50 sets per Army. These instruments were only intended to screen speech, the apparatus required to " drown " buzzer signals being too bulky for use in the field. In October 1916, it was definitely decided to screen the whole front during trench warfare, shutting off the screening buzzers in certain sectors when it was desired to make listening reconnaissances with our own sets. The system, however, proved too cumbersome and not sufficiently

I

safe. It was given a good test on most of the front, but enemy prisoners stated that it was quite possible to hear speech through the uniform screaming produced by the " screeners." The installation was, therefore, only very partially successful and, in view of its comparative costliness and inefficiency, was not long persisted in.

An interesting example of a method by which enemy overhearing was even turned to advantage is afforded by the careful preservation on one Corps front of a single badly-insulated earthed circuit. This was isolated from the other circuits in the neighbourhood and was named by a pretty turn of wit the " Wolff " circuit, after the Press Bureau of that name. On this circuit a series of false orders, information, and conversation, was spoken or buzzed for the enemy's special benefit. No particulars of the results of this effort are available, but the scheme had its possibilities. It is mentioned here as an example of how good may be extracted from the worst circumstances and use made of a situation which from every other point of view was as bad as it could well be.

# CHAPTER VII.

APART from the question of enemy overhearing which occupied a considerable portion of the attention of the Signal Service in 1916, as in 1915, the principal feature of signal evolution in the later year was certainly the building up of the deep buried cable system.

The earlier shallow buries were intended to be splinter-, shrapnel- and traffic-proof only. It was recognized that a direct hit from a high explosive shell of any but the smallest calibre would in nine cases out of ten sever the cables or damage them sufficiently to cause faults and necessitate repair. In 1915, and even in the early spring of 1916, the percentage of direct hits had been so small that breaks in the 3 ft. trenches, which were then the rule, were few and could easily be repaired by the linemen available for the maintenance of the routes.* In January, 1916, a Divisional Signal Officer inspecting his lines after a minor attack, reports :—

" Every surface cable and airline was cut. An ' S ' substitute line in a trench not filled in was cut by the direct hit of a small shell. A brass-sheathed quad† cable line four feet down in an open ditch was cut in four places. All lines buried 3ft. 6ins. held with the exception of one which was cut by a direct hit from a big shell. An armoured G.P.‡ twin line was hit by a 150-mm. shell, which lifted the cable so that you could get a hand underneath it. This cable ran to the most advanced trench and remained through."

This description of the investigation of the behaviour of cable in a small action is interesting in several ways.

To begin with, it gives some idea of the small percentage of direct hits received by a complete Divisional system at this date. This is exceptionally interesting in view of the marked change in this

---

* The only marked exception to this rule was the Ypres salient. Here the shelling was so intense that the shallow buries were often broken by direct hits. The nature of the country was, however, not suitable to the development of the deep bury, and for some time signal officers had to devise as safe a system as possible by alternative routes in shallow trenches.

† Armoured cable with four pairs.

‡ Gutta-percha insulation.

respect which was to come about within two or three months and which was indeed already setting in along the northern portion of the British line. Another respect in which the report has particular interest is the reference to various types of armoured cable which were now being issued in fair quantities for the first time.

Although it was intended for burying, it was natural that the new issue should be taken largely into use as trench and ground cable. The authorities who issued were, however, wiser than the officers who diverted the armoured and brass- and lead-sheathed cable from its original function. It soon became evident that the new cables, though more resistant to traffic, were not immune from the effects of splinters and shrapnel. They were also difficult to repair, needing the attention of specially-trained men. Their use as ground cable soon became quite obsolete, except in emergency at cross roads, and other much-traversed points beyond the limit of enemy shelling.

Even here, the steel-armoured cable alone was utilized, for both brass- and lead-sheathed cable were very easily bruised.

In the trenches, these cables could be used only in places where they could be partially protected, as for instance in the angle at the bottom of a trench nearest the enemy—or beneath the duckboard. Their use on a large scale as trench cable was restricted by considerations of bulk, and weight, and by the fact that far more than was at any one time available was always required for the buried cable routes.

The rival merits of the different types of armoured cable were amply tested in the months which followed. Each had its own good points, each its own disadvantages. Steel-armoured cable was liable to kink and was resilient and therefore somewhat difficult to handle. Brass-sheathed cable was rather more easily damaged, but handled with care was quite suitable for burying both by day and by night. Lead-sheathed cable was easily distorted, even by its own weight if carelessly laid, and required particularly careful handling, and level laying. Any inequalities in the trench in which it was laid would sooner or later cause faults and the trench bottom had, therefore, to be levelled off more carefully than could well be done at night. The lead cable had also to be handled very gingerly for fear of straining the sheathing and so weakening the insulation and the resisting power of the cable. It was, if carefully handled and laid, perhaps the best of all the cables, while it was issued in lengths containing many more pairs than the other two types. Some of the best buries of the early 1916 period were undoubtedly those in which the large twenty pair, lead-sheathed, paper-core, multi-cable had been used. However, owing to the drawbacks already enumerated, its use was confined to trenches which could be dug at leisure and in daylight. It could, therefore, be employed in the forward buries to a comparatively small extent only.

Armoured and brass-sheathed cables, on the other hand, were much more suitable for burying than " D5 " cable, which was not originally intended for the purpose. The earlier issues were often faulty, but as time went on the quality of the cable improved, until a very good working standard was obtained. At first, only " twin " and " quad " cables were issued, but soon " seven-pair " cable was also standardized, and proved to be the most useful of all. From that time " D5 " was practically restricted to the one or two pairs which, in almost every trench, were reserved for Signal Service purposes. Difficulty of identification of pairs was overcome by the adoption of a standard system of colouring of individual pairs or lines, and by careful labelling. The other great problem—that of repair—was solved by the training of large numbers of linemen as " jointers," and, perhaps even more, by the universal use of the cables, which forced all linemen engaged in the maintenance of " buries " to become familiar with armoured cable and able to mend breaks in it.

It was in the Ypres sector—always, since the early days of 1915, a favourite target of the German guns—that it first became apparent, in the spring and early summer of 1916, that deeper buries were required. Hitherto, direct hits on cable routes had been the exception rather than the rule, but, as the number of enemy shells poured on to the forward area increased, breaks in the buried cable became alarmingly frequent.

The 5·9 howitzer was already commencing to play a predominant part in the enemy's artillery preparation and retaliatory fire. Even a 77 mm. shell could be relied on to break the present buried cables if a direct hit was scored. Something more was required, if line communication forward of Divisional headquarters was to be reliable even in normally quiet times.

From the first, scarcity of labour had been the main obstacle in the way of the adoption of buried cable on a large scale. It had already been accepted as an axiom by signal officers that the deeper the cable was buried, the safer the route would be. Commencing with the traffic-proof buries of a few inches to a foot in depth, the tendency had ever been to go deeper and deeper, until the shallow splinter-proof buries had been standardized at a depth of 3 ft. From time to time, particularly energetic officers would achieve buries of greater depth than this, some being dug even to 4½ ft. It was found, however, that this small measure of extra depth was of very little use. The routes were still not safe from a direct hit by a shell of average size. The only effect of the greater depth was to make the repair of breaks more difficult.

Shortage of labour was already restricting the number of routes which could be dug. Induction troubles prevented the concentration of all circuits in one or two deep buried routes, although such a policy was already visualized by many signal officers as the ideal.

It was in early 1916 that the latter difficulty was first overcome by the manufacture and employment of twisted cable. As supplies of the latter and of armoured twin and quad cable increased, so the concentration of all routes into one, or, at most, two buries in each Divisional sector became a realizable ambition. The labour that had formerly been dissipated on comparatively numerous shallow buried routes was now concentrated on a few deeper buries, and it was found by experiment that 6 ft. was the ideal depth. At that depth in normal soil the cables were safe from a direct hit from a 5·9-inch shell, and the 8-inch shell was not yet sufficiently common to be a dangerous menace to continuity of line communications.

Of these first, somewhat haphazard, deep buried systems, by far the most interesting historically are the pioneer examples laid down in the Second Army area at Ypres and Kemmel. In both cases, special factors led to the early adoption of deeper buries than were in use on the rest of the front. One factor common to both places was the intensity of the fighting which took place during the spring and early summer of 1916 along this portion of the British front. Shelling in the Ypres area reached an intensity far surpassing that of 1915 or on any other portion of the front at the same time. Shallow buries were broken right and left, in front and in rear. Circumstances thus forced the possibility of deep burying on the attention of the officers concerned, while other special features local to this particular theatre of war—the sewers of Ypres and the exceptional observation facilities afforded by Mount Kemmel—contributed largely to the comprehensiveness of the schemes adopted and the thoroughness of their execution.

At Ypres, signal communications had always been a problem of the greatest intricacy. The adoption of the shallow bury eased matters for a time, but this proved to be a very temporary respite. Deep buries through the town seemed to be the only alternative to a complete abandonment of line communication. Many lives had been lost, more linemen had been wounded or gassed, in endeavouring to maintain the system already in existence. The strain on the personnel of the Signal Companies of the Divisions manning the salient was too great to be borne, and by far the greatest number of breaks, and therefore of casualties, occurred in or about Ypres itself which acted as a concentration point for the enemy's fire. The problem of intercommunication through the town itself seemed insoluble until attention was drawn to the system of underground sewers which underlay the streets.* It was soon discovered that these would give good protection to the lines—for they were covered by no less than 6 ft. of road metalling. Once it was laid there was little fear of the cable being broken except by direct hit from shells of large size.

* A small Belgian boy was paid to go through the sewers with a line, since they were too small to admit of the passage of a full-grown man.

A careful investigation of the whole sewer system soon showed that the laying of the lines was quite practicable, while only 300 yards of normal bury trench would need to be dug. In this way, the problem of communication through Ypres was solved. Labour was obtained and the execution of the system was put in hand at once. Signal personnel ran the cables through the sewers, and infantry working parties were employed in excavation of that portion of the route where a trench was necessary. The cable was here laid to a depth of four feet, the lines being protected above and below by sandbags. Road metalling was then piled back on top and the result was a route only slightly less safe than that in the sewers themselves.* ·

A similar sewer system on a much larger scale was also laid down in Arras, where, however, conditions of working were much easier than in Ypres. The sewers here were easy of access, large enough for several men to pass each other, and as much as 40 to 60 ft. underground. The cable used was twisted " D5 " supported on insulators above the water level and the route was practically invulnerable. It was fortunate that it proved possible to substitute this system for the earlier buries. Many of the old pairs, particularly many circuits of " pernax " twin, were becoming very faulty and the old routes were rapidly becoming unworkable. On digging them up and examining the cable, it was found that the insulation of the " pernax " cable had completely rotted away, its unsuitability for burying work being thus conclusively proved.

The second of the pioneer deep buried cable schemes which is of particular interest was that laid down, mainly for artillery observation purposes, in and about Mount Kemmel. It was here that the first 6 ft. bury was laid down by the Canadian Corps. At the end of March, 1916, deep buried cables were accepted as a standard solution for the intercommunication problem on the Corps front in which this valuable observation post was situated. Work was at once commenced on a uniform system of deep buries on the whole Corps front and particular attention was given to the routes leading back from the hill itself. Into these were collected the telephone circuits from the observation posts which were scattered on and in the hill and the neighbouring spurs. Work was continued steadily from April 1st to June 30th, and during this time 420 miles of metallic circuit was laid six feet deep within this single Corps area.†

The systems above described, and others like them, were the forerunners of the more uniform buried cable schemes which were planned on the southern portion of the British front later in the year.

* The sewer system at Ypres was finally destroyed by the enemy's 17-in. howitzers. It was not a great success as the sewers were nothing like big enough.

† The work begun by the Canadian Corps was completed by the IX Corps.

It was in the north that the uses and the limitations of the deep bury were first systematically studied. The Ypres system was naturally anything but ideal for tactical purposes. The position of its exchanges, the route of its cables, were entirely decided by the network of sewers. These in their turn followed the plan of the town and were based on purely architectural and sanitary considerations.

At Mount Kemmel, again, the needs which the system served were very special. Everything was subordinated to the requirements of the artillery. Kemmel was an observation station *par excellence*. No general tactical considerations could be allowed to interfere with communications designed primarily with this in view. Indeed, all the northern buries of this period were improvised in a somewhat haphazard fashion as the exigencies of the moment dictated.

The shortcomings of such systems were not allowed to pass unnoticed. If an illustration is permissible, the growth of the buried system here and that which occurred later further south, may be likened in their broad outlines to the growth of two towns at different periods in the life of a nation. A good example is afforded by Sydney and Melbourne. The capital of New South Wales was founded when the colony was in its extreme youth and grew up bit by bit, street by street, like the cities of the Old World. It is a picturesque town, but by no means ideal as regards convenience and accessibility. In contrast, we have the newer and more business-like town of Melbourne, founded at a later stage in the history of Australia, and built on an ordered plan with streets running north and south and east and west. A further illustration of the same contrast can be seen by a comparison of the town plan of any ancient English town which has not been rebuilt on a large scale, with that of any of the newer towns in the west of Canada or the United States. In the same way, exactly, from a study of the failings of the earlier unco-ordinated and unsystematic buries, the ideal buried system—the grid system— which came generally into use in the winter of 1916-1917 was evolved. The germ from which it sprang originated in the minds of officers who watched over and studied the earlier northern buries. It was developed on theoretical grounds by others, and finally appeared in the form which is shown in *Plate* XIII., which was accepted as the standard system of line communications in the forward area during stationary warfare.

Much was to happen before the evolution and adoption of this standard system. As early as May, 1916, the centre of interest on the British front gravitated to the Somme area where the preparations for a great battle had already commenced. The first systematic offensive by the British Army on a grand scale was planned to begin on July 1st, 1916. Preparations for the battle started early in the spring and activity increased as the time for the casting of the die approached. The Signal Service, in common with the rest of the administrative services, rose to heights of feverish activity. In the preparations for the battle two things in particular needed great are and the exercise of careful forethought and creative imagination. The first was the preparation of an adequate and safe system of intercommunication within our own lines in the sector from which the assault was to be launched ; the second was the successful bridging of " No Man's Land " during the assault and the carrying forward of the main line system as soon as the situation had settled down. The solution of the first problem in itself required months of unremitting work.

Our own guns had increased in number tremendously, and at last the supply of shells was in some measure commensurate with the needs of the Army. It was known that the enemy, too, was straining every nerve to increase his output both of guns and ammunition. That he was succeeding was only too evident from the tornado of fire under which our French Allies at Verdun had suffered a veritable martyrdom during the long months from February onwards.

It was hardly likely, in view of the magnitude of preparations involved, the increase in numbers and efficiency of the air services on both sides, and the length and intensity of our preliminary bombardments, that the British attack would come as a great surprise. If it did, the enemy artillery fire was likely to be comparatively feeble for some days, but as time went on and one of the main objects of the attack—the relief of the pressure on Verdun—was achieved, the weight of the fire directed on our own lines might be expected to increase from day to day. The French Signal Service authorities assured their British colleagues that nothing but 6 ft. buries could be expected to survive within the zone of heavy shelling. This, in its turn, now reached almost to Divisional headquarters. A colossal amount of labour was thus involved in the building up of a safe line system.

The quantity of work involved is not easily realized from the mere recital of totals compiled from statistics sent in by the units engaged. No figures of the preparatory construction by itself are available, but, during the preparation and the battles themselves, the amount of wire erected on overhead construction was no less than 43,000 miles. Over 7,000 wire miles of cable were also buried to provide the forward line system, and large quantities of cable were laid overground. The figures in themselves are stupendous when the size of the units upon whom the technical work fell is considered, but the difficulty of the task was increased tenfold by the circumstances under which the greater portion of the forward work had to be carried out.

It was no question of steady work carried out under genial conditions and Trade Union rules, in the comfort and safety of home surroundings. On the rear lines, airline sections and construction detachments were at work night and day in all weathers, harassed occasionally by long range fire, and spurred on to labour to the limit of their strength by a realization of the extreme importance and urgency of the work they carried out. No time could be allowed for rest, no leisure even for the grumbling so dear to the soldier's heart. Every man was worked to the full limit of his capacity all the time. The only reward of self-sacrificing work was the contemplation of a growing and efficient system. It was sufficient. As the last touches were put to the routes towards the end of June, all concerned might well be proud of the work they had done.

As the parties departed to their maintenance stations, to tasks elsewhere along the front, or to await orders for the work which might fall to their lot in pushing forward the routes in the wake of a victorious army, they left behind them a line system which was unique of its kind. It was soon to be surpassed by their own efforts and the efforts of their comrades in the battles of the later stages of the war, but none the less it was a triumph of skill, organization, and well-directed energy.

Forward of Divisional headquarters, the work was carried on under the circumstances always closely associated with trench warfare. Three months of preparation was only just sufficient to permit of a good system of buried cables being laid down. In April, 1916, orders were issued that future buries must not be less than 6 ft. deep. This decision was based on evidence provided by our French Allies and on our own experience. It had been abundantly proved that it was the last few inches that counted. 5 ft. was not much more secure than three, and it certainly took far longer to repair cable buried at that depth when it was once broken.

Buries at a depth of 6 ft. were immune from the direct hit of the dreaded 5·9 shell. In the Ypres operations in June a bury of this depth had been hit several times without being broken. The same day, the one weak spot in a Divisional route several miles long was neatly severed, although the area of insufficient protection only extended for a length of 10 ft. Again and again such experiences showed the danger of leaving any weak places at all.

The deep bury was thus accepted as the standard method of line communication, and during May and June every effort was made to complete such a system on the front of as many Divisions as possible. Once again, the question of the supply of cable was a serious obstacle to reform. Divisions possessing a good system of shallow trenches were unable in every case to obtain either cable or labour sufficient to replace this system with deep buries. The result was soon seen on July 1st. When the enemy's barrage fell on the area behind our front lines, communication remained through automatically, where buries were 6 ft. deep. Where they were less, line communication forward of Brigade headquarters, and often also between Brigade and

Preparing a Route of Buried Cable.

Division, was intermittent. Such measure of continuity as was achieved was only secured with the greatest difficulty and at the expense of many casualties.

The striking superiority of the 6 ft. bury had already been demonstrated in individual cases in the desultory fighting of the earlier summer. It had been proved beyond doubt to our French Allies at Verdun. The lesson was now once and for all driven home to the whole of the Staff and Signal Service of the British Army. Given the necessary labour—and the demonstrations of early July were sufficient to secure this—and enough twisted cable—and the supply of cable was improving every month—and there need be little trouble with communications behind battalion headquarters either in stationary warfare or in the preliminary stages of an attack with limited objectives. The problem of forward communication during an attack and in semi-mobile warfare was a different matter, though much light was also to be thrown on these two questions during the Battle of the Somme.

As the offensive continued, the value of buried cable was indicated with even greater emphasis. Cases were recorded again and again of routes sustaining 30, 40 or 50 direct hits by shells from guns less than 8-inch calibre without interruption of signal communication. As the months passed and the battle continued, the area between battalion and Divisional headquarters was kept bridged with deep buried routes whenever the situation was sufficiently stationary.

As the use of deep buries became more universal, other modifications in Signal Service practice and even in Staff methods necessarily followed.

One feature of the 6 ft. buried system was the immense expenditure of time and labour involved in its construction. It was, therefore, comparatively rigid. The less time and labour required to build up a signal system, the more adaptable will it be. A deadlock at once arose with the general use of the deep bury. It was no longer possible for formation headquarters to move about at will. Already the shallow bury had tied down all but the most *exigeant* Staffs to permanent headquarters. With the installation of the deep bury, it became a physical impossibility for the signal office to follow its Staff about. Spurs could not be built off deep buries ; if labour was available it was more urgently required on the main routes. Headquarters Staffs must settle down close alongside the main signal routes or they must risk overground lines which were almost certain to be destroyed in the first intense bombardment. Experience brought wisdom in its train. The deep bury persisted and the headquarters of formations and the major units conformed closely to the broad outlines of the signal system.

This system in the meantime was also modified by similar considerations and this modification was expressed in two main ways.

One was in the evolution of the " grid " already referred to earlier in this chapter. So far as possible the new line system must permit of constant movements of formations, including that pernicious manœuvre from the signal point of view—the " side-slip." The movements of formations sideways, crabwise, along the length of the front had always been a fruitful source of trouble to signal officers and of disorganization to their intercommunication system. The only method of ensuring that change of formation and change of front should take place with the least measure of interference with " Signals " was by means of the adoption of a skeleton network of front-to-rear and lateral main routes. At the junctions of these main routes would be commodious test or signal offices with comfortable living quarters for the personnel detailed to maintain the routes and to oversee the continual alteration of cross-connections.

At frequent intervals, along both front to rear and lateral routes, would be situated smaller unmanned test-boxes from which spare lines could be led up along protected ways on to terminals. By means of these off-shoots of the main system, connections could be made by the signallers and linemen of the units to whom the lines had been allotted either for the period of their stay in the area, or until the circuits were more urgently required for some more important purpose.

An important point was the relative frequency of the front-to-rear routes, and the selection of the best position for the lateral routes of the grid-iron trace. The former varied, of course, according to whether the system was serving a defensive or offensive front. Also, throughout the war, it was of course modified by conditions of supply of cable and of labour. The form generally adopted was that of one route per Divisional front. If an offensive was imminent and other Divisions likely to invade a particular front, extra labour was provided, and a sufficient number of extra routes were built. The position of the lateral routes was never in doubt once the principle of an ordered system was resolved upon. The main purposes served by the complicated trench warfare intercommunication system were those of " Command " and " Artillery observation and *liaison*." The obvious zones that required good service were those of formation and unit headquarters both of infantry and artillery. The exact position of these zones varied to some extent with the range of the chief types of artillery, both of our own and the enemy.

As can be seen from the illustration of the ideal grid system, four main routes were run in the depth of a Divisional sector. Nearest the front line were the forward centres serving the battalion headquarters and the forward observation officer ; next came the observation centres at the forward edge of the battery zone serving battery headquarters and sometimes Advanced Brigade headquarters. The third route at the rear edge of our own battery zone served the artillery group headquarters and the greater number of Brigade headquarters, while finally the Divisional centres, just beyond the extreme limit of enemy shelling, served Divisional headquarters. This fourth lateral route usually coincided with the forward limit of the airline in the maintenance of the Corps. It was well into 1917 before this system had been fully developed. Later in that year, the same orderly system was continued further back with excellent results, and this policy, with slight modifications which will be referred to later, continued in practice until the end of the stationary period of warfare.

In the meantime, the same consideration which led to the crystallisation of a fairly rigid system of line communication along definitely-planned lines, caused attention to be turned also to the fortification of the manned dug-outs which formed the nodal points of the " grid," and also of the signal offices of formation and units.

Telephone exchange operating, the manipulation of delicate telegraph instruments, the docketing and recording of messages, even the constant adjustments in the cross-connecting field of a big test-point, are all delicate operations which call for the undivided attention of the personnel concerned. In the same way that the members of a Staff could not be expected to produce their best thinking combinations under the constant menace of extermination, so telephone and telegraph operators and linemen, if they were to do good work, required adequate protection.

In the constant bombardments which were the marked feature of the Somme battle, and also of the great position battles of 1917, it was essential that all vital points of the intercommunication system should be protected against the direct hit of everything but the very heaviest shells. The bury itself required protection against the heaviest shell normally used in large quantities in a barrage or in an area bombardment. This was done by making all buries 5·9 proof. Much more was required at all nodal points in the signal system, as these, however well concealed, were liable to attract the deliberate concentration of long-range heavy artillery fire. Before the end of 1916 it was laid down as a principle that all signal offices should be sufficiently protected to be unaffected by the direct hit of an 11-inch shell. This was the ideal. Very often it was not nearly approached, but in all cases great efforts were made to afford security to the men who carried out vital rôles in spots which were exposed to great danger of bombardment by the very nature of the system of which they formed an essential part.

During this year and the next, heavily concreted emplacements for test-boxes and for signal offices became a definite part of the signal communication system. As in 1915, these " nerve-centres " of the line system were made as inconspicuous as possible, but it had become recognized that in the face of aeroplane activity, and particularly of aeroplane photography, it was impossible to attain complete invisibility. Camouflage improved and was used to the greatest possible extent ; strict orders were issued and enforced to prevent unnecessary traffic in the neighbourhood of signal offices and test offices. Everything possible was done to avoid attention. In spite of all precautions, both our own and captured enemy photographs showed up almost all main structures in the system of intercommunication as in that of fortification. This was still further shown by the accuracy of the enemy's long-range fire, particularly in 1917. It became gradually recognized that immunity could only be purchased by greater expenditure of labour, material and thought, in improvement of protection even at the expense of concealment.

All this extra protection both of cables and of offices could only be achieved by the exploitation of the labour of thousands upon thousands of men. From the commencement of the era even of shallow buries, it had become clear that the Signal Service, kept down as it was to the smallest limit compatible with efficiency, could not provide the necessary labour. Infantry, Artillery and Pioneers, all were called upon in their thousands to help, and with the employment of vast bodies of non-signal labour the task became one which was beyond the power of the Divisional Signal Officer. Nothing in the history of Signals was destined to shift the balance of power to the rear more than the labour problems presented by the adoption of a universal deep buried system.

Already the resources of the Brigades were severely taxed to carry out the complicated series of trenches and works required in the forward area under stationary warfare conditions. R.E. working parties were busy day after day and night after night. Men, nominally in rest, were employed for a great part of their time either marching to, carrying out, or returning from, tasks. It is not surprising that an outcry arose when the Signal Service was obliged to put in a claim for a considerable quantity of Infantry labour.

The tasks in contemplation were so great that they could not possibly be dealt with by individual Divisions. Such a policy would also lead inevitably to that lack of continuity of policy which had already caused endless trouble. The necessary machinery for Corps and Army control already existed. In February, 1916, the senior signal officer at the Army had been created Deputy Director of Signals to the G.O.C. with the status of an Assistant Adjutant General and the rank of Colonel. About the same time, the senior signal officer of a Corps was appointed Assistant Director of Signals to the Corps Commander with the rank of Major (afterwards raised to Lieutenant-Colonel). Both officers had been relieved of their executive duties by the posting of other officers as Officers Commanding Army and Corps Signal Company respectively. The avowed intention of the reform was to " facilitate the supervision of signal

communication both of the Signal Service and units of their formation
and to secure efficiency and economy in the expenditure of material."

In both respects, no better subject for the exercise of these super-
visory duties could have been found than the " buries " which grew
and prospered under their hands in 1916 and 1917. Schemes were
prepared and revised at Corps and Army headquarters. Labour
was arranged for by Corps or Division according to the size and
urgency of the scheme. Cable for burying was provided by the Army
and distributed as required by the Corps. Records were insisted
upon and kept up-to-date. Area personnel was supplied and kept
up to its work by a system of the closest inspection. New methods
of working were experimented with and particulars freely circulated.
In every way, the work was co-ordinated and improved, and the
value of a central authority and a central system of control was
perhaps more thoroughly demonstrated here than in any other branch
of signal work.

Finally, before passing to the lessons of the Somme battles in the
forward areas and in the swifter-moving scenes of the more successful
attacks, some consideration should be given to the evolution of
methods of burying cable. From the first, thought and energy had
been directed towards the diminution of the wholesale labour difficulties involved, but for a long time without more than local effect.
Pipe-pushers were used with good results for passing underneath
roads, railways, and other obstacles. Various ingenious devices were
utilized for crossing streams and protecting stream crossings. Considerable use was made of iron water-piping and rails for strengthening
weak places in the bury. An endless succession of water-tight and
more or less shell-proof and easily accessible test- and joint-boxes
were devised and patented by different signal units. The latter
ranged from the simple joint-box, filled with paraffin wax or pitch,
of the earlier shallow buries, to the elaborate test-boards and cross-
connecting fields of the 1917 systems. In fact, as time went by,
ingenuity constantly improved the technique of buried cable until
the final standardized system was evolved which formed the basis
of the recommendations embodied first in *Technical Instruction*,
No. 11, of 1918, and later in *Signal Training*, 1919, Part IV.

The attempts to save labour by the use of mechanical means of
trenching were not so successful. Comparatively early in 1915, a
horse-drawn plough was used in some Corps with good results, but,
with the passing of the shallow bury, the usefulness of the plough
also departed, if we except the special use which was made later of
cable-burying tanks.

What was required for the deep buried cable system was the
mechanical excavator capable of digging a trench 6 feet deep in
reasonably quick time and with sufficient reliability to enable the
time element in the scheme to be calculated with fair accuracy.

In August 1916, the French Army was using with success two such excavators capable of digging a trench 6 ft. deep by 2 ft. wide at a rate of 20 yds. an hour. These machines were used in chalk country and their success seemed sufficient to warrant the adoption of similar machines in those Corps of the British Army which were also operating in chalk districts. They had their limitations, however. It was found that the type of wheel rendered them quite unsuitable for use in muddy ground such as was prevalent in the northern portion of the British front. The machines sank in the mud and—far from saving labour—they required the help of large labour parties to extricate them from the difficulties into which they often fell themselves. Their size and the noise they made also unsuited them for work in forward areas. Many buries were perforce carried out under conditions where night work and comparative silence were essential. In such cases mechanical excavators were quite useless and they were at once ruled out as regards forward work.

There remained then the possibility of making use of them out of sight and hearing of the enemy. There seemed little doubt that they would be of great use in the rear portion of Divisional areas and in that portion of Corps areas where, for particular reasons, burying was considered advisable. Six such tractors were, therefore, ordered from America in December, 1916. The first of these arrived in France in February of the following year and extensive trials were at once carried out, with varying results. Finally, in February, 1918, the Director of Signals reported that the excavators in their present form were not worth their keep. Owing to constant breakdowns and to the difficulty of obtaining spare parts, it was estimated that the personnel employed with them would have performed more work with pick and shovel in the same time.

Further trials were ordered but were never satisfactory, and with the passing of the summer of 1918 the occasion for the employment of the mechanical excavator ceased. If suitable machines and a supply of spare parts had been available in 1916, a considerable saving of labour could have been made in 1917, particularly since the Buried System was then extended far to the rear in the endeavour to counteract the increased activity of the enemy's long range guns and bombing aeroplanes. As it was, however, mechanical trench excavating was, throughout the war, always just a little behind what was required of it and was never of great importance.*

* In justice to these machines it should be recorded that occasions did occur when they did good work. In V Corps area in 1918, for instance, several miles of first-class cable trench were dug in hard clay and chalk in the Toutencourt area. Buried communication was established for some 2¼ miles forward of and 2 miles behind Divisional headquarters. The impression created here was good and with proper spares for maintenance much better and more general results might have been obtained.

The foregoing discussion of the technique of buried cable has strayed far in advance of the general narrative. The end of 1916 and the conclusion of the Somme offensive saw the Signal Service definitely committed to a deep buried system lying in the main between battalion and Divisional headquarters. To the various junctions of a grid composed of the intersections of lateral and front-to-rear routes, all formation and unit signal offices within these limits were connected as desired. The original system, starting with 10 or 20 pairs, had increased to 50 or 70 pairs, according to the details of the situation which had to be met. A certain number of spare pairs had always to be provided to meet emergency concentrations, often of guns, more seldom of formations. The increase of the artillery with the Force had already permitted of the formation of the mobile Heavy and Field Artillery Groups which appeared, sometimes here, sometimes there, as harbingers of an approaching offensive This accession to the number of guns engaged was accompanied by a greater precision in artillery methods which involved special lines for wire-cutting and many more observation posts than had formerly been considered necessary. When the situation was favourable, as at Mount Kemmel, special systems were built up which varied from the normal grid in proportion as the command system of lines was more or less subordinated to artillery requirements. In other places, where observation was from isolated posts or from the fire trenches themselves, lines from observation posts were concentrated through the forward test-boxes, and sometimes through battalion headquarters, to the Observation Centres of the battery zone.* Thus the ever-increasing demands of the artillery were accommodated more and more by the main command system and this was an additional argument for more complete control of artillery signals by the Signal Service authorities.

The extension of the buried cable system beyond battalion headquarters was limited as a rule to the preparation for an approaching offensive. One fact which much reduced its usefulness near the front line in normal quiescent times was that buried cables, however deep, could not withstand shells from heavy trench mortars. Trench cable was therefore used to connect up important forward posts and company headquarters to the battalion, and also for lateral communication forward of the latter headquarters. Before an

---

* The introduction of central observation exchanges in 1916 was undoubtedly the greatest reform in artillery practice so far as it affected signals. By means of the concentration of lines from individual O.P.'s to these central points, it was possible to make the most universal use of the limited number of observation posts available. For the successful carrying out of this plan, central control of artillery lines was essential; the policy could only be carried to its logical conclusion by close co-operation and by the full utilization of the facilities offered by the main command signal system.

K

offensive of any magnitude, however, the deep buried system was continued by night work right up to a cable head in the front line. Often, indeed, it was taken right out by means of saps and mines across " No Man's Land " and even in some cases beneath the enemy trenches, the work being left to be completed after the assault had been launched.

Such cable-heads were usually the limit of reliable line signalling. Attempts were not made in this year to follow up the troops with deep buries, though when an attack had taken place and the situation had once more settled down to a modified form of siege warfare, the buried system was again advanced to the new battalion headquarters. In the preparation for the next attack it would again be carried forward to a cable-head in or near the new front line. This was, however, a normal procedure and was not marked by any features other than those already described. Labour was not available to permit of the buries being hurried forward in the interval immediately following an attack when the enemy shelling was comparatively weak. Many signal officers advocated the formation of a permanent labour party of 200 men per Corps during stationary warfare and 1,000 men per Corps during active operations. Some such system was already in being in the VI French Army and would have prevented the casualties inseparable from the pushing forward of the routes in the face of heavy fire from the German artillery, reinforced as it soon was by reserves rushed up as early as possible to the scene of a fresh offensive. The general tactical situation and the situation as regards man-power did not, however, permit of the adoption of the same policy in the British Army.

Within the limits already described the new system was a very safe one. It was, indeed, for the period which we are now considering, relatively safer than any system of signal communication had been since the war began. The anxieties of the Signal Service as regards line communication in the forward area during stationary warfare were almost removed. Occasionally a bury would be interrupted by the direct impact of an 8-inch shell ; occasionally a signal office dug-out, or test-point, insufficiently protected, would be blown in by a projectile from a long range gun. In either case the interruption was a matter of a few hours or minutes only, and always alternative routes were possible in a well-devised and well-executed grid. So secure, indeed, was the system, that supplementary signal communication was seldom needed in this zone.

The Corps wireless station was able to confine its attention almost entirely to the control of the forward stations working under it, the Divisional central visual stations were able to be sited entirely with a view to picking up signals from forward stations during an offensive. In most Divisions, a supplementary visual communication scheme was formulated and stations were selected and heavily protected.

In the most elaborate cases these took the form of a heavily-protected central receiving station with several periscopes and binoculars or telescopes aligned on to various forward transmitting stations sited near the positions of the Divisional and Brigade observation offices. These intermediate stations were themselves fitted with receiving apparatus devised more with the idea of receiving from any position within their field of view than of communication with any particular fixed stations. The visual system was, however, seldom needed to reinforce or replace the line system further to the rear than Brigade or even (towards the end of the year, when the deep buried system had developed to its full extent) battalion headquarters.

Before leaving for a time the study of the evolution of the buried cable system, it will be interesting to compare the experience of the German higher command with that of the British and French armies. In a report on the Somme battles, the enemy attributes his failure to withstand our initial attacks mainly to the failure of his telephone system, and the comparative absence of alternative methods of communication such as visual and wireless. The latter aspect of the question is of interest in connection with the facts related in the following chapter, but as regards the line system, generally, his conclusions are also very applicable to the experiences of the British Signal Service. The German report on the Somme battle stated definitely that " telephone communication cannot be maintained unless routes are systematically buried not less than 10 ft. in the open and 6 ft. below the sole of a trench." This sweeping statement was a tribute, both to the power and thoroughness of the British artillery preparation, and to the enemy's confidence in a capacity for elaborate fortification which made it possible for him to contemplate such a scheme as a realisable conception.

# CHAPTER VIII.

IN the general discussion on the evolution of the 6 ft. buried system in the previous chapter, reference has been made to the important part played by this system in the battle of the Somme. Where the 6 ft. bury had been completed to battalion headquarters before an attack, or better still, to the front line or well out into "No Man's Land," anxiety was relieved as regards intercommunication in rear of cable-head. Where this did not prove feasible, on the other hand, the shallow buries or trench cables were a source of constant anxiety and loss. Telegraph and telephone communication was at best intermittent, and often non-existent.

The lessons of the battles of the Somme, and the modifications in signal practice and organization which were brought about as the result of this first great offensive carried out by the British Army, are best considered in two main sub-divisions. These are, respectively, the alteration in methods of forward signalling, and the general modifications of signal organization and policy considered in their broader aspects. It is the former that it is proposed to consider somewhat in detail in the present chapter.

Never before had the Expeditionary Force been engaged in warfare approaching in intensity that of the Somme battles. The enemy was well-hidden and well-protected in a system of trenches and redoubts on which he had spent eighteen months of painstaking and intelligently directed effort. Across the face of France stretched at least four series of completed lines, immensely strong, with all salients converted into self-contained forts, and with the fullest possible use made of the opportunities for enfilade fire. In front of the lines of defence were belts of barbed wire, 40 yards or more in breadth, and of great strength and intricate entanglement. True, it was the task of the artillery to demolish, and of the infantry to assault and over-run these defences, yet the Signal Service was equally concerned, for it was the thoroughness of our own bombardment—necessary for the obliteration of wire, trenches and strong-points—which formed one of the great obstacles in the way of following up the advancing troops with a line system capable of serving their needs.

The features of the Somme battles were undoubtedly the length and power of the preparatory bombardments which preceded each attack, and the weight of the enemy's retaliatory barrage which fell upon our front line and the country immediately in rear of it immediately an attack was launched or even suspected. The growling thunder of the guns which was part of the normal routine of trench warfare, rose on occasion to an inferno of shrieking shells and crashing explosions as the barrage or area bombardment blasted out of its path every living thing that could not seek instant shelter in bomb-proof dug-outs or deep communication trenches. The very villages and towns which stood across the path of our advancing troops and which had been converted by the enemy into miniature fortresses, were obliterated and shot away. In many cases, not even a pile of bricks marked the places where once tranquil village life flowed on as if war were not and could never be. For the first time, the Germans themselves experienced what the fury of modern weapons really could achieve. When the battle commenced, the main weight of the enemy's own artillery was concentrated further to the south, supporting and enforcing his assault upon the Verdun fortresses and defences. As the attack was pressed home, however, and he realized that his boasted defences were not impregnable, he concentrated more and more guns opposite to the menaced portion of his front. What with the battered and sodden nature of the country over which the long drawn-out conflict took place, and the weight of metal brought to bear on the contested area by the enemy artillery, the problem of forward signals was well-nigh insoluble.

The battle of the Somme in 1916 may be divided from the point of view of the British Army into three main phases. The initial attack of July 1st with its comparative success on the southern portion of the front, was followed by some months of a moving siege warfare. In the second phase, attack after attack was carried out, now on a Brigade front, now on the front of a Division, now on that of a Corps. Each attack had a definite objective of limited extent ; each was carefully prepared ; each was followed by a period of comparative quiescence or by enemy counter-attacks by which he endeavoured—usually without success—to oust our men from the ground they had gained. The third and last phase of the battle was concerned with the pushing of the enemy down the forward slopes of the plateau. A conspicuously successful general attack was accompanied by a series of voluntary withdrawals by the enemy and was succeeded by a few smaller actions which left the British line in favourable position for the coming winter.

The intercommunication problems of the campaign are also best considered under three headings. Three distinct problems were presented for solution by :—(1) the individual carefully-prepared attack with a limited objective ; (2) the successful surprise attack which involved an advance sufficiently widespread to cause movements of headquarters, and (3) the slow-moving siege warfare which took the fighting formations off the deep-buried system and made necessary temporary reliance on a far less secure line system. It is proposed to deal with these three phases separately in the order in which they are given above. In the first two cases the problem was that of crossing " No Man's Land " and following up the advancing troops with the best measure of signal communication possible. The main requirements of troops in an attack were three in number. The supply of reinforcements and ammunition must be maintained. Sufficient direction must be given to the batteries to enable them to lengthen their range, and concentrate their fire on more distant objectives, while the infantry carried by assault the defences already pulverized. Information of approaching counter-attacks gained from other sources than direct infantry observation must be conveyed to the first line troops and artillery in good time to enable them to crush the attacks. In addition, for the benefit of the higher command, information must be brought back by some means to keep the Brigade and Divisional Commanders in touch with the situation and able to ask for help from higher formations and to utilize their own general reserves to the best advantage.

These requirements appear simple as stated in broad outline, but for the efficient conveyance of orders and information some measure of signal communication was essential. Telephone communication if possible ; if not, any supplementary means which best suited the situation. During the battles of the Somme, forward signal units had at their disposal visual, including communication to aeroplanes and kite balloons, contact patrol aeroplanes, pigeons, mounted and motor cyclist orderlies, runners, wireless and the new untried earth induction sets. The main feature of the story of forward signals during the offensive consists in the combination of all or some of these means into schemes, and their organization individually to form a chain of intercommunication between the most advanced troops and Brigade and battalion headquarters or cable-head.

One thing that early stood out among the lessons of the battles was the fact that different means must be used to suit different sets of circumstances. At one time visual would prove successful ; at another pigeons and runners would save the situation. On occasion, wireless or the new power buzzers and amplifiers would prove the salvation of some isolated body of men hard beset in a captured stronghold. Again, favourable circumstances and a careful study of the enemy barrage would permit of the running of lines by a route safe enough to enable them to be maintained without undue sacrifice of life. Almost always, by one means or another, signal touch would be kept. Runners, for instance, could always be found who would make the effort to cross the shell-swept, corpse-strewn barrage zone. The lives of these men were precious, however. They must not be lightly thrown away. Casualties amongst battalion signallers and runners were normally heavy and at times 50 per cent. and over fell in a single battle. The advantage of visual, wireless, pigeons, and earth induction sets was that each—under suitable conditions—would successfully bridge the dreaded barrage zone. By their means news could be flashed or otherwise despatched through the ether or air from protected emplacements to stations situated at a safe distance beyond the zone of heaviest shelling. Air-signalling vied with ground-signalling, now one, now the other triumphing as the situation changed. The problem before the forward signal officer resolved itself into one of organization more than anything else.

Means of signalling were ready to his hand. It was his task to organize his personnel in such a manner that the greatest use was made of the most suitable means of communication with the least number of casualties. The measure of the success achieved may be judged from the official tribute to the Signal Service in the dispatches which describe the battles of the Somme.

" The Signal Service, created a short time before the war began on a very small scale, has expanded in proportion with the rest of the Army, and is now a very large organization.

" It provides the means of intercommunication between all the armies and all parts of them, and in modern war requirements in this respect are on an immense and elaborate scale.

" The calls on this service have been very heavy, entailing a most severe strain, often under most trying and dangerous conditions. Those calls have invariably been met with conspicuous success, and no service has shown a more wholehearted and untiring energy in the fulfilment of its duty."

To consider the different situations a little more in detail, the simplest case worthy of particular attention is that of the attack on a Brigade or Divisional front with a limited objective. A certain section of the enemy's defences was subjected to a fierce whirlwind bombardment of a few hours, or at most one or two days, and was then assaulted by the infantry. The advance was usually to be a few hundred yards only in depth : it seldom would exceed a mile. The outstanding feature of this type of attack was the absence of movement of any of the major headquarters. Battalion headquarters, possibly even Brigade headquarters, might move forward after the consolidation of the captured position. Such a move, however, was carried out at leisure and could be catered for by the forward extension of the deep buried cable on an ordered plan and by means of organized working parties. During the attack itself, and during the period when the enemy counter-attacks might be expected to materialize, no such forward move would be likely to take place.

The essential preliminary for such an attack was to have the cable-head of the deep buried system as near as possible to the front line. If two or three days' notice had been given, this would be carried out; if not, the proportion of the line communications which must be considered unsafe included all lines in advance of cable-head, and additional supplementary communication must be provided accordingly.

In either case, the position of cable-head would be published in operation orders. One of the main lessons of the Somme battles, and of other offensives also, was that the position of signal offices, cable-heads, test stations with spurs to which units could connect, central visual stations, pigeon posts, wireless stations, and all other means of despatching messages could not be too widely circulated.* It was of no use establishing stations unless their position was known to all the officers, and as many as possible of the rank and file, of the troops whose needs they were intended to serve. Cases occurred on the Somme when, for longer or shorter periods of time, the situation was obscure and the Staff had to rely partially or wholly on news collected by Signal Service officers and N.C.O.'s. Indeed, this difficulty of obtaining information was so real and so pronounced that it was legislated for in the Manual on " Intercommunication in Battle," issued by the General Staff in 1917.

Forward of cable-head, lines up to the front trenches were made as safe as possible, but it was recognized that all or some were certain to be cut during the attack. Various methods of making the trench line system safe were tried. Laddered lines were still in favour, but were used more in the general attacks to be referred to later. Rabbit netting was also still used on occasion. Narrow, open cable trenches were frequently dug. Armoured cable buried beneath the sole of the trench was much used at first, but was not very satisfactory.

Generally, the only marked development of trench cable for attack in 1916, was in the direction of a greater orderliness of system and more attempt at protection. In one case " D2 " cable was buried in a communication trench, by undercutting the side nearest the enemy to a depth of one foot, and filling earth in on the cable. Eight days' heavy bombardment completely destroyed the trench, filling it in and obliterating it in many places, yet this cable was never damaged.

The employment of cable with the assaulting troops differed with the ideas of signal company commanders and brigade section officers, with the requirements of the situation, and with the *terrain* over which the attack was to take place. In an attack with a limited objective it was usually possible to take light cable over with the the first assaulting troops. Provided several cables were taken by alternative routes, and were laid with due regard to the avoidance of places likely to be shelled, one cable at least might remain unbroken

* Of course with adequate safeguards against leakage of information.

sufficiently long to be of vital use. Indeed, several cases were recorded in which such frail threads remained through until diminution of the enemy's fire enabled the bury to be dug forward towards the new front line. One scheme given as an example of a successful attempt to carry forward line communication is as follows :

" Each company should detail three or more signallers, each with a telephone and a reel of " D1 " cable. The latter should be fixed to an instrument in the front trench and securely tied back to prevent any strain from coming on the instrument during the process of laying. A definite point in the enemy's line, to which these men are to make their way, should be decided on previously. This point should be published in orders and should be explained to all ranks as being the Report Centre to which all messages should be taken.

The signallers should advance with or immediately behind the advancing troops, as it has been proved by experience that, provided the wire entanglement has been properly cut, the first line generally reaches the trench without much difficulty. They should advance, one behind either flank of their company, and the third about the centre, keeping well apart and converging on the point previously settled upon as the Report Centre. With any good fortune, one at least should get through with his line in safety."

The above system was tried in practice, and, on one occasion, communication was kept with the third line of German trenches for six hours and, on another, with the first German line throughout the day. It is typical of the kind of scheme tried with varying success in many attacks by Divisions, Brigades, or battalions, and served as well as any other modification of forward signal practice.

In the great majority of attacks with a limited objective, however, the enemy artillery retaliation was so heavy that lines could not be relied upon to remain through. Once the enemy barrage had come down on the old front line, and his bombardment of the captured trenches had commenced, the attempt to maintain or lay new lines might usually be discontinued as causing useless waste of life. On rare occasions, when direct observation was impossible and the initial calculations of the enemy artillery were at fault, a " patchy " barrage might open up possibilities in this respect. Even if this were so, however, all descriptions of traffic at once converged upon the safe route.

Ground lines, even if they escaped the enemy's shells, could not be expected to survive the constant stream of walking wounded, reinforcements, orderlies, limbered wagons, stretcher bearers and other miscellaneous traffic. A well-worn track appeared at once and momentarily expanded in width. Along this, feet and wheels would rapidly trample and churn out of existence the strongest cable. The signal officer must make the most of the route by organizing thereon a runner service, or possibly, if distances were sufficient to warrant their employment, or the road dry enough to permit of the use of motor cycles, a service of mounted orderlies or motor cyclist despatch riders. By one or all of these means, communication could be kept up between the report centres and the cable-heads in rear of our original front line.

Even where, as more often was the case, no well-defined shell-free path could be picked out, runners were still of necessity used in spite of heavy casualties. Cases often occurred where messages, although sent in duplicate by successive runners, failed to reach their destination. Visual and pigeons were used to supplement the runner service, but each means had its limitations. Pigeons could not be used at night * or in heavy mist ; visual was impossible either in mist or through the smoke and dust of a heavy bombardment. Another factor which acted against the use of pigeons was a shortage of birds which kept down the allotment per company for specific actions to two birds. In such cases, one of two things was quite likely to happen, according to the temperament of the company commander. Either he might be anxious to establish communication immediately and liberate both birds with comparatively unimportant messages, or he might, on the other hand, consider his pigeons as his last resource and hesitate to part with them at all. In the latter case, he would as often as not retain the birds while opportunity after opportunity for their use passed, until, finally, they were released with a quite formal message at the close of the 48 hours which was by rule the limit of their stay at any one time in the forward trenches. Some nicety of judgment was required in the use of the birds, but they were often of the utmost value at crises when all other means of communication had failed and the bombardment was of such intensity that to despatch a runner would have been to send him to certain death.

The short distances involved in the type of attack at present under consideration, were within the range of all visual appliances. When conditions were favourable, that is, in lulls of the barrage in clear weather, or even when wet weather prevented a great accumulation of dust in the atmosphere in spite of the constant explosion of shells, this means of signalling proved of the greatest use. Flags, discs, and shutters were used over short distances ; lamps of several

---

* It was not until much later in the war that attempts were made to train pigeons specially for night flying. The French intercommunication service were the pioneers in the new departure, but after the return from Italy, Second Army signals also experimented with a special loft. The birds were kept in red light and were trained at night. Excellent results were obtained in practice flights, the only light required being a powerful one with its rays projected on to the special landing stage. This light could of course be screened from the sight of the enemy's aerial observers. By the time the training of the birds was completed, the last advance had commenced and they were therefore not actually flown during an attack.

types gave good results both by night and by day. The detailed consideration of the long-range visual apparatus is better considered in connection with the second and more general type of attack where greater distances were involved. The Dietz and " ping-pong " discs have already been mentioned, for they rose to favour in the 1915 battles. The Louvre * shutter was, however, new. One little device connected with the latter is perhaps interesting as being the direct outcome of the experience of the Somme battles. As in the case of the Begbie lamp, one great drawback of the earlier type of shutter was the noise made when the springs were drawn out to their full extent and released. This was overcome by the employment of a " stop " which prevented the movable leaves of the shutter from completely opening and closing. A further improvement in order to increase portability and decrease the conspicuous character of the first rigid shutters was the invention of a fold-up pattern which could be unrolled for use and fixed to the end of the signaller's rifle, to a fixed bayonet, or to any convenient pole.

An even less conspicuous type of visual apparatus of the same order was the " Watson " signalling fan, which was designed for signalling over short distances. When closed up, this instrument was very inconspicuous. It had also the additional advantage of being suitable for use, if spread out on the ground with the light face uppermost, for pointing out the presence of the troops to the contact aeroplanes which played a prominent part for the first time in these battles.

--------

The second case to be considered is that of intercommunication during a general attack carried out with the avowed intention of breaking the enemy's line. Here the same main features repeated themselves, but in addition the problem was complicated by the entrance of two further important factors :—advance to a considerable distance, and the movement of formation and unit headquarters which this involved.

Once more, the system of forward signals was based upon a good deep buried system carried forward to cable-heads as near as possible to the front line. In the case of the first great attack on July 1st, the situation was complicated by the fact that the decision to bury cable had not been taken early enough. Where shallow buries were still in existence they were invariably broken in many places on the first day and were a continual menace to the efficiency of the Divisional intercommunication systems. They were often reinforced by alternative routes and by omnibus lines of poled cable run through all Brigade headquarters, but even so, line communication could not be considered certain. More reliance had, therefore, to be placed

* A signalling shutter with slats after the fashion of a Venetian blind.

on the alternative visual system or on the trench wireless sets installed at Division and Brigade headquarters.

Forward of the buried system, line communication in the first stages of the battle was usually impossible. In many cases, Brigade section officers organized " forward parties " to carry forward wires with one or other of the assaulting waves. Usually, however, such parties were swept out of existence—as parties—during the first few minutes of the advance. Casualties were high and the loss of one or two links in each chain was fatal to the attempt to link up the points in the enemy system which had been selected as Report centres.

Everything possible and reasonable to expect was attempted. A careful study of plans of the enemy defences, and of the aeroplane photographs from which these plans had been prepared, enabled a definite programme to be mapped out beforehand. Signal instructions were issued as part of the General Staff Operation Orders for each attack. All ranks were informed where they might expect the new Report centres to be in existence. Staffs agreed to accept these spots as the sites of their new headquarters.

The problem was not, however, so simple as it seemed. The devastating character of the preliminary bombardment altered the appearance of wide stretches of country. The strong points were, to all outward seeming, obliterated from the face of Nature. Without surveying instruments it was often impossible for the parties to locate them at all. Men wandered about the country for hours before they finally set up their office in a convenient crater or partly-destroyed redoubt or trench, and advertised their presence as best they could with flag or other marker. It was impossible to work to a time-table or conform to anything beyond the broad principles of the original scheme. Constant experiences of this nature convinced the signal officers concerned that it was better to wait until the situation had settled down before attempting anything in the way of a line system. When the enemy barrage was discontinuous, advantage was taken of the fact to run lines through the gaps and thus to lay out a system of laddered cable, wire netting, or even of simple ground or poled cable. Laddered cable in particular was often used with success, communication being carried on in dry weather in spite of over 50 breaks in the ladder.

In a successful attack which involved a considerable advance, battalion headquarters usually moved forward within a few hours. By careful selection of a route it was then often possible to connect up to the old cable-head with " D1 " lines, which were later substituted by " D5 " cable. These forward lines were poled as soon as possible and were then maintained by means of a suitable system of lineman's posts which were sited in captured German machine gun emplacements or dug-outs.

Quite apart from the shelling, the establishment of this forward line system was by no means easy. The bombardment had converted the country into an indescribable chaos of overlapping shell holes and craters of various sizes. Any man-made obstacles, it is true, had been shot out of the way of the cable detachments, but the hindrances put in their way were incomparably greater than those removed. Distances of the order of two or three miles had to be traversed over ground which even in dry weather was like the troughs and ridges of a sea lashed into fury by a myriad gusts of wind. When the wet weather which signalized the later months of the offensive set in, the ground became almost impassable. Indeed, the advance of the infantry was ofttimes limited by their physical endurance. When the ground was dry, men could make fair progress with reels on which were wound quarter mile lengths of " D1 " cable, and in this way the initial light line was usually laid. The " D5 " cable which was run out as soon as possible to replace these " D1 " lines was, however, a different matter. The provision of a single-horsed vehicle which would accommodate two or more " drums, cart, cable," was advocated by some signal officers. Proposal was even made that a petrol-driven plough might be used with advantage to lay traffic-proof lines across this much-trampled zone, but the circumstances under which the machines would have been of use were so seldom realized that this was never attempted in practice.

The pack cable horses of the Infantry Brigade had been abolished in the previous year as being unsuited for stationary warfare. Had these been available they might have been of use under certain sets of circumstances, but these occurred so seldom that the pack horses and equipment were never really missed.* In many cases a pair of shafts were fitted to the normally man-drawn barrow which was part of the equipment of all forward signal units. These improvized cable carts were often of the greatest use and were employed largely both in the battles of the Somme and in the position battles of the next year. On one or two occasions in October, when the enemy made slight voluntary withdrawals to more suitable positions than those to which he had been forced back, cable wagons were used in the forward areas. Their use was, however, so exceptional as scarcely to merit mention. Finally, on the extensive mudfields which supervened all over the churned-up battlefields after the autumn rains, yet another type of transport appeared. The laying of many lines was only made possible by the use of the flat-bottomed sleighs which were specially built to meet a situation which bade fair to bring operations to a standstill.

Thus, by one means or another, it sometimes proved practicable to establish a measure of line communication within a few hours of

* One Corps alone in the Thiepval sector lost several hundred horses through their becoming bogged in impassable country.

the advance. Some means had to be devised, however, to keep touch during those first few hours and also to bridge the gap that here, as in the attack with limited objectives, always existed forward of battalion headquarters. These supplementary means must also be carried back to cable-head, wherever that might be, for line communication forward of cable-head was never anything but intermittent. Various means by which this was achieved have already been indicated in studying the attack with limited objectives.

The problems due to the greater distances covered and the movement of headquarters involved in the more extended attacks were solved by more careful organization. A general line of advance was decided on beforehand and the signal communication was mapped out along this line, the only variations permitted being strictly local ones due to the unexpected situations which must always arise even in the best-planned attack.*

Once the lines had been carried forward, there was a tendency for other means of signalling to " bunch " on to the same route. This was only to be expected since the lines went by the safest way, and this concentration much simplified the problem of organization of the despatch rider and runner service, which was still one of the mainstays of the Division and Brigade intercommunication system.

The chief supplementary means of signalling, placed in order of frequency of use in 1916, were runner, visual, pigeon. Nothing much remains to be said about either.

Pigeons were reliable, but few in number. Those which were available were found to be of more use if concentrated at battalion headquarters than if scattered amongst companies. In the latter case, the casualties increased out of all proportion to the number of useful flights made by the birds. At battalion headquarters, on the other hand, it was found that the birds were comparatively safe except when actually in flight. One small fact brought to notice by the experience of the Somme battles was the comparative immunity of pigeons to " tear " gas. One slight innovation which is of interest was the use by the dismounted cavalry Division in January, 1916, of a wireless station to connect its loft at H.Q. at Sailly-la-Bourse with a receiving set in the front trench system. By this means, two-way working was established in a novel fashion. The experiment was, however, an isolated one, and, though successful, was rendered redundant by the fact that on the particular front where it was tried the situation was stable and the cables held.

The main lessons learnt by the organisers of the pigeon service during the Somme offensive was the necessity for an increase in the

* Examples occurred, for instance, when signallers of the forward parties were obliged to take to their rifles and fight their way forward or even to capture the positions they would afterwards use as a signal office.

number of birds available for active operations. In the absence of an unlimited supply of birds, this need could only be met by an increased mobility of the service as it then existed. The result was the introduction of the " mobile " loft by means of which birds could be trained to a new front in a few weeks. As the number of mobile lofts increased, concentration on active fronts became a more practical possibility, and much more could be done with a given number of birds than under the old system of " fixed " lofts. The reconstruction of the pigeon service at the conclusion of a prolonged advance would also be much facilitated by this reform. A mobile pigeon service would have many advantages and at the end of 1916 the proposals for the formation of such a service were definitely put forward, the original figures being six motor and 60 horse-drawn lofts. Each motor loft contained 50 and each horse-drawn loft 75 birds, thus giving an addition of 4,800 pigeons to the service as formerly constituted.

The main lessons in visual signalling have already been summarized. The principle adopted was the establishment of as many protected receiving stations, both on the ground behind our old front line and on captured territory, as could be manned by the available personnel, or as topographical conditions would permit. A large proportion of the signallers accompanying the advancing troops were equipped with flags, discs or shutters, or with lamps. On captured ground, German machine gun emplacements were naturally ideal sites for forward visual stations.

First line troops also set up visual stations in convenient shell-holes or half-obliterated trenches, and flags were used from behind the remains of enemy works, though this latter method was the least popular of all. The feature of the procedure used was D.D.D.D. working, i.e., messages were sent from front to rear without an answer. They were repeated two or three times according to the individual faith of the signal officer concerned. Experience showed that triple repetition was advisable and this procedure was subsequently standardized in an order issued by the Signal Directorate.

Opinions differed very much as to the advisibility of an acknowledgment to important messages. Certainly, the enemy were far too busy and disorganized in the opening stages of an offensive to permit of particular attention being paid to individual stations either with a view to reading the signals sent or of directing artillery fire against them. Equally certainly, visual signalling was not used as much as it might have been, because battalion signallers were doubtful if their messages were being received. Nothing seems more futile than signalling into space without any sign of the vigilance of a receiving station. On the other hand, the number of stations receiving was so great and they were usually so well-disposed, that almost all messages sent under conditions when visual was possible were received, often by several stations, certainly by one or two. The case might perhaps have been met by a single acknowledgment of the whole message, which would have been unlikely to provoke retaliation and certainly would have given away no information of value.

While signalling by day and over short distances was successfully carried out with discs, shutters and fans ; long distances both by day and by night were frequently bridged by means of lamps. Of these, there were several types now available, amongst them being the French projector lamp No. 24, which gave good signals by day up to distances of 2,000 yards with the naked eye and 3,000 yards when a telescope was employed. The second type of lamp used, the service electric signalling lamp, was very much less powerful. It gave fair results by night, but was of little use by day. Two new types which were introduced for signalling to and from aeroplanes were the " Aldis " and " Hucks " lamps. These threw a powerful beam, but were worked by accumulators and were therefore not very portable. They also had too great a dispersion of the beam to be satisfactory for horizontal use between stations working within the possible field of view of a vigilant enemy.

These lamps, however, provided the main idea on which the future signalling lampe were based. Once again a decisive step forward in Army signalling was achieved as the result of individual enterprise when the " Lucas " lamp was designed by a gunner subaltern. Two types of the new lamp were produced—one, worked by accumulators and very powerful, for use with central visual stations, the other a smaller variety with a battery of eight dry cells as the source of power for forward stations.

Both lamps were distinguished by the strength and general efficiency of their component parts and by a most marked reduction in the dispersion of the beam. They were thoroughly tested on the Somme, enthusiastically reported upon by the Corps which had introduced them, and were later adopted with but slight alterations as the new standard signalling lamp. With their adoption visual signalling was once more given fresh impetus and gained markedly in efficiency. Daylight signalling by means of the Lucas lamp became the most popular and easily the most effective of all means of visual signalling in all climates which included a considerable proportion of over-cast weather, while the range of dispersion of the lamp made two-way signalling without enemy " overseeing " more practicable

Before leaving the subject of visual signalling in the Somme battles, mention must be made of a specialized form of signalling which first succeeded on a large scale in this offensive. The Somme battles were marked by the general employment of aeroplanes as a means of keeping touch between the forward infantry and the higher command. Certain aeroplanes were definitely detailed to serve specified formations and keep their headquarters informed of the progress of events.

This could be done in two ways, both of which involved the use of some means of identification of the forward infantry.

For the latter purpose various means were employed, all of them at present in the experimental stage, and many of them giving indifferent results. Perhaps the most successful were those which depended upon direct observation from the aeroplanes. The observer would call by means of his Klaxon Horn for forward troops to identify their position.* One long blast, meaning "Where are you?" would be replied to by the burning of flares or the display of discs, fans or shutters on the ground.

At battalion or Brigade headquarters, large numerals or letters of white cloth on a black background were displayed to identify the headquarters; and for the first time the ground panel was used to send messages in a clumsy code. It was not, however, successful. The aeroplane observers were too slow at reading; the signaller on the ground was too impatient to be read. Messages sent by lamp were also seldom received, and, even if acknowledged, more seldom delivered at their destination. The new experiments in visual signalling were only of use as indicating the lines along which future progress might take place. By far the best reports from the aeroplane observers were those which were based upon their own observation, assisted by the use of flares or the display of other prearranged signals by the front line troops.

Once the observation was made, it might be conveyed to the Staff by two methods : by personal visit, or by dropping a message. The first method was more satisfactory if anything of paramount importance was to be delivered, but it involved a certain amount of delay and some risk, for good landing grounds were not common round about Divisional headquarters. As a rule it was far better for the aeroplane to drop its message on a selected spot where watchers were permanently stationed as long as daylight lasted. This means was more generally adopted and led to the establishment of definite headquarters "dropping grounds," the establishment of which became at a later date one of the responsibilities of the signal company of the formation.

Before the subject of visual signalling can be considered as adequately dealt with, something should be said of the battalion signaller. On these men the brunt of forward signalling fell. Among them occurred the greater proportion of the signal casualties. All forward signalling under battle conditions, whether it was the maintaining of the lines, the conveyance of messages by hand, or the watching for visual signals, involved a considerable measure of risk. From front to rear of the forward signal system casualties were common. Among

---

* In some cases, discs of tin were sewed on the backs of the men's tunics, but the device did not prove successful and is in any case somewhat outside the scope of Signal Service activity.

L

the battalion signallers, however, battalions often reported the occurrence of 40 or 50 per cent. of casualties in a single action. This could not be permitted to continue. In the early days of the battle, many signallers fell in the ranks of the attacking infantry or on special duties which had nothing to do with signalling at all. The dangers of the situation were early realized, and pressure was brought to bear to enforce the policy of holding at least one-third of all the signallers of each battalion in Brigade reserve. These men were withdrawn from the battalion before it went into action and were used to replace casualties or to improve the forward signal system as occasion arose.

A further extension of this policy was later achieved by the formation of the " Brigade Pool." This consisted of eight signallers from each battalion in the Brigade who were permanently retained at Brigade headquarters under the orders of the Brigade Signal Officer. They were trained specially in visual appliances and with the power buzzer and amplifier. In action, they were utilized on any forward portion of the Brigade system of communications and in particular to keep communication between Brigade and Battalion headquarters by either of the above means, or to help man the Divisional visual system.

The whole question of the " signals " of a battalion was shown by the Somme battles to be on a somewhat unsatisfactory footing. The abolition of the Battalion Signalling Officer had been followed by a gradual deterioration in the qualifications of the battalion signaller and the organization of intercommunication within the battalion. As time went on, this was remedied to a certain extent by force of circumstances. In many battalions the Adjutant gave more time than he could well spare to the supervision of the signalling system. In others, the Assistant Adjutant was expected to devote a considerable proportion of his attention to the same work. In yet other battalions an unofficial signalling officer was appointed and gave his whole time to this very important duty. Success was achieved in proportion as the problem was taken seriously, but it was not until December, 1916, that the proposal that the post of battalion Signal Officer should be re-created was seriously put forward. Discussion went on for months, during which time many battalions anticipated the decision of the higher command. Finally, in December, 1917, the necessary amendment was made to the War Establishment and the new appointments, which by now had become general, were officially recognized. A marked increase in the efficiency of battalion signals was the immediate result wherever officers were appointed, while another important side-issue of the decision was the re-opening of a channel through which a supply of most efficient junior officers flowed into the Signal Service.

It may be said of the temporary signal officer that, the nearer the front line he gained his early experience, the better was his signal practice and the more use was he in an emergency. Quite the most efficient officer for forward signal work was the battalion signal officer who had seen service and had then been sent home for a six months' course of technical training. In future wars, this method of choice might with good results be made more general and a much smaller percentage of totally inexperienced material taken into the commissioned ranks of the Signal Service. An ideal forward Signal Service would be that officered by men who represented the pick, either of the battalion signal officers, or of the rank and file of the forward signal units. In such men will be found a knowledge of the conditions of modern war which has been gained at first hand combined with a working knowledge of signal practice as modified by these conditions. A comparatively short course of training would serve to equip them to grasp the more technical work they would necessarily have to supervise as they rose in the Service and were appointed to more exalted posts further to the rear. On the other hand, the man chosen without experience of war, however well trained technically, is an uncertain factor when exposed to the soul-testing and nerve-racking experiences which he cannot fail to meet when he takes up his duties in the fighting area. He may do untold damage both to the lives and the morale of his unit before he becomes acclimatized. He may not ; but the risk is there.

To certain technical posts in the rear, however, this argument does not apply. Technique will here often be of paramount importance, and to fill such posts no better men could be employed than those who have spent their lives grappling with problems similar to those they would have to face in the Army. Thus, for such posts, sometimes at Corps, more often at Army, still more frequently on the Lines of Communication, personnel with the necessary technical experience, but little military knowledge, would often be admirably suited.

Another effect of the high percentage of casualties amongst battalion signallers and Brigade sections was the rejuvenation of the Divisional Signal Schools. Whenever a Division was in rest or holding a quiet part of the line, sometimes even when the Division itself was battling in the full tide of war, the Divisional Signal School was established at some convenient village or hutment camp well to the rear. Here, artillery and infantry signallers were trained in visual and in new types of forward signalling appliances. Special attention was given to improving the speed of forward signalling. Great care was taken in teaching the men the principles and practice of telephone and fullerphone working. All men were taught also to repair the simpler type of lines—" D5," " D3," " D2 " and " D1 "—and to lay them in the safest and most efficient manner to suit various tactical situations. Here, also, the new recruits—partially trained in the Depôts at home, but totally unfamiliar with service conditions—were given a final polish before taking up their work in the field. Usually an officer for the Signal School was found from the Divisional Signal Company, either by appointing one of the supernumerary officers allowed to these companies by a wise policy, or by using a Brigade section officer whose place would be taken by a supernumerary. The latter, of course, might be expected to give the best results. During these long years of trench warfare the Divisional Signal Schools played a predominant part in maintaining at a high level the efficiency of the signal communications within the Divisions. They were never officially recognized, but their importance cannot be over-rated, and the need for them is almost certain to recur under similar conditions. There is a certain type of training which is best carried out, indeed, it can only be efficiently undertaken, within reach of the atmosphere of the fighting line. The Division is the fighting formation, and training within the Division can hardly be replaced.

---

A principle which must be recognized throughout in modern warfare is that no means of signalling within the area of heavy shelling is infallible. All are liable to break down or become non-effective from one reason or another. The deepest buried cables yet achieved can be severed by the direct hit of an 8-inch shell.* Visual is dependent on atmospheric conditions and is often impossible through smoke and dust. Wireless sets may have their masts and antennae destroyed by shell fire. Pigeons cannot normally be used at night.† The acme of good signalling organization is the combined use of all these means, with the runner as a last resource. A runner service is a slow and expensive means of intercommunication. Especially is this so in the case of the type of attack at present under consideration when comparatively long distances have to be covered. Where distances were greater than 500 yards, and where mounted orderlies and motor cyclists could not be employed, runners were worked in relays and relay posts were arranged at 200 to 500 yards apart according to the ground.‡

The runner relay posts were frequently made coincident with lineman's posts and, in many cases, the runner was taught to keep his

* On several occasions six foot buries were cut by "dud" shells which penetrated to a depth of 8 or 9 ft. Delay action shells intended for the destruction of dug-outs or other counter-sunk works would, of course, have a similar, but much more devastating effect.

† See note, page 138.

‡ It should be noted that the opinion of experienced battalion signal officers and runners is that it is better to have through runs, as relay posts are impossible to supervise, sometimes unreliable and difficult to ration. Relay posts under half a mile apart are also very extravagant of men. When installed under pressure of circumstances they should be temporary and closed as soon as possible.

eyes open and to mend obvious breaks in the cables on his way back after delivering a message. Runners during the Somme battles became differentiated in the main into two classes :—(1) officer's personal runners who always accompanied the officers into action ; (2) general runners who were at the disposal of the signal officer or sergeant and who were attached to companies or to battalion and Brigade Signal Officers.

The first qualification of a good runner was bravery. He took his life in his hand day after day, and many times a day, as he jogged to and fro between front line and company headquarters, between company, battalion and Brigade headquarters, or between relay posts. Sooner or later, almost certainly, a machine-gun or rifle bullet, or a shell would claim him as a victim. The danger attending the duty was accompanied by none of the generous heat engendered by the excitement of an action and the prospect of a hand-to-hand encounter with the enemy. Under no particular eye, with nothing but a sense of duty to prevent him from seeking the comparative shelter of the nearest shell-hole, only the most courageous men could be expected to traverse the barrage zone many times a day in the course of his duty. Every battalion and company commander, every Brigadier, counted his runners among the best of all his men.

---

It is now necessary to discuss one of the features of the Somme battles which probably gave the Signal Service more trouble than any other. This was the conversion of the initial successes of the general attacks, not, as was hoped, into mobile operations, but into slowly-moving siege warfare. In the first few hours of such a general attack events might move comparatively swiftly. Sooner or later, as the element of surprise ceased to have effect and the enemy accumulated reserves and guns, the initial impetus would be slowed down although the advance was not brought to a standstill. The Signal Service was then faced with all the inconveniences and difficulties of an intensely-raging battle and yet with such comparative stability that the Staff claimed and expected to receive all the conveniences which had come to be admitted as their right during stationary warfare.

Labour was not available for the forward extension of the buried system. Some makeshift was required which would enable lines to be carried forward with, at any rate, a fair prospect of success. Various methods were tried and the most successful was found to be the laying of cables in spade-wide trenches, one or two feet deep, which gave protection against anything except a direct hit or a splinter from directly overhead.

Occasionally a system of German cable trenches could be utilized, and these had the additional advantage that they led straight between

German dug-outs or strong points which could be used as our own headquarters. Shallow buried cable was also tried but it had serious disadvantages. Cables covered with earth were very little more immune from damage than those in open trenches, while they were much more difficult to repair. The principal trouble with the open trench was found to be that all units were liable to use the trenches of the command line system to protect their own lines. Gradually the confusion along such routes almost vied with that which had nearly ruined the line system in 1915. The identification of the original lines could be secured by means of seizing them with spunyarn to stakes in one corner of the bottom of the trench and by careful labelling every 50 yards or so. Induction troubles, however, were not so easily overcome. In such an advance, neither transport nor cable was available in sufficient quantity to permit of all circuits being made metallic. It was recognized, too, that in a swiftly-changing situation the danger from overhearing was much reduced. The enemy was losing ground and had to keep his listening sets well back, while several such sets had been captured or destroyed. Induction trouble was, however, a great drawback to these open trenches and prevented them from becoming really popular. From every other point of view they were easily the best substitute for the deep buries, for, in addition to the other advantages already detailed, they gave a certain measure of protection, and therefore of confidence, to the lineman responsible for the maintenance of the routes. In the special situation described it was to such open trenches that the credit for the retention of a fairly complicated system must be attributed. As soon as practicable, labour was obtained from the General Staff and the deep buries were pushed forward. With the completion of the latter to a well-protected cable-head near battalion headquarters, the situation could once again be considered normal until the next advance.

It was in such situations as the above that wireless found its principal opportunity in the Somme offensive. Attempts were made in some formations to push forward wireless sets with assaulting parties, but without success. A wireless station required a carrying party of several men and an efficient system for the interchange of charged and discharged accumulators. Under the conditions of the battles this difficulty usually proved insurmountable. Party after party was dispersed—sometimes destroyed—by shell fire or machine-gun fire, and finally, it was definitely ordered that wireless was not to be carried forward during an attack.

When the situation had settled down, attempts were made to use wireless to communicate with special isolated positions where communication was liable to be cut off for days at a time. Sometimes the wireless station also failed, maintenance of the aerial being impossible in the overwhelming shellfire to which the posts were subjected. In other cases, however, better results were obtained and, on occasion, wireless was the only means of communication left, and important tactical messages were dealt with by the set.

At, and in rear of Brigade headquarters, the wireless sets although easily kept through were little used in normal times, as the deep buried cables were seldom broken. When, however, Brigade and battalion headquarters had moved forward off this system, they were often invaluable. It is significant, however, that it was reported that enemy jamming stations immediately ceased operations when they realized that a British ground station was endeavouring to send a message of technical importance. This is particularly interesting in view of the evidence given by captured German documents concerning the German attitude towards field wireless.

As late as the spring of 1917, Field-Marshal Hindenburg was strongly against the use of field wireless of any description. He attributed his victory at Tannenberg entirely to the fact that during the whole of the action he was able to overhear and follow the plans of the Russian higher command as transmitted by wireless to the fighting formations. He was greatly in fear of similar indiscretions and considered the function of wireless should be the interception of information which might be obtained from a less careful enemy wireless service. His objections were overruled, and the Germans soon developed field wireless to a considerable extent, but this attitude bears a distinct resemblance to that of the British Divisional and Brigade Staffs, and such an uninformed dislike to wireless was a potent hindrance in the path of its development.

On the whole, we may say of wireless on the Somme that its use was the exception rather than the rule. It was not until the next year that forward wireless achieved a measure of popularity.

Before completing the recital of the lessons of the Somme battles, a few words should be said of certain new methods of signalling which were at that time on trial or in the experimental stage. The appliances referred to are the power buzzer and amplifier, the message-carrying rocket and bomb, and various acoustic forms of apparatus.

The last method referred to has, for the present, dropped out of consideration, except in the one specialized instance of the Klaxon horn which since its great success in the Somme battles has become a standard method of signalling from aeroplanes. Indeed, the consideration of this type of signalling instrument may be despatched at once with the single remark that the intention was to make use of the Morse code as interpreted by two horns of differing tones, one being chosen to represent the dot and the other the dash. The instrument was based on a French device and was tried with success on the Somme up to a distance of 1,500 yards. It had many disadvantages, however. The signals were liable to be drowned by the noise of bombardment. They were audible to any enemy near the sending and receiving station and could therefore only be used for code messages. The conditions under which the apparatus might be of sufficient use to justify its existence were so few that the experiments were not persisted in.

The history of the development of the power buzzer and amplifier will be reserved for consideration under the position battles of 1917, when this instrument was first used with really decisive success and on a large scale. Its possibilities in action were first shown during the Somme battles, but its exploitation as a practical means of bridging heavily shelled zones in the forward area properly belongs to a later period of the history of signals.

The use of message-carrying rockets and bombs, on the other hand, never became general throughout the Army and may be dealt with once and for all in the present connection. The use of rockets as light signals had been universal from the beginning of trench warfare. In the Somme battles,* S.O.S. signals were practically confined to different-coloured rockets. So general did their use become that the Germans went to the trouble of copying the type of rocket in use in the British Army with a view to the confusion of our artillery. The display of rockets from both sides of the line became to a greater and greater extent the most picturesque feature of the night until stationary warfare ceased. One particular application to signals was the use of rockets as an acknowledgment to D.D.D.D. visual messages. This method was suggested and employed by some units, but was accompanied by disadvantages which prevented its general adoption.

It was early suggested that rockets might be employed for carrying messages and lines. The first specialized line-carrying projectiles were those used by the personnel of the forward wireless stations for erecting wireless aerials. A piece of light line was attached to a " dummy " rifle grenade which was fired above the projection over which it was desired to pass the wire. An insulator and aerial wire were then attached and the aerial drawn up into position. The device was successful and was standardized, rifle grenades without detonators being issued as part of the usual equipment of trench wireless stations. From this to the line-carrying rocket was one step only, and the latter was given extensive trial but never with much success. Cases are on record where lines were laid this way, but sufficient accuracy could not be obtained and the experiments were dropped.†

The evolution of the message-carrying rocket was more successful. Proposals were first made from First Army based on the personal

* Trials took place in 1915 with the idea of the use of coloured rockets by the Cavalry in the event of a break-through at Loos.

† An attempt was also made to carry listening post earth connections across " No Man's Land " by means of trench mortar bombs but without success.

experience of the Lieutenant-General commanding one of its Corps, who had used a blank rifle grenade successfully for this purpose. Later, in November, 1915, the 3rd Corps brought to notice a German rifle flare with a range of 500 yards. It was suggested that a similar flare might be devised with a recess in the weighted end. Into this recess might be put a message written on pigeon paper and rolled up in a cylinder.

The rifle grenade was, however, soon ruled out of the question on account of the difficulty of identifying and locating the message-carrying projectile, and rockets accompanied by a trail of smoke and burning a bright flare on alighting were substituted. Experiments were continued throughout 1916—a side line being experiments with message-carrying bombs which proved to be of no practical value. In September, 1917, two types of the " Wynn " message-carrying rocket were adopted ; one long-range rocket with a radius of action of 2,300 yards, the other, a lighter type for short ranges. 15,000 were ordered at once and a monthly supply of 6,000 arranged for.

In 1918 supply was made in fair numbers and the rockets were advertised by carefully-arranged demonstrations carried out by the O.'s C. Divisional Signal Companies before Brigade and battalion commanders. The demonstrations were carefully stage-managed and uniformly successful and the new rockets were used to some extent in the position battles which preceded the advances of the autumn of 1918. Difficulties of supply, however, prevented sufficient practices being carried out to enable all ranks to become familiar with them, and this precluded their employment on a large scale. In individual cases they were made great use of, the extent of their popularity being largely dependent on the particular experience of individual battalions.

# CHAPTER IX.

# A REVIEW OF SIGNAL SERVICE ORGANIZATION WITHIN THE ARMIES BETWEEN 1914 AND 1917.

Factors For and Against Increase of Establishments.—Three Recognisable Stages in A.S.S. Re-organisation between 1914 and 1917.—Increase of Divisional Signal Companies, 1914.—First Temporary Adjustment to Meet Position Warfare Conditions, May, 1916.—First Great Re-organization in Winter of 1916–17.—Difficulty Experienced in Finding Men to Complete New Establishments.—A Review of Organization in Wireless Telegraphy.—Appointment of Army Wireless Officers.— Formation of Army Wireless Companies.—Decentralization of Wireless.—Growth of " Intelligence " Wireless.—Portable Electric Lighting.—Visit of Post Office Representative to France.—Appointment of *Liaison* Officer at G.H.Q.—Formation of F.W. 7.—Signal Service Training in France.—Army Signal Schools.—Appointment of A.D. Signals.—Training in 1918.

INCREASE in the strength of any branch of a growing Army, such as was the British Expeditionary Force during the European War of 1914–1918 may be divided into two main types. Of these, one is that directly caused by the growth of the Army as a whole. More and more formations proceed to the theatre of war, and each carries with it its recognized quota of every arm of the service. In this way the increase of the Signal Service of a growing Army is progressive and automatic.

The second method of increase, which is more definitely associated with the subject of the present chapter, is that which must take place to enable units to cope with changes in war practice within the formations of which they form a part. This can only be achieved by a series of successive changes in establishment. An increase is required here, a decrease there, a rearrangement elsewhere ; all tending to adapt the constitution of units to the peculiarities of the situation as it varies from month to month or from year to year.

As has been shown in the preceding chapters, the growing intensity of the warfare during 1915 and 1916 had produced many and decisive changes in signal practice, together with a great increase in Signal Service responsibility. Yet, perhaps the most important result of all the experience of these two years was the great reorganization of the Signal Service which was conceived and approved during the winter of 1916 and carried out in the spring and early summer of 1917. At its completion, the Army Signal Service—for the first time since the very mobile warfare of the 1914 campaigns—approximated in numbers and organization to the strength and disposition necessary to enable it to meet its responsibilities with success.

During the whole period under consideration a gradual evolution had been taking place. For several reasons, however, this had lagged far behind what was necessary if efficiency was to be maintained without undue strain. From the time of the commencement of position warfare, it was recognized that the war had entered upon a phase which might be indefinitely prolonged. Until a marked preponderance of men and guns could be decisively applied by one or the other side, no solution of the deadlock could be expected. It was quite likely that stationary warfare might be drawn out for months, or even for years, as eventually proved to be the case. In these circumstances, the man-power reserves of the Empire might be expected to be strained to the utmost. From the very beginning, therefore, orders were issued that every increase of Establishment must be carefully scrutinized and not allowed except under the absolute pressure of necessity.

This policy was cumulative in its effect as the struggle continued. It was in 1917, indeed—*i.e.*, before the situation was relieved by the entrance of America into the war—that it bore most heavily on the whole of the Expeditionary Force and particularly on such branches as the Signal Service. Its results were, however, apparent from the very first, for it is to this factor of the situation that the failure of Signal Service establishments to keep pace with the development of the tactical employment of signals must be attributed.

Another circumstance which tended to prevent Signal Service establishments from keeping abreast of the times was the kaleidoscopic nature of the technical developments which revolutionized signal practice in the early years of the war. The development of the telephone, of wireless telegraphy, of the carrier pigeon service, or permanent lines and buried cables, all involved modifications in the duties and therefore in the qualifications of the personnel of signal units. Not only were increases required in the number of men of trades already recognized, but, as in the case of telephone switchboard operators, new trades had to be created. In addition, the technical development and growth of other arms of the service, which could not easily be foreseen by a specialized and over-taxed Signal Service, were a further source of trouble. A good example is the growth of artillery which was responsible for more modifications of Signal Service establishments than any other single factor.

These, and other obstacles, almost equally formidable, effectually prevented a continuous and automatic adjustment of the Signal Service to the changing conditions amidst which it was called upon to work. Months of discussion, reference and counter-reference were necessary before the final form of the desired changes could be settled upon and officially approved. It was, therefore, on all counts considered best to carry on for long periods at a time by the help of minor concessions wrung with difficulty at widely-separated intervals from a critical Staff. Necessities were permitted to accumulate until an overwhelming case could be presented ; luxuries were never considered at all.

Three principal increases in establishment can be recognized in the years under review. With the commencement of position warfare in the winter of 1914 and the early increase in artillery requirements, both for purposes of command and observation, the first considerable accession to the establishment of a forward signal unit took place. This took the form of the addition to the Divisional Signal Company of two motor cyclist despatch riders for the use of the C.R.A. and of a fourth cable detachment.*

The formation of the first two Army Signal Companies which took place in the winter of 1914 was the direct outcome of the extension in size of the Expeditionary Force, and not of any difference in function of the Signal Service. As the number of Corps increased, decentralization of command for administrative purposes became imperative. Any such decentralization must inevitably have its due effect on all the ancillary services.

One other type of increase to signal units which requires a bare mention also occurred for the first time in early 1915. This was the adoption of a sliding scale to adjust the signal companies to the variations in the number of subordinate formations controlled at each step in the chain of command which took place from time to time at the will of the General Staff. Such variation was especially common in the lower formations in this year. Reinforcement units came out for the most part as isolated battalions and the number of battalions in many Brigades increased from three to four, five, six, or even more. To meet this increase, a temporary increase of an extra telephone detachment was made to Brigade sections serving a Brigade with five or six battalions. In the case of Armies, Corps and Divisions, the addition of an extra Corps, Division, or Brigade involved a considerable increase of work. It was, therefore, definitely laid down that, for each such formation above the normal number, a corresponding increase of office telegraphists and motor cyclists should be added to the headquarters of the signal company of the higher formation.†

* Modifications of less importance which belong to the same period were a slight increase—for the same reason—to the Corps Signal Company, and certain alterations due to the gradual supersession of horsed by mechanical transport in all signal units as far forward as Divisional headquarters.

† Another type of increase was that due to an Army or lower formation holding an unusually wide or deep front. This was met by temporary loan, either from the signal company of the next higher formation or from the Signal Depôt. An example of this was the loan of permanent linemen to certain armies or Corps to assist in the maintenance of permanent lines of unusual length.

At the time they were proposed, the alterations in establishment enumerated above were the bare minimum to enable efficiency to be maintained. As the months wore on, it became ever more clear that all units were quite unable to deal satisfactorily with the increasing work which fell to their lot. In early 1916, therefore, further proposals were put forward as a temporary measure pending the general reorganization which was quite clearly essential if the Signal Service was to be adapted to the requirements of position warfare.

The machinery for advancing the interests of the Signal Service with the Armies had been immensely improved in February of this year by the appointment of the D.D.A.S. Army and the A.D.A.S. Corps. Orders had been issued by the General Staff that in each formation the senior signal officer was to hold virtually the position of Staff Officer for Intercommunication to the Formation Commander, and the new status of these officers added great weight to their representations of the urgency for reform in Signal Service organization.

This second series of additions to Signal Service units which was approved in May, 1916, was entirely devoted towards the partial and temporary solution of difficulties which had arisen through the changes in signal practice which had attended position warfare of an intensive character. The growth of the telephone system had given rise to two main deficiencies :—(a) A shortage of constructive power within the Armies which was dealt with by the addition to each of one motor airline section and one extra cable section—making totals respectively of four and three. (b) A lack of telephone exchange operators which was partially solved by the addition to all signal companies of a number of Pioneers trained to perform this duty.*

At the same time a pool of 50 men of similar qualifications was created at G.H.Q. to fill vacancies in the G.H.Q. area and on the Lines of Communication.

The lack of continuity due to frequent reliefs was partially solved by the addition of 40 permanent linemen to each Army to serve as area personnel. Airline sections also were made more fitted for the work on permanent routes which so often fell to their lot by the addition of eight men of this trade. Finally, the Corps Signal Company was still further augmented by four office telegraphists and four motor cyclists to deal in some measure with recent increases in heavy artillery.

It was recognized, however, by the heads of the Signal Service, and admitted also by many responsible commanders, that the concessions granted by the War Office letter authorizing the above additions were already insufficient, even at the date of their

---

* Permission to create a new engineer trade—telephone switchboard operator—was at this time refused. The question was raised again some months later with more satisfactory results.

promulgation. Artillery requirements were not catered for on anything like an adequate scale, while the 40 linemen given to each Army for area maintenance were altogether out of proportion to requirements. The Army cable and airline sections were drawn upon to such an extent to provide men for these duties that they were of little use for the construction purposes for which they were really intended. The Battle of the Somme was destined to emphasize the inadequacy of the establishments, and it was only by the most self-sacrificing and devoted work of all ranks that it proved possible to maintain an efficient standard throughout these critical months.

The necessity for further reorganization was never lost sight of, and discussion as to the form the alteration should take formed one of the principal subjects at all the signal conferences which were held periodically in the higher formations during 1916.

The original proposals, which emanated from Second Army and which formed the basis of the earlier discussions were very far-reaching. They contemplated, indeed, the taking over both of the artillery and the infantry signal system right up to the front line. In the battalion, for instance, it was proposed that an officer and 20 battalion signallers should be attached to the Brigade section, and should deal with all forward lines. These proposals were not adopted, mainly because it was considered that in mobile warfare each branch must still control its own personnel. If the Signal Service were made entirely responsible for regimental signals, the change would involve the transfer of all regimental and battery signal personnel and the appointment of Signal Service officers to every unit. This was not practicable. The alternative suggestion, that the Signal Service should take over responsibility under position warfare conditions only was also vetoed because it would mean that signal service personnel must be duplicated and that regimental signallers reserved for mobile warfare were not likely to be properly trained.

There remained to be considered, therefore, the question of the general modification of the Signal Service units proper to suit the conditions of stationary warfare. The new establishments must be capable of dealing with three main things which were not contemplated when the original establishments were formulated. These three developments were : (1) The increase of construction made necessary by the new telephone system ; (2) The necessity for area maintenance and supervision ; (3) The immense development of the various branches of the army for whose intercommunication the Signal Service had become responsible.

Artillery, Flying Corps, Kite Balloons, Anti-aircraft Guns, Survey Companies, Tunnelling Companies, Trench Mortar Batteries, and a host of other units, were all daily making fresh demands upon an overworked Signal Service. Those which existed before the war were considerably increased in size and complexity of organization ; many were entirely new. All desired, and indeed must have, a more complicated system of signal communications under position warfare conditions. The artillery alone, with their allied services—kite balloon, sound ranging, flash-spotting, anti-aircraft sections, etc.—required considerably more intercommunication now than had been allowed to the whole Expeditionary Force as originally constituted. (See *Plate* XIV).

After mature consideration of the problems connected with the reorganization of the Signal Service, there appeared to be only two alternative suggestions. Either it should be divided into two different portions—" siege " and " mobile ; " or a large proportion of the signal units which were originally designed for mobile warfare conditions must be pinned down to definite areas for the duration of position warfare. The policy to be adopted, however, was never seriously in doubt. From the beginning of the war, the axiom which had throughout been considered and treated as of paramount importance was that all decisive warfare must be mobile. To ensure the mobility of an Army, every formation must be composed of mobile units and this rule was particularly applicable to the Signal Service. It was, therefore, decided that reform must take place by the adoption of the latter of the two alternatives set forth above, and that signal units must be modified to suit the new requirements without detracting in any way from the mobility of the Army, Corps, and Divisional Signal Companies which would still form the nucleus of the reorganized Signal Service.

A certain proportion of the newly-formed units would be intended for area maintenance, and the main functions of such units would cease with the disappearance of position warfare. Such units need not be made as mobile as the remainder of the Signal Service, but they must be easily identifiable, so that when the Army marched off the area in which their activities were concentrated, they could be readily switched on to other work, such as salvage, or collected to form a pool for the replacement of casualties. On the other hand, such units or details as were intended to deal with the signal communications of the formations and units of a rapidly-advancing Army must be provided with transport to enable them to keep pace with the headquarters they served.

The problem was discussed from all points of view and always with the recognition of the policy of the Adjutant General in the background. The general attitude of this branch of the Staff to modifications in the establishment of the Signal Service was summed up in the words " any rearrangement you consider necessary, but no absolute increase in numbers can be authorized." It was, however, impossible to meet the situation without some concession being made. One man could not be expected to do the work of three for an indefinite period, and a substantial increase in the numbers of the

Signal Service had finally to be allowed. The form actually taken by the first great reorganization in late 1916 is tabulated below :—

TABLE IV.

*Amendments to Existing Establishments.\**

| | Increase. | | Decrease. |
| --- | --- | --- | --- |
| | Offrs. | O.R. | Offrs. |
| Divisional Signal Company .. | 2 | 10 | 0 |
| Corps Signal Company .. .. | 0 | 7 | 1 |
| Army Signal Company .. .. | 0 | 24 | 0 |

*New Units.*

| | Offrs. | O.R. |
| --- | --- | --- |
| Corps Heavy Artillery Sections (one per Corps) .. | 1 | 36 |
| Signal Construction Company (one per Army) .. | 3 | 116 |
| Heavy Artillery Group, Sig. Section (one per Group) | 1 | 36 |
| R.F.A. Bde. Signal Sub sections (one per Bde.) .. | 1 | 19 |
| Area Signal Detachment (eight per Army) .. | 1 | 15 |

A glance at the new units shown in *Table* IV. at once betrays the fact of a considerable increase. This was, however, kept as low as possible. The nucleus of the new artillery signal units already existed in the regimental establishments of telephonists possessed by artillery headquarters, who had been from the first more generously treated in this way than other arms. In a similar way, the nucleus of the area detachments was ready in the form of the supernumerary officers and the pool of 40 linemen per Army which had been authorized in May, 1916.

A considerable number of extra men were, however, required to complete the artillery signal units, area detachments, and signal construction companies, and the resources of the home signal establishments were taxed to provide these men. Indeed, it was not until April, 1917, that it proved possible to complete the forces in the field to their new establishment even with partially-trained personnel. To provide the extra men, the general use in the Expeditionary Force of men fit for field service at home and even for sedentary service at home was seriously considered for the first time. Certainly, men fit for sedentary service at home were capable of performing duty as telephone exchange operators on the Lines of Communication and with any formation which was not likely to be called upon to move frequently or at short notice. As time passed, more and more such men were taken into use in the rear offices, and fitter men, equally highly-skilled, were released for work in the forward areas where

* The individual alterations in establishment are shown in the comparative Table of Establishments which forms Appendix I. of this volume. Wherever possible, an addition was made at the expense of a decrease elsewhere.

Detailed establishments of the new units are also shown in the column marked "1917" in the same Appendix.

they were sorely needed. At the same time, men of medical category "B1" of other trades were sent overseas and absorbed, while, also in 1917, women telegraph operators and telephone exchange operators were used in considerable numbers on the Lines of Communication.

In the meantime, an immediate reinforcement of considerable magnitude was required and this could not be supplied by such a process as has been outlined above. Nevertheless, the men must be found from somewhere and every possible source of technical personnel was carefully reviewed. The extension of the age limit to 45 was productive of a considerable number of valuable recruits. The Post Office and railways were largely drawn upon for skilled operators and linemen. In addition, large numbers of men were at this period transferred from field companies to the Signal Service. To all these sources, too, must be added the normal quota of recruits allotted to the Signal Service at home by the recruiting authorities. In one way or another the men were obtained and the new establishments were filled up, either by transfer of R.A. personnel and orderly officers,* or by reinforcements from home. By April, the Signal Service may be said to have been reconstituted on a suitable basis for position warfare and, by the opening of the 1917 campaigns, considerable progress had been made in the training of the very raw material of the new drafts.

Thus was accomplished the most important of the signal reorganizations, but side by side with this, and preceding and following it, there were taking place yet other changes in specialist branches of the Service.

A review of the general growth of wireless organization and its relation to the other branches of the Signal Service can perhaps be best achieved by carrying the development of wireless forward at one bound to the early summer of 1917, when decentralization was recognized as the most efficient policy and was carried out both overseas and at home. This policy obliterated once and for all the differences which had gradually and almost inevitably grown up between wireless and the elder branches of the Signal Service.

When writing about the earlier battles of the war, mention has been made of the formation of " Q " Wireless Section—the rudimentary G.H.Q. wireless unit from which was to grow the whole great organization which is in 1919 taking its rightful place as one of the greatest assets of the Signal and of the Intelligence Service. In January, 1915, " Q " Wireless Section became the G.H.Q. Wireless Company and the addition of a wireless headquarters was authorized for the first time. From early in 1915, as both the intelligence and

---

* Officers in Artillery Brigades who acted as assistants to the Adjutants and part of whose duties was the supervision of the Brigade intercommunication.

M

the tactical side of wireless continued to develop apace, differentiation set in and the two branches gradually grew further and further apart. Each developed its own specialists and its own particularly qualified personnel, though both were still controlled by a central wireless authority representing the Director of Signals at General Headquarters.

The next stage in the development of the tactical side of wireless involved a certain measure of decentralization. In September, 1915, an officer was appointed to each Army to further the interests of Army wireless telegraphy and to act as the adviser to the O.C. Signals of the Army on all matters connected with this branch of signalling. In particular, the appointment was made with the direct intention of localizing control over the new trench stations, which, using short wave lengths as they did, were likely to cause much interference with the sets in the aeroplanes of the Royal Flying Corps.

The early days of wireless in the Armies were marked by a constant struggle for recognition, waged whole-heartedly by the wireless officer, and backed to a greater or less extent—according to his faith or lack of faith in this means of signalling as a possible solution of many of his greatest difficulties—by the O.C. Signals himself. The time of the wireless officer was about equally divided between superintending field experiments and educating wireless operators. The early experiments were sufficiently promising to warrant the formation of pools of wireless personnel and the provision of a large number of the new forward sets. In October, 1915, the Army Council ordered sufficient of these sets to provide for two for each Division in the British Army. There was, however, destined to be a very long time interval between provision and supply, though the gap was well filled by enthusiastic officers in training personnel in anticipation of the time when the sets should become available.

In February, 1916, the O.C. Wireless, G.H.Q., was officially charged with the co-ordination of all wireless throughout the Expeditionary Force. His representatives at Army headquarters were the officers i/c Army Wireless already referred to, who exercised under the Army commanders such control as was necessary within the Armies.

Control was thus definitely centred at G.H.Q., and, though proposals for the formation of Army wireless companies were put forward in the same month, it was a considerable time before the new establishments were approved. The situation remained much the same until July in the same year.

As the provision of sets improved, it became more and more difficult to provide skilled operators in sufficient numbers. The problem of finding the necessary personnel, and training them when found, formed no small part in the work of the G.H.Q. Wireless Company, and this was recognized in April, 1916, by the formation of a Wireless Depôt and School.

The expansion of the older and better-recognized branches of the Signal Service was in itself a great task, but the building up of a forward wireless service, with the high degree of skill required from the personnel composing it, was even more difficult, while the undertaking was made more onerous by the fact that wireless during these years was never more than barely successful. It was recognized by most people to have sufficient possibilities to make it worthy of experiment, but very few had any great faith in its ultimate success on a large scale. Indeed, the idea at the back of its development in the early days was that it should be entirely an alternative, to be used as a last resource. It was even suggested that no special personnel should be allotted, but that telegraph operators, when their lines were down, should turn to wireless in their extremity and work the local set themselves.

The next step in the evolution of the wireless organization took place in July, 1916, with the authorization of the formation of the Army Wireless Companies, which included sections and sub-sections for each Corps and Division in the Army. By the creation of this establishment wireless was for the first time organized throughout the Force as far forward as Divisional headquarters.

The chief points worthy of notice about the new establishments were the admission of the necessity for special personnel for working the trench wireless sets, and the centralization of control in each Corps under the Corps Wireless Officer as the most forward representative of the O.C. Wireless, G.H.Q. Since the original proposal to give stations to Divisions—dating back to November, 1915—divisional control had not been satisfactory. This was so for several reasons, chief amongst which was the absence of special personnel to work the sets. The Divisional Signal Company establishment was not nearly equal to its other responsibilities ; while it was only by sheer accident that any Division possessed personnel with a knowledge of wireless. The typical attitude taken up by the Division at this date was that, owing to its unreliability, and to the code and cipher restrictions which attended its use, wireless was better left alone. The personnel at the disposal of the Division Signal Company commander was much better employed upon methods of signalling which were better known and more likely to give paying results.

It is not to be wondered at, therefore, that little or no progress was made under a *régime* where operators were untrained and the responsible officers unsympathetic. By the centralization of control at Corps headquarters, on the other hand, organization was improved, but close supervision was made quite impossible. Try as he might, the Corps Wireless Officer could not visit his six or eight sets * as often as he wished. Inter-battalion and inter-brigade reliefs were among his

* These were always located at forward points where intercommunication was difficult to maintain.

principal troubles, for the incoming units were often unaware of the existence of the wireless sets. Such reliefs frequently took place without his knowledge, and Divisional signal officers could not help him to any great extent. The consequence was that message traffic was irregular; stations were sometimes mislaid altogether; and men were frequently discouraged by being left without rations for long periods.

To remedy this state of affairs, classes for Divisional signal company commanders and Divisional signal officers generally were inaugurated at wireless headquarters, while at home, also, the training of all signal officers in the use of Army W/T sets was commenced.

It was clear that decentralization and a close approach to the other branches of the Signal Service were the two lines on which, alone, Army wireless was likely to reach the efficient standard and find the popularity which was necessary for its salvation.

In all other branches of the Signal Service—notably in the pigeon service, which was in about the same state of development—decentralization, involving a large measure of control by Corps and Divisions, was contemplated. To a certain extent, wireless was a definite problem in itself with special characteristics, but, as education of the mass of the Signal Service progressed, this became less true. Through the winter of 1916–1917, while the first great reorganization was being carried into effect, everything was being gradually prepared for another reformation which was to embody the wireless branch in the Signal Service as it had never been before.

In June, 1917, this took effect, and the wireless service as a separate and integral branch of the Army Signal Service virtually disappeared on that date. The O.C. Wireless, G.H.Q. whose independence had become rather too marked was abolished. In his stead an A.D. Signals, Wireless, was appointed on the Staff of the Directorate of Signals with similar functions to the other members of the Director's Staff.*

At the Army, Corps and Division, the headquarters, sections, and sub-sections of the Army Wireless Company were absorbed and re-appeared as sections of the signal company of the formation. The O.C. Army Wireless Company himself was attached to the Army Signal Company and in effect became a Staff officer for Wireless to D.D. Signals.

The independence and isolation of wireless was at an end—in name

* At G.H.Q. the principal unit after the re-organization was the G.H.Q. Wireless Observation Group, whose duties were the watching of the traffic and movements of the high-powered German stations working in the rear and the movements of the larger bombing aircraft. In addition, there were two Motor Wireless Sections for intercommunication between G.H.Q. and Army H.Q. These latter were ultimately administered by the O.C., G.H.Q. Wireless Observation Group.

if not in fact—and, as the months passed, this became more and more a factor for good in its development.

While consideration was thus being given to putting tactical wireless in the Armies on a proper footing, Intelligence wireless was also decentralized in the spring of 1917. Until this time, detachments of G.H.Q. Wireless Company had been placed as required from time to time in the Army areas. These detachments had gradually assumed certain well-defined forms. Each had its own establishment of officers, N.C.O.'s and men, but all were centrally controlled from G.H.Q. As most Armies possessed one of each type of station the organization was unwieldy, and, in April, 1917, orders were issued for its standardization and control from Army headquarters instead of from G.H.Q. A definite establishment was laid down and all the Intelligence stations in each Army were completed to the allotted scale and combined to form a Wireless Intelligence Section of the Army Wireless Company. The reorganization in June which abolished the latter, transferred the stations and personnel to the Army Signal Company, and they were known thereafter as the Wireless Observation Group of that company.

From a single intercepting station in 1914, " Intelligence " wireless, technically controlled and administered by the Signal Service, but working under the direct orders of the Intelligence branch of the General Staff, had grown by 1917, until it was sufficiently important to warrant the creation of a special branch of the Intelligence Staff at G.H.Q. to direct its activities and co-ordinate the results obtained. Originally intended for the interception of enemy messages and calls, it developed by the introduction of the direction-finding station in 1914 into a means of locating enemy wireless stations. By plotting on a map the position of these stations, the headquarters of enemy formations could be identified.

Before finally leaving the question of the growth of wireless establishments, there is one other branch of signal activity which became the particular charge of the wireless officer and can perhaps be best reviewed here. In 1914, G.H.Q. and 1st and 2nd Corps headquarters took overseas with them portable electric lighting sets to light their headquarter offices and the signal offices. These had not at that time any direct connection with the Signal Service, but each set was cared for by a corporal who worked directly under the formation Staff. The sets were no one's particular charge and did not flourish until the Signal Company, as the nearest R.E. unit, was asked to supervise them unofficially.

During the autumn campaign of 1914, several Divisional headquarters managed to secure small lighting sets unofficially by one means and another (in one case, at least, by salving an abandoned lorry during the retreat) and the new sets proved such a boon that a demand arose for an official issue to all Corps and Divisions. The demand was first recognized by G.H.Q. in November, 1914, and the Director of Signals was requested to take over charge of the provision, administration, and upkeep of these sets.

From this time, the history of electric lighting at the headquarters of formations becomes a portion of that of the Signal Service. In the early days, it was one chiefly of difficulties of supply, while a prominent feature was always the gradual increase in the power of the sets and in the ideas of headquarters as to the number of lights required. An organization for the repair of portable electric light sets and lorries and a system of inspection by an officer appointed for the purpose were soon inaugurated. In 1917, decentralization affected this department also, and the revision of the establishment of the wireless companies and the army signal companies resulted in the break-up of the central G.H.Q. unit and the formation of small electric light repair workshops at each Army headquarters. Rather later—in November, 1917—the replacement of all existing sets by the 3-kw. Lister set was ordered and in the winter of 1917 and the spring of 1918 standardization was fully accomplished. The old locally-purchased " Eallot " sets and the obsolescent service sets, which had done yeoman service until this date, were withdrawn and scrapped.

This was the only example of Signal Service responsibility in a department which had nothing to do with intercommunication. It was undoubtedly successful and it is questionable whether any other arrangement would have worked more smoothly in the past. Its continuation in the future is a different matter. The care of the sets was an extra responsibility for the shoulders of signal officers already overburdened with work. On the other hand, it cannot be denied that their control over the sets had two great advantages from the point of view of the Signal Service. For one thing, it was possible to make certain of an unfailing supply of efficient lighting for the signal offices at the major headquarters. This in itself is a boon that will be appreciated by everyone who has endeavoured to run signal offices in badly-lighted and ill-ventilated dug-outs and cellars. In addition, it was most useful for the signal officer to have a point of contact with his Staff which was entirely separated from his official signal activities. Whether these two considerations out-weighed the extra work and responsibility involved, is a question to which different answers would be given by different officers according to the degree of smoothness of their personal relations with their Staffs. Logically, it would appear that the electric lighting services should be controlled by the R.E. or R.A.S.C. rather than the intercommunication service. The sole point of contact with the latter was their occasional use for the purpose of charging the accumulators of the small power wireless sets. With the arrival of the small A.B.C. charging sets this use of the P.E.L. lorries gradually fell into abeyance. It is likely in the future that the tendency will be to eliminate the accumulators from forward wireless as far as is possible.* If this be so, the Signal Service will have still less reason to be burdened in future wars with the responsibility for a service foreign to its nature and, in all probability, largely increased in size and in complexity.

Three unrelated incidents in the history of signals in 1916 which still require mention are (1) the first visit of a Post Office representative to France ; (2) the appointment of a *liaison* officer on the Staff of the Director of Signals at G.H.Q. ; (3) the formation of Army Signal Schools. All three occurred in this year.

The visit of an official of the General Post Office Engineering Department to the Directorate of Signals and to the Armies in the Field was the outcome of a suggestion from the Director of Signals to the D.A.S., Home Defence. It was made in furtherance of the already existing policy by which supply was made to the Expeditionary Force of Post Office types of apparatus and of instruments made up in Post Office workshops.

From the first, use had been made of Post Office telephone and telegraph apparatus and telephone exchanges on the Lines of Communication, but the question of supply of apparatus more robust and therefore more suitable for forward conditions, was now urgent. Many of the more delicate Post Office instruments were not at all suitable for use in the Field. In the Post Office workshops, however, were a skilled staff, a good reserve supply of standard parts of instruments, and a great eagerness to help in any way possible. All that was required to enable this help to be as well-directed as it was skilled in execution, was a knowledge of the active service conditions under which the instruments were destined to be used. This was achieved by periodical visits to France by a G.P.O. representative, when typical signal offices of all degrees of magnitude were visited in the course of a week's tour. Personal contact was also established during these visits with the D.D. Signals of Armies, with the A.D. Signals of Corps, and with the O.'s C. Divisional Signal Companies. A free interchange of views resulted in many useful adaptations of Post Office instruments and apparatus to suit particular Army needs.†

One of the few advantages of the Armies of three nations being grouped together in a common effort to overthrow an aggressive and efficient enemy was the attention which was necessarily directed towards the improvement of *liaison* in the combined forces. The

---

* At the present time, May, 1921, the tendency is the other way.

† Perhaps the most typical example of apparatus which owed its origin directly to these visits was the 4-plus-3 buzzer exchange, which is familiar to all forward signal officers who served in France between 1916 and 1918. The original instrument was improvized at II Corps headquarters from a spare strip for a five-line exchange and French receivers.

word "*liaison*" has indeed gained a significance in the war of 1914–1918 which it has never had before, but which it is to be hoped will be perpetuated, with all that it means, in the future history of the British Army and of the Signal Service in particular. The very peculiarities of the situation forced the idea on the Directors of all services. From its original employment to mean the encouragement of free circulation of opinion and thought between one ally and another, the word advanced to have a more specialized application to a similar interchange between and within the different branches of the Expeditionary Force.

In July, 1916, this policy found expression within the Signal Service in the appointment of a *liaison* officer at G.H.Q. The duty of this officer was to visit signal units and research departments of our own and of the French and Belgian armies, and to keep the Director of Signals informed of everything in signal practice and invention that was new and likely to be useful. Similarly, he was to visit the research departments working under the Director of Fortifications and Works, the Postmaster-General, and the Munitions and Inventions Committee. Not only could he bring to bear on the problems that were exercising their attention his own practical experience of conditions in the field, but he could collect and disseminate the most practical of their ideas and help to test and popularize the more practicable of their inventions. A judicious selection from the information gained by him in the course of his duties could be cast into readable and easily understandable form and circulated throughout the armies and the training establishments at home. This was actually carried out in the form of Signal Notes and Memoranda with good effect and soon grew to be an important branch of Signal Service publication.

An extension of the idea of a *liaison* officer, which also originated from the Directorate of Signals in France, was the formation of a Signal Service Committee for the co-ordination of signal research. In the original letter suggesting the appointment of an authoritative body, the Director of Signals pointed out the number of isolated bodies* which were working in an entirely, or almost entirely, unco-ordinated fashion on closely-related problems.

In July, 1916, this proposal found more than realization in the appointment both of a committee of three members, and of a special branch at the War Office.

The latter was authoritative in character and was organized as a separate department of the Directorate of Fortifications and Works (F.W. 7).

* F.W. 4a, War Office. Munitions and Inventions Committee. National Physical Laboratory. Marconi Company. R.F.C. W/T School. H.M.S. Vernon. R.N.A.S. at Eastchurch. R.A.F., Farnborough. R.E. Wireless Training Centre, Worcester.

The formation of the Army Signal Schools, which is the third of the unrelated items which conclude the present sketch of the development of signal organization, was a matter intimately connected with the development of the whole policy of signal training in France. Training in the Expeditionary Force was intended to be confined to a final polishing up of signal units and of individual signallers in modern signal practice and was carried out as far as possible under field service conditions. There were, however, many factors which extended the scope of training in France far beyond what was originally intended. The decisive influence on which all others depended was of course " position warfare." The latter, by its encouragement of complication in signal systems and by its long-drawn-out character and absence of hurried movement, both made necessary and permitted a much greater proportion of training in the field than could possibly have been carried out in a mobile campaign.

As early as January, 1915, unofficial schools were opened by Army headquarters to enable the training of signallers in buzzer operating and lineman's work to be started on the necessary considerable scale. For some time these schools, whether at Army, Corps or Divisional headquarters, remained unofficial, were kept in existence or abolished at the discretion of formation commanders, and were manned by the allotment of personnel from signal units serving in the line. By the end of 1915, circumstances had forced them upon the majority of formations within the Expeditionary Force, but it was not until May, 1916, that the first Army school—that of Second Army—was recognized. Corps schools were not recognized until 1917, and Divisional schools, which were the most usual of all, and probably the most useful in the aggregate amount of training carried out, were never officially recognized to the extent of being granted an establishment of their own.

It was to be expected that a certain overlapping of syllabuses would take place in the earlier unco-ordinated schools. This was of course the case, but with the appointment of D.D. and A.D. Signals and the official recognition of the schools, a system was arranged which, while differing in detail in different armies, was in agreement in its main features throughout the Expeditionary Force. During 1916 and 1917 the signal schools of the higher formations confined their attention mainly to the training of officers, to refresher courses for Signal Service personnel, to the training of instructors, and to wireless training. Throughout, the Divisional Signal Schools devoted their energies to refresher courses for regimental signallers, and to teaching the elementary principles of forward signal practice and the use of the simpler types of signalling instruments to the raw material provided by batteries and battalions.

In 1918, the formation of the Central Wireless School* which was controlled from Abbeville Signal Depôt, still further restricted the activities of the Army Signal Schools. Early in 1918, also, central control was brought to a head by the appointment of an A.D. Signals, Training, at the Directorate of Signals. With this reform, signal training in France entered on a new phase which outlasted the war, the existing establishments being retained after the Armistice and devoted to the service of the new campaign of education which was the salient feature of the period of demobilization.

* The Central Wireless School was created in order to co-ordinate instruction in Wireless Telegraphy. The headquarters of the school was established at Abbeville. The scheme was for the formation of seven or eight centres spread over the back areas and sited at or near other instructional centres. Wireless instruction was still carried out at Corps schools, but if the war had continued, it was intended that the whole of the wireless instruction, both C.W. and Spark, should be concentrated at the Central Wireless School.

# CHAPTER X.

THE final attacks of the offensive in the autumn and early winter of 1916, which had left the British armies in a more favourable position than they had ever held before, were destined to have their reflection in the early actions of the following year. Throughout the winter months, particularly in the months of November, 1916, and in January and February, 1917, though warfare on an extended scale was impossible, continual small attacks were carried out on the front between the Ancre and the Scarpe. The result of this policy was seen in March, 1917, when the German retreat became general. For a short distance—about fifteen miles in greatest depth—the British forces pressed close upon the heels of the retreating Germans and for two or three days conditions of mobile warfare once more came into existence along a considerable portion of the front.

The retreat had been well thought out beforehand and, although considerable dumps of stores, such as permanent line and airline stores, passed into our hands in good condition, the German telephone and telegraph system had been so thoroughly destroyed that it was of little use. Many poles had been cut down and all lines had been cut and dragged aside until the tangle of wires was such that it was necessary to re-lay the routes in order to obtain speedy and reliable intercommunication. Most of the poles, indeed, had been so thoroughly destroyed that the stumps could not even be utilized to support comic airline or poled cable. They were so short that lines thus suspended would have been a constant menace to traffic and even to dismounted troops.

From the signal point of view, the main interest of this short interlude lay in the approximation to mobile warfare conditions. This came in very timely fashion to test in a real advance the results of the training schemes which had been persisted in whenever signal companies and sections were in rest during position warfare. It had long been an axiom of signal training that " fast " cable should be laid by all cable sections when in rest, and that airline sections should be employed frequently in moving schemes. Opportunity was now given to test the efficiency of the sections. Cable detachments with Divisional Signal Companies followed up their Brigade headquarters with lines six or more miles in length, a thing that had been unknown since the autumn of 1914. Corps, Divisions and Brigades, all moved forward across the evacuated country by graduated stages— Brigades moving frequently, Divisions less often, and Corps head- quarters once or twice only by large stages. In the meantime, the new Signal Construction Companies pushed forward the permanent routes as quickly as possible to the new Corps headquarters, Corps airline sections followed up the Divisions with semi-permanent or comic airline routes, and Divisional Signal Companies kept pace with the movements of Brigade headquarters, building poled cable which would be replaced by buried cable as soon as the situation should once more settle down.

For two or three days, with the exception of the small local actions with the German rearguards, the conditions of peace manœuvres were approached. Staffs accustomed themselves to less general telephone facilities ; a system of wireless was often of great value when the advance outran the cable ; and two-way visual with lamps, heliographs and flags provided all the communication required forward of Brigades. As the enemy's retreat was accelerated by our advanced guards, the isolated forward actions were almost exact replicas of field-days at home. Lines to Report centres were through shortly before the Staff arrived, and they remained through through- out the battles. A series of messages describing the course of the operations was delivered to the Staff rapidly and at regular intervals, and when the battle ended with a further withdrawal of the German rearguard, the signal office was closed down and the advance resumed. There was an air of unreality about the whole proceedings to the officers and men who had been engaged in the intensive fighting of the previous year.

For the troops on the front affected, it was a pleasant breathing space before position warfare of an even more intensive character was resumed in the immediate neighbourhood of the immensely strong " Hindenburg " line in front of Cambrai and St. Quentin. The smoothness of the signal communication achieved reassured signal officers as to the efficiency of their units under mobile condi- tions, and the effect of this slight practice was to be demonstrated in the more far-reaching of the operations of the coming summer.

As the outlying bastions of the new trench system were approached, the resistance of the German rearguards stiffened and once more the enemy artillery, which had been silent for some days, opened up in full fury from their new positions in rear of the prepared defences. Assault on superior forces in a position chosen by the enemy and without adequate artillery support or any prepared positions west of the old evacuated German defences, was out of the question. Isolated actions on short fronts for particular objectives were pressed home, but the general advance slackened and finally stopped. By the end of March the situation was stabilized and signal activity was confined to the building up of a new position warfare system over the new country.

The result was a buried system which approximated far more closely than any previous system to the ideal grid. The German buries were examined, but proved to be of little use. They contained far too few pairs to be equal to accommodating our own artillery and they were ill-adapted in many ways to the requirements of the British Command system. The history of the Signal Service on this portion of the front during the next few months—in fact until the Cambrai offensive in November—contained little incident of special interest. The modifications in forward signals which were the result of the isolated actions having for their object the penetration of the Hindenburg line will be included in the general discussion of the position battles of 1917.

With the settling down of the situation in the southern portion of the British line, the centre of interest shifted further to the north. The plans for the offensives of the summer had long been made and the unexpected happenings of the spring were not allowed to modify them in their main outlines. Commencing with the Battle of Arras in April, the summer and autumn of 1917 were characterized by a series of fierce position battles which culminated in the Third Battle of Ypres and the capture of the Messines and Passchendaele Ridges. For three or four months the British armies battered their way forward steadily, the objects in view being to break through the German lines if that should prove possible of attainment, and, if not, to attract large enemy forces to the threatened front and to inflict as many casualties as possible upon them. Artillery action on both sides was vastly increased even over that of the Battle of the Somme. Troops on either side advanced to the attack or defended their lines under a hail of shell from guns of every calibre. Villages and hamlets disappeared in a rain of brickdust and stone ; larger towns were shelled until they were a hotch-potch of stones, bricks and rubble without definitely recognizable features. Whole stretches of the open country were churned into an unholy devastation which resembled nothing so much as a storm-tossed sea, frozen into immobility in the height of its fury, and strewn with the *débris* of countless wrecks.

After this increase in artillery action, the feature which had most effect on the nature of the battles was the adoption by the enemy

of the principle of " Defence in Depth." From the point of view of
signal practice, the new policy had two direct effects. The depth of
the advance of our troops in the early stages of a well-prepared attack
was much greater (reaching on occasion to as much as from two to five
miles), while the process of mopping-up was so prolonged that the
signal forward parties became quite frequently involved in the fighting
and on many more occasions found it difficult or impossible to occupy
the positions laid down in operation orders.

By the deepening of the advances—far beyond the limits of the
Somme battles—the warfare was liable to become temporarily of a
semi-open character. Advances of over two miles needed re-arrange-
ments both of our own and the enemy's guns. On the one hand,
movements of batteries and groups took place during the battle,
involving the improvization of a fresh series of artillery signal communications, often without a buried cable system on which to base
them. On the other hand, such an advance often involved the capture of considerable numbers of the enemy's guns and the hasty
withdrawal of the remainder to positions well to the rear of the new
line on which he had succeeded in slowing down our advance. Thus,
in each battle of greater magnitude, where the British attack was
attended by a considerable measure of success, the Signal Service
could rely on a short period when enemy retaliation was feeble and
overground lines could be laid and maintained with a fair degree of
ease and certainty. Such temporary revivals of the field line system
where ground and poled cable, and even comic airline, crept up for
a few days to well within the Divisional areas, was a decided feature
of the 1917 battles. This was, however, a phase which, while
extremely useful and often responsible for signal successes at critical
periods, was temporary only. Such conditions might persist for some
days, but, as the enemy artillery reserves once more accumulated and
the retreating guns again came into action, artillery retaliation rapidly
increased. The signal officer was then compelled to get his lines under
ground or, if this was impossible, to rely to a great extent upon
alternative methods of communication.

The main phases of the battles of this year can be readily
distinguished. The offensives were all of the nature of set-pieces.
Preparation and rehearsal had both been brought to the status of a
recognized science. The former, as in 1916, involved the laying down
of an extensive preliminary intercommunication system. This was
planned to include lines for all units that might reasonably be
expected to swarm into the area during the last few weeks before the
offensive. Once more the buried cable system was the main feature
of the signal preparations in the area of frequent shelling. Behind
this was an ordered system of permanent and semi-permanent lines ;
while parallel with it was an alternative visual and wireless system
which was, however, seldom used. In front of the buried cable

was carried out a standard policy of forward signals which will be referred to later in more detail.

Rehearsal was also an important part of signal preparation for the 1917 offensives. The principle of detailed dress rehearsals of all main attacks, over ground prepared by artificial means to resemble as closely as possible the actual terrain over which the advance was to take place, was a feature alike of Infantry and Engineer preparation during the year. The forward signal parties were practised daily with full equipment and apparatus over country prepared with replicas of the landmarks where their relay posts and report centres were to be set up. These rehearsals were of great value and much diminished the chances of detachments losing their way and failing to reach their destinations. As shown by the records, however, a considerable margin of error still existed. Everything possible was done, it is true, but no amount of careful preparation could enable parties to find landmarks which had been obliterated by their own artillery. No amount of training, either, would teach unarmed or partially-armed and overburdened signallers how to oust machine-gun posts and garrisons from cement emplacements or pill-boxes. In such cases the best had to be made of a bad situation and an office was set up in a shell-hole or crater short .of the original destination until a suitably-armed mopping-up party, a tank, or, in extreme cases, a friendly section of field artillery, had come to the rescue and dealt with the human element of the obstruction.

The first period of the offensive—that of preparation—lasted for two or three months, and the last week or two was usually accompanied by considerably increased enemy artillery retaliation. It was very unlikely that three months of extensive preparation, carried out necessarily by day as well as by night, would escape notice. The word " surprise " has taken on an entirely different meaning in position warfare in modern days. The aeroplane had taken the place of the cavalry as the " eyes " of the Army and with the aid of its own " eyes "—its observer, and still more its camera—it was much more efficient than its predecessor. It was no longer possible entirely to conceal happenings far behind the line. The most that could be hoped for, was that a march might be stolen on the enemy by concealing from him the first few weeks of preparation and the actual day and place of the main attack. Some time before the offensive could be launched, his aeroplane photographs would betray to his Intelligence Staff the steadily increasing network of light and other railways opposite to a certain portion of his front. The fine tracery of tracks and buries would also alter and increase in definition from day to day. His artillery would then commence to play its part in countering these preparations and delaying the offensive by harassing fire.

It was now that the greatest test of the Corps and Divisional system might be expected. If the buried system had been carried sufficiently far back, had been conscientiously dug to a depth of 6 ft. or deeper, and had been adequately planned, the signal officer might sleep in comparative peace. His system would not fail him and, with one solitary exception, might reasonably be expected to serve his needs until his formation advanced beyond it and he was faced with an entirely different problem which would indeed tax his ingenuity to the utmost. The solitary exception occurred when the system was planned so that the main trunks passed close to battery positions or other places likely to be systematically shelled by the enemy, or when enemy shelling was so widespread and continuous that it was impossible to fill in the frequent shell holes along the route. In either case, it was found by experience that no buried system, however deep, could be considered safe. The deeper it was, too, the more difficult it would be to repair when it was broken. Fortunately such cases were not of widespread occurrence. It was seldom that enemy attention was so universal that it was impossible to repair the ravages made by his shells along the routes. Usually he fired to a time-table at certain definite positions and tracks which could often be determined beforehand by the exercise of forethought. The real solution of the difficulty lay in the direction of the greater perfection of *liaison* between artillery and " signals." One of the lessons learnt during these battles was that the artillery must be kept well-informed of the main signal routes and must exercise some consideration in their choice of positions. Sometimes sufficient alternative positions were not available and then the best had to be made of a difficult situation. More often, the exercise of co-operation between the artillery command and the signal officers of the higher formations would practically eliminate this source of trouble.

One of the main troubles of the senior signal officer during the preparation period of the great position battles, was an absence of full knowledge of the amount of artillery he might expect to come into his area for the operations. Estimates which appeared on the extreme liberal side at the time they were made were frequently falsified in the event. The number of pairs carried forward in each main trunk route was limited by the supply of cable and had always to be kept as low as possible. If this consideration was given too much weight, on the other hand, preparations proved hopelessly inadequate and endless confusion resulted. If similar situations recur in future wars, an effort should be made to forecast with more accuracy the needs of the artillery. This can only be done by the General Staff, since it involves calculations based on policy and on the supply of new guns and ammunition.

Another respect in which the Signal Service was much hampered in carrying out a general scheme of signal preparation was the lateness of arrival of formations and units at their posts for the offensive. Here, it must be admitted by anyone who seriously studies the records, that the Staff did not in many cases live up to the standard laid down by themselves in " Intercommunication in the Field." One of the principles enunciated in this book was that all new units and formations should be in position at least a week before an offensive commenced. Artillery groups, Tank battalions, heavy and field batteries, and all the other free lances of position warfare, were usually still dribbling into position 24 hours before the attacks were arranged to commence. The result—from the Signal Service point of view—was that the connection and allotment of circuits was hopelessly congested in the last two or three days and much unnecessary confusion resulted.

Another result, equally disastrous, was that impatient artillery commanders, finding that their needs could not be attended to at a moment's notice, began to revert to their former practice of strewing the field of battle with numerous ground cable lines. These as usual were destructive of all attempts at order, were a menace to free intercourse on the battlefield, and were destined in many cases to betray the batteries that relied upon them. Such lines were swept away in their dozens by peripatetic tanks or were flung to the four winds of heaven by the enemy barrage in the opening phases of the battle. They brought discredit on the signal unit which laid them and they nullified to some extent the shooting of the group or battery which endeavoured to use them. To these defects, they added the grave drawback that at this stage of the battle they were entirely unnecessary and thus a waste of so much field cable that might have been invaluable later in the action. More care in organization and an earlier concentration would have enabled the main signal system to have accommodated by far the greater number of the units using such lines.

One other way in which the Signal Service suffered at the hands of many units of other arms, deserves mention in the hope that it may not recur. This was the interference of impatient battery and battalion signallers with lines allotted to other units. In a carefully-planned system such as was the main feature of the Corps buried systems of the battles of this year, refusal or neglect to abide by the decision of the Area Signal Officer was productive of unnecessary confusion. The *esprit de corps* and discipline of all intercommunication personnel, should have been too high to permit of any such defiance—whether wilful or thoughtless—of the orders of even the most junior signal officer, provided always that the instructions given referred to lines which were under his direct control. Intelligent, self-sacrificing co-operation is essential to the maintenance and working of the intricate modern intercommunication systems. So long as the reports of signal officers contain strictures on signal

N

personnel for interference with lines and test-boxes, and neglect of instructions, then the Signal Service cannot claim to have reached the high level of efficiency and comradeship to which it properly aspires.

Following the preparatory phase of the battles, when the main signal system received its first great test, came the actual attacks themselves. Here the same phases may be recognized as have already been referred to in the consideration of the Somme battles. The attack with limited objective, the far-reaching general attack, and the slowly moving siege warfare were all represented and each gave its characteristic features to the intercommunication problems connected with it. The main methods by which these problems were met and solved remained much the same, though the difference in their application marks the principal advance in signal practice in 1917.

Before proceeding to examine more in detail the signal organization and the changes in signal practice which characterized the battles of this year, there are two aspects of the general problem which require consideration. Both are connected with forward signals and mark important developments which gave distinct form to the Signals of the year.

Enemy overhearing had first been countered with definite success in the winter of 1916–1917. The danger of the indiscriminate use of telephones and buzzers within 3,000 yards of the front line had by now been driven home to all ranks both within the Signal Service and without. Telephones were still installed, in many cases as far forward as company headquarters, in some cases in the front line, but except for artillery observation their use forward of battalion headquarters was forbidden in normal trench warfare. Many officers were already in favour of entirely forbidding their use forward of Brigade headquarters. The buzzer had by this time been replaced to a great extent by the fullerphone and definite orders had been given that no messages were to be sent by buzzer or vibrator in advance of Brigade headquarters. This was tantamount to the abolition of these instruments during periods of stationary warfare, for sounders were now installed at most Brigade headquarters. The latter instrument was universally preferred to the more clumsy vibrator with its raucous, nerve-wearing note. The early troubles with the fullerphone were by now largely overcome, and improved instruments and a well-directed educational campaign were rapidly popularizing these substitutes for the " D3 " buzzer. The summer sun of 1917 shone on a front which approached much more nearly than ever before to the silence which was the ideal of the Intelligence Officer and which it was the aim of the signal officer to achieve. How was such a state of affairs going to suit offensive warfare ? This was a question which was of paramount importance, for an Army compelled to advance in telegraphic and telephonic " silence " and hedged about with cipher and code restrictions, was going to be deprived of a very large proportion of its available means of communication.

It was admitted by the Intelligence Staff, however, that the enemy would be too much occupied when our attacks had commenced, to be able to pay much attention to individual remarks made over the British telephone system. In addition, a successful British advance would involve the destruction, capture, or withdrawal of his listening posts. Also, even if news of importance was overheard, it would be practically impossible to convey it to the responsible Staff in time for it to be of use before the situation had radically changed. All these considerations tended to revolutionize the whole situation immediately the advance commenced. Particular care was, therefore, taken that nothing was given away before the date fixed for an offensive, but, once the attack was under way, all restrictions on the use of the telephone and telegraph were either swept away or allowed to go by default. Buzzers, forward telephones, even earthed lines, made their appearance whenever and wherever the situation demanded. Wireless code and cipher regulations were not entirely relaxed, but much more latitude was allowed to the individual officers who framed the messages transmitted by this means. Earth induction sets, also, played their very important, if restricted, part in these operations. It was not until the situation hardened once more and position warfare conditions again set in, that precautions were resumed and restrictions re-imposed. In the meantime, it is likely that little harm was done and there is no doubt that persistence in restrictive legislation would have so crippled the signal system that an infinitely greater amount of damage would have resulted than can ever have been the effect of the uncontrolled use of the telephone and buzzer and the temporary suppression of code and cipher regulations.

Perhaps the most interesting aspect of the reaction between the ever-changing conditions of warfare and signal practice as applied to the position battles of 1917, was the development of signal forward policy which found its expression in this year. Now, for the first time, a great reform in signal policy owed its inception to the direct co-operation of the General Staff with the Signal Directorate. The operations of the Signal Service had come to assume an increased importance in the plans of the General Staff, while its co-ordination with the rest of the Expeditionary Force, and its position with regard to the other branches of the Army, was still far from satisfactory. Recognition of this fact had already found expression in the greatly enhanced powers given to senior signal officers. The situation was now ripe for a decisive step which should put the coping stone on the new policy and at the same time standardize signal methods throughout the Army and give to the heads of the

Signal Service an authoritative manual to which they could point when they required to enforce the recognition of the principles on which their system was based.

Hitherto, every formation Staff and every formation signal officer, had held his own theories about forward signals. These were based partly on individual experience, partly upon what they had heard or seen in other formations, partly upon the literature which embodied the experience of other officers in other battles and which was freely circulated, if less freely read and acted upon. Systems of forward signals had gradually been evolved which were similar in their main outlines but which differed in many details in individual formations. If a formation had recently come from a low-lying inundated country, the signal officer placed his faith less in buried cable and more in alternative means of signalling. If a signal unit had recently been operating over a good and safe buried line system, its alternative chains of visual and wireless stations might have been neglected. Further forward, some officers had had unfortunate experience of pigeons, some considered the power buzzer worse than useless, some disliked visual, few had much use for forward wireless telegraphy. All had, however, been compelled to recognize one underlying truth. Successful forward intercommunication depended upon the thorough organization of some or all of these means, side by side with the best forward lines it was possible to lay and maintain.

From the other side of the question, there were similar anomalies which were often the cause of trouble to the unfortunate signal officer. His Staff might have a particular fancy for some method of signalling which he was convinced would not suit the particular set of conditions he had to face. It is true that in the last resort he could follow his own judgment, but he did this strictly at his own risk and had the uncomfortable and enervating feeling that in the event of a quite possible failure the " I told you so " of his General or G.S.O.1 might carry sufficient weight to transfer him summarily to other and less congenial scenes of labour. He had no authoritative written support either for the adoption of a general policy or for the exercise of a measure of discretion in fitting means to ends and adjusting his somewhat meagre resources to serve his needs and the needs of his Staff under all conditions. Then, again, unreasonable Staffs recognized no obligation to keep their signal officers informed in advance of their intentions in the event of the various contingencies which might arise in the forthcoming operations. Also, it was still not nearly often enough recognized that changes in disposition at the last moment were productive of disorganization to a rigid signal system which was quite irreparable at short notice.

The arrival of three or four Brigades of artillery in a Corps area within 24 hours of zero of an important offensive was enough to make the signal officer concerned wring his hands in despair. Yet such occurrences happened commonly without the slightest notice and had to be dealt with as best could be. Altogether, the relations between the Staff and the Signal Service, though immensely improved, were, at this date—early 1917—capable of considerable further improvement.

Most of these anomalies were swept away by the appointment in March, 1917, of a combined Staff and Signal Conference and the publication, as the result of its deliberations, of S.S. 148 *, the first Staff manual devoted entirely to intercommunication problems. The book, as it originally stood, was by no means ideal, the principal failing being a certain rigidity in the advocacy of particular methods which was not justified in view of the varying conditions to which the standardization must necessarily be applied. It was, however, an immense advance in signal policy and marks as does nothing else a revolution in Staff and Signal Service relations. By its publication the Signal Service was definitely recognized as a collaborator of the General Staff. The necessity for mutual consideration between Staff and Signal Service was explicitly pointed out in such paragraphs as that which laid down that formations and units must arrive in a new theatre of operations one week before an offensive was scheduled to begin. It is true that this was often not lived up to, but the occurrence of the regulation in an authoritative manual was a constant reminder to the Staff and a comfort to the signal officer. In many ways, the possession of " Forward Intercommunication in Battle " was a support and a clinching argument in the discussions which were inevitable between signal officers and the best-intentioned Staffs.

Amongst other things which were recognized as the basis of the standardized intercommunication scheme, the control of the A.D. Signals of the Corps over the main telegraph and telephone system as far as the forward limit of the buried cable was laid down for the first time in authoritative form. Divisions still had to provide a proportion of the personnel for maintenance of the system in their areas, but it was intended that the buried cable system should be carried out under the orders of the Corps and that lines in that system should be allotted at the discretion of a Corps signal officer appointed to supervise it. Signal instructions, which were already in very general use, were insisted upon, and were, so far as possible, to conform in type to a standard form, a list of essential points being

---

* S.S. 148 was produced in eight days—a four-days' conference and four days writing up notes. The proofs were corrected and the book in print within a fortnight. Its early publication was so vital that there was no time for that considered discussion which might have served to relax the rigidity with which the main principles were laid down.

given in the Manual. It was laid down that such instructions should be prepared by the General Staff in conjunction with the senior signal officer of the formation. In point of fact, they were usually prepared by the signal officer and submitted by him to his Staff for approval. In any case, if the greatest effect was to be obtained from the support which the General Staff was expected to give according to the new Staff Manual, it was best that they should be signed by the Chief of the General Staff and issued from his office as an integral part of the operation orders of the formation. As such, they were binding on all arms and carried the weight of a mandate. When issued by the signal officer himself, as was frequently done in earlier days, all subordinate commanders were at liberty to misconstrue them or to ignore them at will. The worst that could come of such misinterpretation or neglect was a failure in the local communications of the officer concerned which his own signal officer was expected to put right and for which the latter was in any case compelled to accept responsibility.

Complete sections of the new manual were devoted to the consideration of forward signals in the attack from entrenched positions, from captured country, and in open warfare. These were amongst the most debatable portions of the book. It was here that a certain rigidity and tendency towards dogma somewhat invalidated the usefulness of the earlier edition. Sufficient play was not left to the imagination of the individual signal officer, or regard paid to his special knowledge of local conditions. In the coming battles, the most successful signal officer was he who did not follow too slavishly the precepts of S.S. 148, but, on the other hand, all reports and all individual experience went to show that the most successful units were those who based their intercommunication systems on the broad principles enunciated in this book. Modifications were necessary to cope both with local conditions and with the succeeding phases of a long-drawn-out action. It was to the incorporation of these modifications and to the adoption of a more tentative attitude towards all three problems that the successor of S.S. 148 (S.S. 191—Intercommunication in the Field) owed its popularity and success.

The first attempt at standardization of methods and at the strengthening of the position of the signal officer was, however, the important step forward in policy. From the point of view of historical interest, therefore, the less valuable book, considered intrinsically, has by far the greater significance. Having regard to the authoritative tone in which it was written, to the source from which it emanated, and to the principles which it advocated, it was undoubtedly the greatest visible expression of that advance in the status of the Signal Service which was the most marked feature of signal development during the war. Considered from this point of view its importance, in spite of its faults, cannot be over-rated.

In order to understand fully the difficulties with which the responsible heads of the Signal Service were faced at the commencement of the 1917 offensives, some reminder of the situation of the Signal Service in April of this year is necessary. The first great reorganization which has been described in the previous chapter had just taken effect. The new signal units specially needed for this type of warfare were just completed to strength, and signal units of older constitution had but just absorbed the raw material which had been drafted to them to swell them to their new establishments. A general re-sorting of signal personnel had been necessary in order to make the best use of the trained men and to absorb as successfully as possible the very raw recruits sent out from the various depôts at home. In the artillery, in particular, where the trained personnel formed the minority of the signal sub-sections and sections, the result of the first essays of the new units caused some dissatisfaction. Sappers transferred from field companies, raw recruits with their civilian habits but thinly veneered by military discipline, even Post Office and railway telegraph operators and linemen, could not be expected to become used at once to service conditions of a peculiarly trying nature. In the first few weeks after their formation it is questionable if the new units were not less efficient than the old skeleton organization, inadequate as that was.

Every effort was made to combine training with the urgent preparative work for the forthcoming offensives. The best possible use was made of the small proportion of trained N.C.O.'s available to stiffen and train the new material. Many signal officers parted with their most efficient and most valued men in the purely patriotic endeavour to help other less fortunate units. Indeed, it was only by self-sacrifice and altruism of this kind that it proved possible to train the new units in time. Success was achieved at the expense of many drastic changes in companies and sections where officers and men had served together so long that it required a real wrench, brought about by a true zeal for the good of the Service as a whole, to permit of close ties being broken, and valuable men spared for duty elsewhere.

Careful selection of the best men to fill the vacancies as N.C.O.'s was the next problem to be surmounted, but this was much easier. Casualties since the Somme had been comparatively few. There were many Sappers in the ranks of the signal units who were fit for non-commissioned rank, and many junior N.C.O.'s who could carry further promotion with ease to themselves and with good results to the efficiency of their units. By these means, vacancies were filled and the large proportion of raw material trained in the way it should go.

At the same time, enemy artillery activity was such that a week or two of forward work would accustom any man to a reasonable amount of shelling. By the opening of the summer offensive, the new units were most of them tested, and though mistakes occurred, and many things at first gave rise to doubts in the minds of the artillery as to the wisdom of the change, things gradually settled down. Units bought their experience dearly in many cases and the casualties to the Signal Service in these battles were higher than they ever had been before.

Nevertheless, reinforcements were steadily absorbed to replace the casualties of war and in the meantime the surviving personnel grew more and more equal to their work. Within a month, the advisability of the reorganization was placed beyond doubt. In a very few weeks more, and only a very small minority of artillery commanders would have still wished to revert to their old tried but insufficient gunner organization. As regards the gunner signallers themselves, their status, their prospects of promotion, and their pay, were all improved by the transfer. In a very short time all but a few " irreconcilables " were glad of the change and would have been aghast at the prospect of a reversion to the old order of things.

The Signal Service as it now existed was destined to survive the war in all its main features, the only changes in the future being minor reorganizations and the redistribution of some of the smaller units among the different formations.* The great position battle experiences of the Signal Service as reorganized for this type of campaign took place in 1917, between April and September. No better place could, therefore, be chosen for a review of the working of the Service on its new basis, and amidst the conditions for which the reorganized units were intended.

* An extensive re-organization of the Divisional Signal Company was approved in the summer of 1918, but was not actually given effect.

## CHAPTER XI.

# ARMY AND CORPS SIGNALS IN THE POSITION BATTLES OF 1917.

### SYNOPSIS.

Army Signals.—General Responsibility.—The Permanent Line and Airline System.—Subdivisions of the Army Telegraph and Telephone System.—Intelligence Centres.—Picture of the Army Signal Units at Work.—Indoor and Outdoor Staff.— Army Wireless.—Control of W/T Stores and all.W/T Stations in the Army.—D.D. Signals' Office Staff.—Corps Signals.—Lighter Routes and More Alternatives.—Corps Artillery Signals.—A.D. Signals' Distribution and Employment of Corps Signal Personnel.—Special Aspects of Corps Signal Work.—Stores, with Particular Reference to Buried Cable.—Corps Wireless.—The Corps Airline System.—Corps Control of. the 1917 Buried System.—Improvements in the Buries of 1917.—Buried Cable in the South and in the North : A Contrast.—Increased Enemy Artillery Attention to Signal Systems.—Refinements of Camouflage and Protection.—Greater Extent of the 1917 Buries.—Duties and Distribution of Area Personnel.—Records of the Buries. —Special Features of the Northern Buries.—Contrast Between Signals in Rear and Forward of Divisional Headquarters.—Rise in Importance of Alternative Means.

THE Signal Service at G.H.Q. and on the Lines of Communication was not vitally affected by the reorganization to suit stationary warfare conditions. Its development to meet the largely increased demands of the growing administrative services in rear of the Armies was normal and without marked changes in organization or method. From Army headquarters forward, however, all signal units had shared in the changes brought about less by the increase in the size of the Armies than by the alterations in technique which were the direct result of the deadlock in the Western European theatre of war.

In the Army areas this had been marked in two ways : first, by the appointment of the Deputy Director of Army Signals and the delegation to him of a large measure of responsibility for forward signals ; secondly, by the immense growth and the profound changes in organization which had taken place in all the technical arms of the Service. The extension of the responsibilities and improvement in the position of the senior signal officer of the Army has already been referred to as the source of a great accession of strength and efficiency to the Service as a whole. It is the latter aspect of affairs that is most important to a general review of the position battles of 1917.

Throughout the two previous years, the R.F.C. and Anti-aircraft organizations, the light railway system, "Intelligence," and all other technical branches of the Army had increased from comparatively insignificant beginnings until each had reached the dimensions of a separate Service in itself. It was no longer desirable or possible to group the intercommunication required for the whole of the various units administered by Army headquarters under one single signal system.

The problem was simplified to a certain extent by the fact that—even in 1917—the Army area proper was well outside the normal range of enemy activity.  Long-distance bombing planes and long-range guns occasionally played havoc with Army communications of all descriptions, but such damage was not yet so frequent as to make necessary any general use of buried cable or other means of protection either of lines or of offices.  That was to come very shortly, but it does not enter into the present problem to any great degree.

On the other hand, the responsibility of the Army signal units had extended considerably further forward than the Army area proper.  Indeed, the work of the area detachments—an important branch of the Army Signal Company—only ceased theoretically at the forward limit of the buried cable.  In a well-regulated buried system the area officer, who was also usually the O.C. Area Signal Detachment, was responsible for the maintenance of the whole system and for the allotment of all lines.  His detachment was attached to, and usually administered by, the Signal Company of the Corps in whose area lay the lines he controlled.  His activities are, therefore, better reviewed in detail when considering the signal system in the Corps area.

To the rear of the buried cable a telegraph and telephone system with permanent, semi-permanent, or " comic " lines was the main-stay of the intercommunication system.  Despatches of less urgency were dealt with by an organized despatch rider letter service with two or three deliveries daily to all important signal offices, and circular runs to less important units in each formation area.  Wireless, on the other hand, was never needed for normal intercommunication purposes, but was confined to Intelligence work and to the various training schemes which were always a prominent part of signal activity in the rear areas.

All urgent traffic was dealt with by telegraph.  All personal intercommunication was by telephone.  The latter was seldom used for the transmission of messages and as a general rule such a use of the telephone was discouraged by the Signal Service.  The available lines would only just accommodate the demands of the Staff for direct conversation with their immediate superiors and subordinates and with the officers of allied services.

The main feature of the Army intercommunication system was, therefore, a network of permanent routes which were of heavy construction and each of which contained many wires.  At least one main permanent route led forward to each Army from G.H.Q., while, in addition, other routes led directly back along the Lines of Communication to deal with purely administrative traffic.  Forward of Army headquarters, there were heavy main routes to each Corps in the Army and, in addition, a number of somewhat irregularly distributed lighter routes with fewer wires, which connected together the locality exchanges and the various scattered units which these latter served.

Much of the preparation for a position battle of any magnitude consisted in the duplicating of these existing routes. Additional main routes had to be built for every extra Corps which it was proposed to employ on the Army front during operations. Besides the new routes, additional circuits were necessary on almost all of the already existing routes to provide signal communication for the extra formations and units whose arrival in the area was part of the normal preliminaries preceding an offensive.

It was during the preparations which preceded the 1917 position battles that it was finally decided to adopt the policy of giving, so far as possible, separate systems to different departments of the Army. Thus, in one Army, seven telegraph and telephone systems were provided. These were utilized as follows :—

(1) Command system.
(2) Administrative system.
(3) R.F.C. system.*
(4) Intelligence and Observation* system.
(5) Anti-aircraft Defence system.
(6) Light railways system.
(7) Reserve areas system.

All of these were linked together at the principal exchanges, but every effort was made to keep the traffic of each to its own circuits. The Command and Administrative Systems were, of course, the most important of all and required adequate connection to all the other five. The reserve areas were dealt with by a series of locality exchanges and were linked up to give telegraphic and telephonic communication between all formations down to Brigades and that immediately superior to them. By means of this system and the connections to the command system, all formations and units in reserve could be ordered forward at a few minutes' notice. Undoubtedly this free circulation of orders in the rear areas played a decisive part in battles where the sudden application of unexpected concentrations of troops was of primary importance.

The most interesting features of the Army signal communications, from the point of view of their historical significance, are the special systems which were the outcome of the growth of the Royal Flying Corps, with its collateral branches, the kite balloons and anti-aircraft sections, the field survey companies, and the Intelligence Service generally.

All the above services had this in common. They were of vital

* A diagram of R.F.C. Anti-aircraft and Field Survey telephone systems in one Army is illustrated on *Plate* XIV. (Sept., 1917).

importance to the welfare of the Armies in the present type of warfare and they had a large amount of traffic to dispose of if their efficient working was to be ensured. Also each had its special needs, and the greater proportion of the traffic of each was confined within the limits of the particular branch concerned. The signal system of each could be to a large extent self-contained and self-sufficient.*

Such a system of independent circuits, connected to common main exchanges had many advantages. The R.F.C. system, for instance, was planned on such an exchange system, and Brigades, Wings, and Squadrons were all connected to exchanges by one or more junctions.

This was found to be invaluable and the increase of Squadrons in the Army areas was accommodated by the allotment of one or two spares upon the main routes, and caused but little extra work. For A.A. defence, on the other hand, direct communication is absolutely essential and a system which could be controlled by the O.C. Anti-aircraft was desirable. Any special instructions he might wish to give, could then be conveyed without any interference with general intercommunication. Light railways equally required a special system apart and merely needed connection to the command system at certain points.

The special feature of the Intelligence intercommunication during 1917 in at least one Army consisted in the formation of a separate system based on a series of Intelligence centres in which the various methods of obtaining and disseminating information were concentrated to permit of all becoming parts of one co-ordinated whole. Scraps of information, apparently unrelated, and obtained by different

---

* It is not intended to convey the impression that separate routes and separate exchanges were utilized for the different systems. This was not the case. All the circuits of the Army system as a whole were concentrated on certain definite main routes unless the scattered nature of the subscribers rendered shorter and lighter spurs necessary—as they often were. Certain circuits between suitable exchanges were allotted to certain departments or services, however, and these were reserved exclusively for their use, and each series considered as forming a self-contained system. Diagrams issued for the information of subscribers showed these circuits—perhaps differently coloured, perhaps identified in other ways. Frequently special diagrams were issued showing the circuits of one system alone. On the other hand, the Army route maps and the main Army circuit diagrams would simply show—the former, the routes ; the latter, the individual circuits—totally undifferentiated except in so far as they might run to subsidiary exchanges which were obviously built for the use of the special branches. The important point, however, is that these specially allotted circuits were considered as separate systems not to be used for the passage of messages alien to the department or branch that they served except in dire emergency. By this means confusion was avoided and a common source of delay— the difficulty of umpiring as to the relative urgency of the " Operations Priority " and " Priority " messages of different arms of the service— was eliminated to a great extent.

means, could be made to yield a much greater amount of valuable knowledge of the enemy's movements and intentions if fitted by skilled brains into their proper places in a general imaginative picture.*

In its most typical case this system took the form of a central exchange at the Army Intelligence centre which was connected by several junctions with Army headquarters, and from which circuits which were devoted to Intelligence traffic branched forward. These, in their turn, connected through the Corps and Divisional exchanges to all sound-ranging sections, observation posts, and other means of obtaining information. By means of these circuits which were placed directly at the disposal of the Intelligence Corps, information received from one source could be confirmed or denied at once by reference to others.†

It is evident that, in spite of recent increases of strength, the Army signal company and its affiliated units had as much work on their hands as they could readily attend to. Even in quiet times everyone was fully occupied. In the feverish preparation for an offensive and while the lines were burdened with the thousands of important " operations " messages which marked the progress of a battle, it was all the Army signal units could do to keep the system in order and to ensure the smooth working of the exchanges. Only the most careful forecast of individual requirements could make certain of a successful sub-division of the available circuits amongst the competing departments and branches of the Army. To be successful, the D.D. Signals of an Army required both the imagination and the courage to anticipate the most unlikely developments. The closest touch with the Staff was essential and sometimes success required that he should anticipate the formulation in the minds of the latter of the plans for a future operation. No officer had a greater variety of considerations to weigh in the balance before deciding on a definite policy ; few were compelled to make quicker decisions if preparations were to keep well ahead of events.

The personnel of the headquarters of the Army Signal Company, itself, consisted in the main of " indoor " staff whose duty it was to work the Army telegraph instruments, to man the telephone exchanges, and to keep in repair the instruments and signal equipment of the Company. The Army signal workshops had become an important part of the signal organization. Here, all faulty instruments not

* The name " Intelligence Centres " originated in First Army, but systems which closely resembled the First Army system were evolved independently in other armies and all had one feature in common. Reform, whatever form it took, was directed towards quicker intercommunication from all sources of information to Intelligence and Artillery headquarters.

† *Plates* XV. and XVI. are diagrams of detailed telephone systems of an Anti-aircraft battery and a Sound-ranging section in September, 1917.

hopelessly damaged were repaired and returned to service. A considerable quantity of improvised apparatus was also made up and despatched to the Army signal stores, there to be examined and issued to units. Decentralization had thrown a heavy burden on the personnel at Army headquarters and whether the Army was on the defensive or offensive, the shops were always in full work and required the entire attention of a technically qualified officer. With them, also, was usually situated the portable workshop which carried out repairs to the electric light lorries of the headquarters both of the Army and of all the subordinate formations down to Divisions.

The outdoor staff at Army headquarters consisted of some 20 or 30 permanent linemen. These had perforce to be considerably reinforced from the personnel of the attached airline and cable sections before they sufficed to maintain the routes of the great telephone and telegraph system to which reference has already been made. Isolated parties of three or four men were scattered throughout the Army area at all exchanges, at important junction points, and at other central positions along the routes. These men constituted the permanent line staff and were responsible for the normal maintenance of the lines. Their work was carefully organized and directly supervised by the O.C. lines and his N.C.O.s. In addition, the special breakdown parties with their own special transport and apparatus—including lengths of " interruption cable " and all appliances for making repairs on a large scale—were stationed at the main offices whence they could be dispatched at a moment's notice to the site of any major breakdown.

The scene at any particular signal office was one of ordered activity. Long before this date, signal offices had been standardized at least within the limits of each formation. All wiring was carried out on an authorised plan. Wires were arranged in an accessible manner, but carried from terminal pole to test panel and from test panel to exchange and instruments, by routes which were carefully chosen to avoid obstruction. Tables and operators' seats were arranged to allow free circulation and the portion of the office given over to the operating staff was planned so as to ensure as little movement and noise as possible.*

A special room was allotted to the despatch riders and orderlies on duty. Here they could await their turn with the maximum comfort to themselves and the minimum interference with the office routine. Above all, constant supervision was insisted upon and an efficient staff of instrument repairers ensured that all instruments were kept in order and all wiring was periodically overhauled.

In the meantime, new construction of permanent routes was dealt with by the Army Telegraph Construction Company, and of routes of

* The ideal office included a separate room for the telephone exchange.

lighter make by such airline sections as had not been absorbed to eke out the maintenance parties and to make up the breakdown gangs. The Army cable sections also had their special duties. Their work varied according to the individual Army in which they served. Some Armies were more fond than others of heavy cable routes. In others they were reserved entirely for attachment to subordinate formations carrying out special duties and needing special help. They were perhaps used more normally for the running of temporary cable spurs where such were necessary and for temporary local lines.

A totally different aspect of Army Signals was cared for by the Army wireless section, and the Army wireless observation group. The former was seldom or never used for the passing of tactical messages. The line system was almost always sufficient to carry the normal message traffic. If a breakdown occurred on one route, there was always a choice of several others available. Nevertheless, the Army wireless stations had important duties to fulfil, Of no method of signalling is it so true as of wireless that central control of message traffic is essential if efficiency is to be obtained. Every spark wireless station can interfere with every other station in its neighbourhood that is working on the same or a near wave-length. Every station can be overheard by special enemy stations devoting their whole energies to this purpose. These are the two cardinal facts that needed to be constantly borne in mind by the officers responsible for Army wireless. The principal activities of the Army personnel resulted from these two facts. It was their business to keep constant watch on all the waves in use in their Army for two purposes. Stations near the front line who could not attract the attention of the stations to which they were working might need the assistance of the higher-powered Army station to help to establish communication. It might even be necessary for the Army station, having picked up such an unacknowledged message, to switch over to the transmitting side and send it out with a strength sufficient to drown all less important but more importunate stations.*

The second duty of the Army wireless station was of yet more general importance. It was its duty to watch for errors in wireless

* An excellent example of the value of the Army control station can be cited from the records of the battle of Cambrai in November, 1917. An infantry Brigade completely cut off by the enemy could not get through by wireless either to its Division or its Corps, possibly on account of the latter headquarters being in retreat, possibly because distances were too great. The Army wireless control station heard its call, took the message and promptly forwarded the latter to its rightful destination.

This is only one of many examples which in themselves justified the retention of these powerful stations which watched and controlled our own traffic.

discipline from the signal point of view. Any serious error would soon be brought home by the Intelligence Staff working through the medium of the wireless observation groups, but, if strict discipline was to be observed, a careful watch for indiscretions must be kept by the Signal Service itself. It was the duty of the O.C. Wireless of the Army to suppress all tendency to individuality on the part of wireless operators. Innovations in procedure, little mannerisms on the key, irrelevant remarks between operators, indiscreet messages, all of these things needed to be controlled and eliminated so far as was possible, since they might give so much away to a presumably watchful enemy. It was in preventing such occurrences and in tightening up discipline, that the greatest utility of the Army Wireless Section lay, though its other functions were also of importance.

The wireless stations of the Army were of the light lorry type with a range extending far beyond the limits of an army area. Their use except in urgent necessity was, therefore, to be deprecated and they were seldom used except for interception.

The duties of the Army wireless observation group have already been outlined in a previous chapter. The stations were manned almost entirely by Signal Service personnel and from one point of view—that of the provision of reinforcements—they placed a great strain upon the resources of the Signal Service. The diversion of wireless operators to these stations lessened the number available for tactical wireless and helped to produce a shortage that was never thoroughly overcome.

In addition to the units already referred to, there were carried on the strength of the Army Signal Company the Signal Sub-sections of the Army R.F.A. and R.G.A. Brigades. The activities of both these, however, when in action, belonged more to an area nearer the front line and are better considered together with similar units which were grouped for battle under the Corps or the Division.

The whole of the great organization just described, was controlled by the D.D. Signals from his office at the headquarters of the Army. He himself spent much of his time touring the Army area, visiting the A.D. signals of the Corps and the O.C. signals of the Divisions in the Army and inspecting their signal systems. A personal knowledge of forward signals was essential for intelligent direction from the rear. At his office at Army headquarters, however, he had a small clerical staff which was usually slightly augmented by details attached from the Army Signal Company. Here, the general plans for signal communications for the whole Army were revised and co-ordinated and it was here that the D.D. Signals presided over the conferences of senior signal officers which did so much to advance the interests and to shape the general policy of the Signal Service. Later in the war, the establishment of D.D. signals was increased by the addition of a Staff officer with the title D.A.D. Signals and of an officer whose duty it was to supervise the Army pigeon and messenger dog service. Before the advent of these officers, however, his only assistant was the O.C. Army wireless and he had to rely upon the O.C. Army Signal Company to deputise for him at those times when his absence from headquarters was essential. No small part of his time was taken up with the scrutiny and modification of the indents for stores submitted by the signal officers of the formations within the Army. In 1917, as already pointed out, the decentralization policy resulted in the formation of comparatively large Army Signal Stores where a considerable reserve was kept of all essential signal equipment and line stores. This, again, meant an increase in staff, and an officer and a few other ranks were added to the establishment to cope with the new departure.

---

The O.C. Army Signal Company was held responsible for the maintenance and construction of lines in rear of Corps headquarters. Further forward the responsibility devolved upon the O.C. Corps Signal Company and the work was carried out by the latter's personnel. Here, also, the main feature of the signal system were the overhead line routes, though in this case the system was modified to a somewhat greater extent by adaptation to minimise interference through enemy action. The main ways in which modification showed itself were in the adoption of lighter routes with more alternatives and in greater care in leading into headquarters and to the principal signal offices. Junctions of routes were made as inconspicuous as possible. At the more important junctions overhead lines were replaced by short lengths of buried cable. Leads in to headquarters were carefully camouflaged, converging routes being arranged to point to some quite different spot from that actually occupied.

The tendency of the routes was to become lighter, both because a Corps must be more mobile than an Army and because more numerous routes containing fewer individual circuits were less likely to be put out of action on a large scale.

One direction in which the researches of the Army and the Corps signal officers were made was the devising of the most suitable light routes for carrying any number of single wires up to sixteen. A large number of such routes were needed for the subsidiary branches of the line communication system and some easily-erected and easily-maintained type was required. This was finally obtained, as already mentioned in the chapter on the rise of the telephone system, by the adoption of the trestle route. (*Plate* VIII.)

" Comic " airline was still much in use, but single and even double airline was almost obsolete except for special purposes. A revival of this type of line might be expected under mobile warfare conditions, but even there one pair of lines would not be of much use for the service of the major formation headquarters. From comparatively early

o

in the war single and double airline were relegated to the construction of branch lines to subordinate headquarters. The greater proportion of the work of the Corps airline sections consisted in the maintenance of already existing routes and the building of semi-permanent and " comic " routes with from four to 16 or even more lines.

In the Corps area also, as well as the Army, the growth of the signal system of the technical services was one of the features of this stage of the war. Indeed, it was at the Corps that the artillery signal communications with their accompanying specialized means of observation were mainly grouped. The artillery signal system in the Corps rivalled the infantry command system in importance and had long outgrown it in size. One of the chief preoccupations of an A.D. Signals before an offensive was the amount of artillery for which lines must be allowed in his system. A typical observation signal system in a Corps in the summer of 1917 is seen in *Plate* XVII. It is a complicated system in itself, and, when added to the ordinary command and administrative systems, taxed the resources of the signal units to keep it efficient.

Since the reorganization, artillery signals were cared for by Signal Sub-sections of R.E. personnel who were commanded by the Brigade or Group signal officer. The strength of Corps signals thus fluctuated with the attachment of a greater or less number of artillery formations. These made necessary a maximum development of the Corps signal system which was sometimes not justified by events. It was, however, impossible to take the risk of falling short of supplying unexpected artillery requirements. Spare lines were made essential by the sudden artillery concentrations which were a feature of position warfare. Any review of Corps signals as a whole must give due importance to this aspect of their development. The heavy artillery signal sub-sections, though always a variable quantity and ever changing from one Corps to another, were an essential part of the Corps Signal Company strength. Each on arrival at its battle quarters, took over the Corps lines allotted to its use and built in front of them a system comparable to, but considerably larger than, the telephone system of an infantry Brigade in the line.

Control of all the Signals within the Corps area was vested in the Assistant Director of Signals who had a small office at Corps headquarters and a small clerical staff to keep his records up-to-date and deal with his correspondence. He usually lived in close association with the O.C. Corps Signal Company whose immediate concern was the administration of the Corps signal units and the supervision of the line system. For the latter purpose a particular officer was usually delegated—as in the Army—with the title of " O.C. Lines " and personal responsibility for the maintenance, construction and allotment of routes and circuits.

A separate captain with a small signal section of his own cared for the signals of the Corps heavy artillery headquarters. This was often situated at some distance from Corps headquarters and, in any case, usually had a separate line system of its own, closely connected with the main system by junction circuits between the exchanges of artillery and infantry formations at each step in the chain of command. It was on this officer that the supervision of the special lines of the Survey and other Corps observation posts fell, and he was so fully occupied that, in 1918, he was given a subaltern to assist him.

Other officers at the headquarters of the Corps were the wireless officers and the stores officer who had charge of the Corps signal stores and who was directly responsible to the A.D. Signals himself. In addition were the officers of the various airline and cable sections whose duty was the construction of such routes as were ordered by A.D. Signals or his representative, the O.C. Lines, or who were given responsibility for the maintenance of sections of the Corps line system.

Few special remarks are necessary with regard to the employment of the available personnel in the Corps signal units. The principle adopted was much as in the Army area. One novel feature was the importance of the attached artillery signal sub-sections and the area detachments. Other variations in the duties of the Corps signal personnel were due to the responsibility of the A.D. Signals for the buried cable systems of the Divisions of his Corps.

Much of the work carried out at the Corps signal stores was concerned with the receipt, the preparation, and the issue of armoured cables of all types for burying. Many Corps at first had their cables made up into ropes containing 20, 30 or 40 pairs according to the numbers required for the buries. This was not altogether a satisfactory method, however, though it served well enough on occasion. The prepared ropes were very unwieldy in size and very heavy. Despite the precautions taken they were still liable to "kinks," while testing them was not more easy, nor testing in the field superfluous. The general decision of forward officers actually engaged in burying was in favour of the issue of individual rolls of cable in coils containing a quarter of a mile each of twin, quad, or seven pair cable. These were carried forward independently by men of the cable-laying party and combined into a rope when alongside the site of the trench. The prepared ropes were, however, used with success in the case of buries to reserve positions or in areas not under observation by the enemy and where good roads existed.

The Corps wireless officers were originally charged with the supervision of all forward wireless, but at the time of the later battles of 1917 decentralization had taken effect and the activities of these officers were confined thenceforward to special duties. The senior officer acted, as in the case of the Army wireless officer, as adviser in wireless matters to the A.D. Signals of his Corps. The junior officer was usually responsible for the running of the Stores, the charging plant, and the listening posts. Both supervised the working of the Corps directing station.

The functions of this set were much as those described in dealing with the Army control station, but on a smaller scale. The Corps station was, however, more frequently called upon to help out the forward sets and was expected to keep a very close watch with a view to facilitating the efficient transmission of messages. At this period, also, the Corps wireless officer was sometimes made responsible for such things foreign to his nature as pigeons and messenger dogs, but these were really part of the responsibilities of the O.C. Corps Signal Company and later, in the next year, a special officer was appointed to supervise the working of these services.

As far forward as Corps headquarters, the number of trunks connecting one headquarters with another was determined practically entirely by the amount of traffic with which they would have to deal. Thus, for instance, two telephone trunks and a telegraph circuit passing forward from Army headquarters to Corps headquarters were considered ample for the needs of the General Staff, and these usually did, indeed, suffice. Forward of Corps headquarters, however, enemy action became more common and partial interruption was practically certain during the heavy long-range shelling which invariably preceded offensive action either by the enemy or by ourselves. Mention has already been made of one method of counteracting this, that is by the breaking up of the heavy routes prevalent in rear of Corps headquarters into several lighter routes. By using numerous light routes it was possible to duplicate the main forward circuits of the Corps. During the summer offensives of 1917, three circuits from Corps to Division were the rule, but as many as six were not uncommon. These were taken forward by different routes, and thus it was extremely unlikely that any Division would be entirely cut off from Corps through enemy action.

It was forward of Division, however, that the near presence of the enemy first gave a definite and entirely different character to the signal system. Within the zone of constant shelling, no airlines could be expected to stand and the whole system was taken underground. In a normal Divisional area it was unusual to see any lengths of airline or poled cable with the exception of the few hundred yards connecting the rear dug-out or test box of the bury with the signal office at Divisional headquarters. In particularly favoured areas a little airline existed and poled cable was not uncommon, but almost everywhere buries were the prevailing means of communication.

One of the effects of the advent of the buried cable system was the consequent concentration of all forward circuits—whether required for Corps or for Divisional units—into two or three main routes in each Corps area. This, in its turn, resulted in the forward extension of Corps signal responsibility and maintenance. The routes were necessarily common to all formations and experience speedily proved that control was best vested in the signals of the highest formation using the bury. This lesson was really learnt decisively during the offensives of 1917. Many Divisions in the early months of this year controlled their own buried system, but it was always found that allotment and maintenance worked most smoothly when control was vested in an area officer working under the orders of the A.D. Signals. The earlier method persisted for some time in certain Divisions, but gradually the later and more efficient procedure was standardized. It was admitted by Divisional signal officers that an efficient area officer relieved them of an immense amount of responsibility and added to the efficiency of the system.

His presence and that of the men under him tended to continuity of policy and to a thorough knowledge of the individualities of the bury. He and his men knew its weak places and its good and bad pairs. He knew what pairs could best be spared for more urgent purposes. He had a superior authority to appeal to in support of his decisions. He was usually carefully chosen and carried out his very difficult, arduous, and often dangerous duties exceedingly well. Last, but not least, he had no other responsibilities as had the Divisional signal officer who had been his predecessor.

The Corps-controlled bury was in many ways much more satisfactory. The final policy was for the A.D. Signals of the Corps to decide on what buries were required in consultation with the O.C. Signals of the Division. The Divisions then carried out the portion of the buries which lay within their respective areas, and on conclusion the Corps took over the system and was responsible for maintenance and allotment of circuits. For the latter purpose certain area detachments were attached from the Army to each Corps in the line, and on these men fell the brunt of this work. The way the area detachments carried out their task was beyond cavil and the new units soon created a record of which their successors may well be proud.

The buried cable system of 1917 was planned on the broad lines laid down after the experiences of the Somme battles. In numerous details, however, progress had been made towards greater secrecy in execution of the work and towards the more successful protection of the cables. 6 ft. buries were still the rule, but many trenches in suitable country were dug to 7 ft., and under favourable circumstances some Corps even insisted upon buried cable 8 ft. deep within a thousand yards of the front line. The 1917 buries were of much greater extent than those in 1916. In this year it was unusual to meet with airline within 5,000 yards of the front line. The rear cables of the buried system usually finished about on the line of Divisional headquarters, leaving a short overground lead-in as the only vulnerable portion of the intercommunication system. Even this was often eliminated by burying the lead-in right up to the walls of the signal office.

Two distinct problems were presented by the buried cable systems of the battles of Arras and Vimy, and that of the third Battle of Ypres. In the former case, the ground was eminently suitable for burying, and a good safe system 6 ft. 6 ins. to 7 and even 8 ft. deep, was carried right up to the front line. Even this was improved upon in places and the system made practically impregnable by utilization of the extensive system of tunnels, caves, and sewers, which were a characteristic of this portion of the front. In the use of tunnels, particularly, much assistance was afforded by the local Tunnelling Companies. Some Divisions were in the fortunate position of being able to go into action feeling absolutely assured as to the safety of all their signal communications in rear of the original front line.

In the Ypres, Messines, and Passchendaele areas, on the other hand, the British forces were under the necessity of preparing for the attack from their positions on low-lying swampy ground and under the constant observation of a vigilant enemy. All work for miles behind the front line had to be done at night. The country was about as unsuitable for burying cable as it well could be. The net result was that, while a buried system of fair safety was achieved by the efforts of the working parties—labouring often under intermittent fire and suffering many casualties—much more reliance had to be placed upon alternative methods of communication until the later stages of the battles. Then, when the higher ground which had been the objective of the earlier attacks had been taken, and made to form the basis of further advance, deeper buries were possible and were again carried forward to cable head as near as possible to the front line.

The chief lessons learnt by the Signal Service in 1917 as regards buried cable were the necessity for camouflage and for even greater protection. Early in the summer it became clear to everyone concerned that the enemy's gunners had added the buried cable routes to their list of targets to which special attention should be paid. His activities took two main lines, both highly unpleasant to the Signal Service personnel and working parties, and both a very decided menace to continuity of signal communications.

A careful watch was kept for any sign of working parties or of parties engaged in staking out buried routes on that portion of the front overlooked by his observation posts. Also, enemy aeroplane photographs must have undergone careful examination for any sign of recent buries or of buries in the making. Evidence of enemy deductions from his photographs or from direct observation was invariably unpleasantly direct. Time after time, working parties on the buries were harassed by fire which was obviously intended for their special benefit. Many casualties were suffered from such bursts of enemy fire and still more casualties to Signal Service personnel were the result of the systematic attempts made by the enemy in the phase immediately preceding our attacks to destroy all buries known to him.

So bad was the shelling in some cases that it proved impossible to keep the shell holes on the buries filled in day by day and it was discovered that this was the one set of circumstances that rendered a buried system—however deep it might be—relatively unsafe. No bury could withstand the continual impact of shells, one falling on the spot already weakened by its predecessors. This persistent attention became a problem in itself which was dealt with in two ways. One already indicated was by choosing the route more carefully to avoid any country likely to be shelled, the other was by improvement in any direction likely to prevent the enemy from finding the bury, either by direct observation or through his aeroplane photographs.

The danger of direct observation was comparatively easily averted. Buries were carried out in the exposed areas by night only. All reconnaissance which required daylight was done by a single officer, either alone or accompanied by a solitary sergeant or sapper. Orders were issued that maps were to be in evidence as little as possible and any other signs which might give a watchful enemy the idea that anything of special importance was about to take place were carefully suppressed. It was more difficult to camouflage the lines. It would be hard to impress on one who had not actually experienced the doubtful pleasure of picking out his own bury from the detail of a photograph taken from some thousands of feet up in the air, the extreme difficulty of hiding such a track from the argus eyes of the aeroplane cameras. To one who has, on the other hand, seen such photographs of the scene of his activities—possibly in the presence of a justly incensed Brigadier, the position of whose headquarters he has unwittingly revealed—no such difficulty of understanding exists. His efforts would henceforth be mainly directed to overcoming the obviousness which seems to be the chief characteristic of the most carefully dug bury. A thin white straight line which could not possibly be mistaken by the meanest intelligence for a track, a stream, or anything but what it brazenly and patently was, too often showed that all the care devoted to " camouflage " had been in vain.

Still, if buries could not be entirely hidden, much could be done to make them less obvious. The earlier types—nice straight lines from headquarters to headquarters, used as convenient guides by all men and trampled upon by day and by night, in season and out of season—were doomed. As much ingenuity as possible was brought to bear on the question of camouflage and this, in 1917, took certain definite forms. Buries were pointed anywhere but at the headquarters they were designed to serve. They were connected to signa offices by trenches run off at acute angles and hidden from observation from above by all the devices known to the camouflage officer and his trained staff. Strips of wire netting covered with stuffs cunningly coloured to resemble the surrounding soil were the latest and most successful devices used. Previous to the evolution of such artificial means of ensuring freedom from observation, already-existing tracks and ditches were made use of or the buries were run in the immediate shadow of hedges or trees. Even so, the unfortunate signal officer was betrayed on more than one occasion by the deciduous nature of the European foliage. Carefully-hidden buries screened from prying aerial observers by the dense summer foliage of shade trees were revealed by the autumn storms in all their nakedness as white streaks, clearly artificial and worthy of enemy artillery attention.

The first step in this campaign for secrecy was an important one in itself. The work on the earlier buries had been haphazard in nature. No steps had usually been taken to suit the task to the power of the men and the time available for work. Long stretches of trenches were half-dug, or wholly-dug, but not filled in, and were then left throughout the daylight hours. They were, however, " noticed " with such painstaking thoroughness that the order was given that work must be completed and the trenches filled in before the working parties were permitted to leave the scene of their labours. This, in its turn, led to a more careful apportioning of the size of the task. Statistics were compiled and all signal officers employed on cable burying grew accustomed to measuring out each man's task for the night so thoroughly and accurately that the work was normally completed and the party out of range and observation before the early morning light made possible direct observation either from observation post or aeroplane.*

Another refinement which was the result of further experience was the reinforcing of the bury in spots where only a comparatively shallow trench could be dug, by building up a mound, two or three feet in height, above the ground. Yet another, was the placing across the bury of obstacles to prevent the rank and file of the Army from using it as a convenient track through otherwise unbroken and uncharted country. It paid the Signal Service to be inhospitable enough to their fellow men to build barricades which could ensure that the ease-loving soldier would find a way forward which was more pleasant and less strewn with unexpected and, from his point of view, entirely unnecessary obstacles. Refinements of "camouflage," again, were (1) the wilful adoption of a zigzag track in which economy

* Exceptionally hard ground and short summer nights were sometimes the cause of the failure of this policy, resulting in trenches not reaching a safe depth.

of labour was sacrificed to the fostering of an apparent inanity of purpose and (2) the utilization of neighbouring crops and herbage to give temporary immunity from observation.

The latter were either plucked at random—if ripe and unlikely to change colour—and flung down across the earth-coloured track of the bury, or—where the herbage was green and likely to die if treated in this way—were transplanted *en bloc* and planted in growing position over the trench and the trampled ground on either side. It became a regular routine in pasture country to remove the upper sods carefully and place them on one side well out of the way of the working party's feet. The last job of a careful signal party was then the replacement of these sods to restore the face of nature as far as possible. Success varied both with the capacity of the men for landscape gardening and with the character of the turf. Still another way of deceiving the hostile observer was the digging of a dummy trench in a quite different direction from the real bury. The ground was turned over to a depth of two feet or so and a realistic scar left. Such " dummy " buries were often useful as decoys to enemy artillery and were, indeed, frequently a source of chagrin to unfortunate pedestrians who followed the false tracks in the hope of reaching the headquarters they expected them to serve.

From the point of view of protection, much had been done during the winter of 1916. Much more was done in the preparation for the 1917 battles. The digging of the trenches to a depth of 8 ft. near the front line has been mentioned. This was somewhat exceptional, for 8 ft. was a depth almost impossible to reach in the unbroken labour of one night. The 8 ft. trench was mostly confined to the buries further to the rear where time could be taken over the digging without unpleasant consequences.

In the principal dug-outs of the 1917 systems in the south, 15 ft. of headcover was aimed at by some Corps. This was, of course, impossible for such systems as those in Flanders. Here, recourse had to be had to reinforced concrete and iron girders, if any measure of security was to be achieved. Still, everything feasible was done to prevent the signal dug-out from being a weak spot in the system either from its conspicuousness or from lack of fortification. The area detachment had a relatively hard time under all circumstances, but as much was done as was humanly possible to make their life bearable and safe.

A feature of the buried cable system of 1917 was, as has already been pointed out, the much greater extent of the individual systems. In one typical Corps system 1,000 miles of cable were laid in preparation for a single offensive. The making of the system took nine weeks with all the labour Divisions could spare. Main routes contained 40 to 50 pairs and even then were found insufficient. At least one main route, and often two, were taken forward on the front of each

Division and it was very seldom that cable head was not within easy distance of the front line. This was the policy aimed at in the Somme offensive, but at that date it had not been possible to carry it out to the full extent. Even routes serving a Brigade front were now completed with at least 20 pairs, in the expectation of their becoming the backbone of the new Divisional signal system in the event of an advance. The year was marked by a multiplication of the number of circuits in the routes which was only limited by the supply of cable. Yet the systems were too often insufficient to meet the needs of the artillery, for 10 to 20 Army Brigades were frequently concentrated on the front of one Army besides those normally part of the complement of the Divisions or Corps.

So much for the buried cable system at the opening of one of the great position battles. To obtain a picture of the forward signal system on the southern portion of the front affected, it is necessary first to visualize for the eyes of the imagination a more or less irregular grid of heavy cable routes securely buried from any single direct hit of a shell of any size less than 8-inch. At frequent intervals the cables are connected through securely protected dug-outs by means of elaborate cross-connecting frames which are equipped with plug and socket boards, terminals and cross-connecting wires, or any other of a dozen devices which might be the particular fancy of the local senior signal officer. At most of the dug-outs and test-points two, three, or more pairs are led up out of the bury and fixed to accessible but protected stakes and boards for the benefit of units whose headquarters are situated in the immediate neighbourhood. At the principal junction points the dug-outs are more commodious, and here, in a kind of warren more or less adequate to their needs, live the maintenance personnel under the charge of a junior N.C.O. or senior Sapper. Certain other dug-outs are manned only during operations. At all, whether manned or not, are notices to the effect that unauthorized persons must not tamper with the lines. At all, also, are diagrams, perhaps only of the immediate connections, perhaps also of the general Corps system. All diagrams are kept up to date and the N.C.O. or sapper in charge at each station is informed daily as to alterations and instructed as to the allotment of his lines.

Finally, at the principal test station lives the area officer himself in constant communication with his A.D. Signals and the "Lines" officers of his Corps and of the Divisions occupying the area for which he is responsible. His books are a compendium of the history and present state of the bury. He should know every detail of its history and the exact state of efficiency of every pair. He should patrol every inch of his bury at frequent intervals to ensure that his maintenance personnel is keeping the routes in perfect order and repairing daily the ravages made by enemy shells.

How is free intercommunication between himself and his men

ensured without interfering with the general working of the system ? The answer is supplied by yet another improvement. This was the allocation of two circuits, usually of "D5" or "D8" to prevent confusion, for the sole use of the Signal Service. Of these two pairs, one is used by the linemen as they make their daily patrol of their own particular section of the line. The other is the general channel of communication for Signal Service personnel. The signal officer who has planned his system without leaving room for these necessary adjuncts to its smooth working has laid up endless trouble for himself, his successors and his subordinates.

To adapt the above system to the northern area of the British front, it is only necessary to remember that deep delving was impossible, being prohibited by the nature of the ground. All extra protection had to be added overhead. It was, therefore, only achieved as the result of unlimited labour, by the expenditure of relatively large amounts of fortifying material urgently required for other purposes, and at the expense of concealment. In other words, having regard to the practical factors of the situation, it was frequently impossible. Security had to be sacrificed in favour of concealment and the economy of stores and labour. The result was a comparatively unsafe buried system, only rendered successful in any measure by unremitting toil at its daily maintenance, and liable at any moment to interruption for the period necessary to repair a complete break.

The success of the northern buries in low-lying country depended largely upon the care with which they were sited and the promptitude with which they were repaired. In any case, the element of uncertainty was such that much more reliance was perforce placed on the alternative methods of communication as far back as Divisional headquarters. This was an added care to the signal officers concerned, but, on the other hand, it was possibly a potent influence in the development of these alternative methods.

So far, in the picture of the signal activity in the rear areas in 1917, stress has been laid on the telegraph and telephone system, with little mention of other means save a passing reference to wireless. This was, however, necessary if a true picture of the Signal Service in action in position warfare was to be obtained. The importance of this system has not been exaggerated. There was, indeed, no reason to depart to any great extent from the most rapid and reliable method of signalling. In rear of Divisional headquarters, alternative means were strictly subsidiary in their functions. Such representatives of wireless, pigeons, visual, etc., as were included in the rear establishments confined their attention mainly to administration and control and to the evolution of signal policy. The rear establishments were a faithful reflection of the rear conditions of signal warfare and the realities of signal practice. Had they not been so, they would have been inadequate and ill-proportioned.

# CHAPTER XII.

## FORWARD SIGNALS IN THE 1917 POSITION BATTLES

### SYNOPSIS.

General Remarks.—Horses of Cable Sections a Problem.—Universality of Training. Aimed at.—Motor Cyclists.—Visual in the Division.—Wireless in the Division.—R.A. Signals.—Brigade Signals.—Forward Signals in the Attack.—Pushing Forward the Buried Cable.—General Policy of Forward Signals Compared with S.S. 148.—Forward Lines.—Forward Visual.—Message-carrying Agencies.—Decentralization of the Pigeon Service.—Formation and Organization of the Messenger Dog Service.—Runners.—Forward Wireless.—Loop Sets.—Continuous Wave Wireless.—The History of the Power Buzzer and Amplifier.

In the previous chapter a picture has been given of the activities of Army and Corps Signal personnel in the 1917 battles and it has been shown how the responsibility of both D.D. Signals, Army and A.D. Signals, Corps had moved forward. This forward extension of supervision had also been accompanied by the use of Army and Corps personnel, in the shape of the area detachments and the heavy artillery signal units, well within the Divisional areas. The tendency was for the buried system, although serving units right up to the front line, to be gradually taken out of the hands of the Divisional signal officer who was relieved more and more of responsibility both for its administration and for the upkeep of the routes.

This policy was never entirely achieved, however. To the close of position warfare, the Divisional Signal Company personnel remained responsible in great measure for the planning, and almost entirely for the execution, of the forward buries, in maintaining which the same unit also provided considerable help.

During the whole duration of position warfare, one great drawback to the Divisional Signal Company had been a lack of modification to suit stationary conditions. Great changes in establishment had taken place ; yet further changes, involving considerable additions in strength, were to take place in 1918. Nevertheless, the Divisional Signal Company was still primarily constituted and equipped for mobile warfare. In no respect did the peculiar consistency of policy of the higher signal command show to better advantage under most insistent pressure than in this refusal to reorganize the Divisional Signal Company's constitution. Almost every Divisional Signal Officer came to consider the horses of his cable sections as little less than a curse at times. Two-thirds of the companies at the least did not use their cable wagons for any purpose other than training until the retreat of March, 1918. One or two had had a reminder of their usefulness in March, 1917, during the German retreat.  Half a dozen or so were to have a similar demonstration in November, 1917, at Cambrai.  One here and there laid a line two or three miles long by cable wagon in the deeper advances of the position battles of 1917.

In the meantime, all cable between Division and Brigade—the extent of the responsibilities of No. 1 section of a Divisional Signal Company—was either buried, laid by hand, or at most from a horse-drawn drum barrow.  When advances were sufficiently deep and shelling sufficiently light to permit of the survival of a six-horsed cable wagon in the forward area, our artillery preparation and the enemy defences had in the vast majority of cases made the terrain impassable for such a vehicle.  Roads destroyed beyond immediate repair defied wheeled transport ; dense and broad belts of wire only partially uprooted barred the way, or the destruction of bridges over unfordable streams effectually put a limit to their activity.

And all this while the sappers of the section, without whose aid it was almost impossible to keep horses and vehicles clean and equipment in good order, were required for work on the position warfare line system.  Cable section operators were employed in the advanced and rear Divisional signal offices or attached to Brigades to work the forward end of the Divisional circuits.  Field linemen (the " cable hands " of the old nomenclature) and general duty pioneers were wanted to lay buried cable or to help maintain the system when laid. To crown all, there was no general officer of Division who did not know all about transport and horses, while there were many who were not versed in the technical details which usually distinguished an efficient from an inefficient signal company.  To such commanders, the only way of judging the discipline and efficiency of the signal company, which was giving at least average satisfaction in its technical duties, was by frequent inspections of the company transport and personnel. It is not too much to say that, in the manifold activities of trench warfare, these recurring inspections were a principal source of trial to the Divisional Signal Company commander.  With the resources of his company strained to the utmost to cope with a signal system almost beyond his power, he was constrained to employ more men upon his horses than he could conscientiously spare.  Apart altogether from the inspections—which were very necessary if the horses were to receive their due share of attention—in fairness to the animals themselves, a considerable proportion of the company must devote most of their time to their welfare.  In some divisions the representations of the O.C. Signals carried sufficient weight to enable him to draw upon certain infantry personnel to help out his drivers ; in others, with the ingenuity which distinguished many of these sorely-taxed officers, he started classes in horsemastership,part of the virtue of which consisted in the pupils attaining a thorough proficiency in grooming.  In most cases, however, it was left to the officers and men to struggle as best they could to keep the company efficient. This aim was attained in the majority of cases, but the struggle was a very hard one and was one of the main reasons why the personnel of the Divisional Signal Company was never " in rest " in the true sense of the phrase. Whether in the line or not, horses had to be cared for, signal offices must be manned, and lines must be maintained. In addition, out of the line, after the first two or three days' clearing up, the whole of the surplus energy of all ranks was devoted to training for mobile warfare.

In view of the circumstances set forth above, it is not surprising that many officers sent in from time to time strong recommendations as to the desirability of a considerable reduction in the percentage of horses in the company. These proposals were very seriously considered, particularly in 1917 and 1918, when the general man-power situation was causing anxiety. The decision very wisely reached, however, was that, though the percentage of men to horses might be improved by the addition of extra dismounted personnel, no great revision involving loss of horses could be permitted. Officers' second chargers disappeared ; a slight reduction was made in spare horses, etc. No considerable reduction was, however, permitted and the Divisional Signal Company entered upon the mobile warfare of 1918 unchanged in any of the essential features of its establishment as they affected the mobility of the unit.

At the date of the present review the company had been substantially increased from the pre-war establishment. It was, however, none too large for the work it had to do. The standard organization included a rear signal office and an advanced one at battle headquarters. All the operators available in headquarters and No. 1 section were required to man the normal shifts in these two offices and to provide two sounder operators for each Brigade. The Divisional end of the Corps circuit was manned by operators attached from the Corps, or the office personnel could not have been made to go round. Headquarter linemen were usually pooled with the linemen of No. 1 section and utilized turn and turn about upon the headquarter circuits, on the maintenance of the buries between Division and Brigades, or on night cable-laying parties.*

* In some Divisions the headquarter linemen specialized on work on the headquarters circuits and the main trunk lines to the Brigades. This was always a matter of individual policy of the O.C. Signals. Both systems had their advantages and disadvantages, but as a general rule one of the principles of forward signals, where casualties were more common, was to carry the principle of universality into the training and employment of the men as far as possible. Indeed, in a thoroughly well-trained forward signal unit, a proportion of motor cyclist despatch riders with a knowledge of lineman's duties would be found ; motor cyclists would be trained as horsemen ; operators would be trained to carry out simple repairs to their instruments ; linemen and drivers

While linemen and operators were fully employed, the D.R.'s and the artificers—instrument repairer, harness maker, wheeler, etc.— were also without much spare time upon their hands. The motor cyclist despatch rider's work had to a great extent lost the romance which made it one of the most interesting aspects of the Signal Service during the 1914 campaigns. The danger of his work had markedly decreased, though the new German practice of putting down shell storms* on the main roads behind our front was once more adding a considerable element of excitement to his routine journeys. He had, however, a great amount of hard work to get through each day. The normal D.R.L.S. kept the various reliefs continually at work, while the Divisional Staff had never overcome their liking for special D.R.'s. Time and again an unfortunate motor cyclist would be called from his well-earned rest to take a single packet which through thoughtlessness or forgetfulness had missed the regular post. Occasions were even recorded when special D.R.'s were utilized to take forward a commander's private mail. The practice of despatching "specials" on insufficient grounds, indeed, became so common and had such unfortunate effects on the working of the service that special legislation was required to deal with it.

Other portions of the headquarters of the Divisional Signal Company, as constituted in 1917, were the "Signallers and Despatch Riders" and Wireless Section. The former were still so few in number that for any position battle in which cyclist or mounted despatch riders were required, detachments of Corps cyclists or Divisional mounted troops had to be attached temporarily to the signal company. It was also—quite apart from the difficulty of the same men being regarded as despatch riders—usually impossible for more than one Divisional visual station to be manned by the personnel of the Company Headquarters. Unless circumstances were particularly favourable, this meant that an alternative route by visual between Division and Brigade was impossible without outside assistance.

In a measure this difficulty was overcome by the appropriation of some portion of the Brigade pool of battalion signallers for this purpose, and in some Divisions the signal section of the pioneer battalion was utilized to eke out the very meagre visual establishment. By means of these men, a system of visual stations could be

were both given practical training in the Morse code. The best chance of promotion for the driver, especially, was by training for the duties of a sapper and passing the necessary remustering tests. The further forward the unit had its position, the more was this the basis of the training carried out. Naturally, too, as the front line was approached, where personnel changed frequently and was not so highly skilled at any one work, such as operating, it became more possible to train all men to a fair level of efficiency both at operating and lineman's work.

* Especially gas shells, which caused many casualties in 1918.

set up between Divisional and Brigade headquarters in any but the most enclosed country. Where the country was flat and very enclosed, however, it was not usually worth while to attempt an elaborate system. The buried cable routes were usually to be relied upon, and, if alternative communication was required, the wireless section was looked to to provide it.

The wireless section was destined to come into its own during the Cambrai offensive and the 1918 battles. It consisted, in its earliest form, of personnel for three trench wireless sets and for two power buzzer and amplifier sets. It was specifically laid down in the establishment that a proportion of the operators were available for work as office telegraphists. This was a regulation which was destined to be much insisted upon. One of the main obstacles to the development of wireless within the Division was the fact that the best wireless operators were seldom available for duty in that capacity. This trouble was not overcome until the appointment of a wireless officer gave to wireless within the Division an authorized champion.

At the present time—the campaign season of 1917—wireless was used principally as an alternative for the buried cable system between Divisional and Battalion headquarters. In such a capacity it was often of great momentary value, especially in the Flanders area. A special use to which the trench sets were sometimes put was observation with the artillery. Here, however, they were at once superseded by the new continuous wave sets which had peculiar qualifications for this work.

In a bird's eye view of the Signal Service at this period of the war, it is necessary to imagine the personnel of the Divisional wireless section either at work in the signal office as telegraphists or, more legitimately, manning a trench set at or near Divisional headquarters and one, or possibly two, others at convenient spots well forward along the main Divisional lines of communication, probably handy to Brigade headquarters. In addition, in a Division where wireless was being fully worked, two or more power buzzer amplifier stations might be in use, either between a particularly exposed battalion and its Brigade headquarters or between isolated posts and the forward Divisional wireless station. Forward of these, again, would be power buzzers installed at company headquarters or at other important strong-points and worked by battalion signallers.

The remaining personnel of a Divisional Signal Company was contained in a R.A. headquarters section, the two R.A. signal sub-sections, and the three Brigade sections (Nos. 2, 3, and 4 sections of the company).

The artillery signal system of a Division was usually run to all intents and purposes entirely separate from the infantry command system. Possibly the artillery exchange might be a different board in the same office, far more often the artillery ran a separate signal office closely adjacent to their headquarters which was itself often at a considerable distance from Divisional headquarters. The system was the special care of a captain of the Divisional Signal Company and circuits ran from the artillery signal office to the various artillery Brigade headquarters which had their own smaller exchanges. From here, again, lines radiated to batteries, to the Brigade wagon lines and the Brigade Staff, to the affiliated infantry Brigade, and to the neighbouring artillery Brigades. Usually, also, subsidiary circuits linked the ordinary Brigade or individual batteries to the local kite balloon and to other means of observation common to more than one formation. The subaltern with the R.A. signal sub-section was responsible for all the signal communication between Brigade headquarters, the Brigade O.P. or O.P. exchange, and the batteries ; forward of the batteries the signal system of each was controlled by an officer of the battery and the work carried out by R.A. personnel.

A general supervision was, however, exercised by the artillery Brigade signal officer, who was held responsible for the technical efficiency of the whole system. An artillery sub-section officer was more important to his formation Staff than even the infantry Brigade signal officer to his. Artillery without good observation is comparatively inefficient. In modern warfare good observation is robbed of most of its value without equally good intercommunication. Fleeting targets could not be engaged at all without both being efficient. Good instances of this were frequently afforded in the autumn of 1918 by the firing of the German heavy artillery during their retreat. All firing for days together was done at random by the map. Shells, patently intended for a local objective such as a bridge across a canal or an important road junction, frequently fell with monotonous regularity two or three hundred yards from the intended target. Entire absence of observation was shown by a complete failure to correct such an error. Poor signal communication was shown when an error which obviously was visible from German occupied territory was rectified only after a considerable lapse of time.

No signal units suffered a greater proportion of casualties in 1917 and 1918 than the newly-formed artillery signal sub-sections. This was especially so with gas wounds. The German artillery systematically shelled the British battery areas at all times. Battery personnel, generally, could take shelter during the periods of heavy shelling. Signal offices must, however, be kept manned and linesmen were continually out in pairs upon the lines. It was seldom that many weeks passed without casualties occurring in such units as were in the line, and the total mounted up far in excess of that of any other class of R.E. signal personnel.

Casualties in the Divisional Signal Company, generally, were undoubtedly minimised by the general use of heavily-fortified signal

P

offices and the concentration of the forward routes into deep buries. The latter were dug and the cables buried under cover of darkness. Breaks were not common and maintenance was therefore reduced to a minimum. After the gunner sub-sections, most casualties occurred in the Brigade sections. Indeed, during the actual offensives the casualties of these sections must have exceeded in number those suffered by the artillery signal units.

Brigade signals in position warfare consisted mainly in the manning of the Brigade signal office, the giving of assistance with the forward portions of the Divisional lines, and maintenance of trench cable and alternative wireless, power buzzer, and visual, to battalions and flank Brigades. The Brigade section is one of the few signal units which remained practically unchanged throughout the war. Its only rival, indeed, in this respect, was the cable section. Both changed to a certain extent as regards the qualifications of the men composing the units, but neither underwent radical changes in organization. Both the Brigade and the battalion signal section shared in the prevalent shifting forward of technical qualifications towards the front line. The battalion signaller of 1914 knew visual only— both Morse and semaphore—but nothing else. Telephones, if they existed at all, were unofficial. The height of position warfare in 1917 and 1918 saw battalion signallers *blasés* as regards lines and the common "D3" buzzer ; versed in the mysteries of the fullerphone ; and familiar with the highly-technical power buzzer and loop wireless set. In addition, he was required to know how to handle pigeons, how to fire message-carrying rockets and how to use small buzzer exchanges. In a word, he was expected to have more qualifications than the old "telegraphists, field line" and "telegraphists, permanent line" of the pre-war classification had possessed.

This needs to be borne in mind when considering the evolution of forward signals, for it was one of the chief difficulties encountered in replacing casualties amongst battalion signallers.

It was impossible for the Brigade section, unchanged in numbers as it was, to keep efficient a normal Brigade signal system in the position battles. This was legislated for by the formation of the Brigade pool of battalion signallers already referred to. These men were specially trained to enable them to work the more technical alternative methods of forward signalling and were controlled by the Brigade signal officer. This fact helped very much to make possible the decisive step which characterized the forward signals of this year— that is, the concentration of signal activities along one main route down the centre of each Brigade area.

On a "peaceful" front in normal times the brigade signal office would be connected by sounder or fullerphone and by telephone with Division ; by telephone and by fullerphone with each battalion and with lateral Brigades. As far as possible, lines would be accommodated in the buried system. Where this was not possible, trench cable would be used. Forward of battalion headquarters, an emergency line system would be laid and connected up to "D3" telephones or fullerphones at company headquarters or the more important posts. Normally, this system would be tested through but not used except for purposes of artillery *liaison* or observation, or in emergency. The line system would be completed by laterals between company headquarters and to the battalions and companies to left and right. It would be reinforced by as complete a system of visual stations as was possible. In addition would be power buzzer and amplifier stations at most Brigade and some battalion headquarters and power buzzers at important company headquarters or at posts particularly likely to be cut off by shell fire or a sudden attack. At battalion headquarters and in each company area would be pigeon posts; normal routine traffic which had no particular urgency and yet could not be passed over the telephone was sent by runner. Buzzer was strictly prohibited forward of Brigade headquarters.

---

This normal Divisional intercommunication system was, of course, modified considerably during offensives. In three ways, in particular, distinct advances from the policy and practice of the previous year can be seen. These three were :—

(1) The pushing forward of the buried system across "No Man's Land."
(2) The adoption of the single Brigade line of signal communications and the formation of Brigade forward parties.
(3) The success of the power buzzer and amplifier and the initial use of loop wireless sets. (Under this heading, also, might be considered the first development of forward continuous wave wireless for use with the artillery).

In the position battles of 1916, no attempt was made as an ordered policy to push forward the buried cable immediately after zero. Two considerations militated against the adoption of such a policy, the first being the shortage of labour, the second, the casualties which would certainly be inflicted on the working parties by the enemy's barrage. In 1917 both considerations were over-ruled and in some cases the buried cable system was pushed forward well into the captured zone within a few hours of the commencement of the action. The best examples occurred in the advances opposite Arras and in the battle for the Vimy Ridge. Here, circumstances were particularly favourable, and on one occasion a short bury of 60 yards only had to be dug to connect up the British mined cable head with the extensive tunnels on the German side of the line. In such circumstances, the best results might be expected, but even without the use of such adventitious tunnels good work was done in pushing forward normal buries. One Corps reported the completion of 1,500 yards within 15 hours of zero, and a further 1,000 yards by zero plus 31 hours.* The whole system was installed and connected up and working by the time quoted and gave good results. In other cases, results were not so good and the opinion of Divisional signal officers was by no means generally in favour of persevering with the new policy. It would seem that here, as in most other aspects of forward signalling, regard must be had to the particular circumstances of each individual case. The deciding factors in 1917 were the position in the Corps as regards the supply of labour, the weight of the enemy barrage on the country to be crossed, the depth and speed of the advance, and the presence or absence of aids on the German side of the line. Under any but the most favourable conditions, only the most carefully worked-out schemes could be expected to achieve a reasonable measure of success.

The weight of the enemy's shelling varied very much in different actions. If the attack was pressed home well and the enemy forced to withdraw his guns, his shelling was so reduced that for some time a ground line system could be maintained with ease. The interval between the advance and the normal forward extension of the buried cables was thus bridged with a sufficiently good temporary system. If, on the other hand, the enemy barrage was extraordinarily heavy and widely spread, buried cable was out of the question on account of the casualties involved. It was necessary to wait until our own guns had engaged the enemy batteries or the latter had shifted to individual targets. It was then often possible to pick a good way forward, along which the cable could be extended without undue loss. In the meantime, alternative methods must be resorted to and in such situations pigeons, visual, and wireless carried the essential traffic.

The depth of the advance was also a powerful determining factor. It was useless attempting to keep up with a deep advance by means of buried cable. Signal communication was required at once and must be extended forward by the most rapid and not by the slowest existing means. Fortunately, such deep advances implied relatively little enemy retaliation. In such a case it was therefore possible to follow up the advancing troops with poled cable and airline routes. Thus, for brief periods, comic airline and poled or treed cable crept up once more into the Divisional areas. Once the overground

* Out of 21 pairs in the first 1,500 yards one only was faulty ; there were no faulty pairs in the other 1,000 yards of route. The route remained uncut until the sector was handed over three months later, since which date no record is available.

system was completed and working, a portion of the outdoor signal personnel was told off to maintain it, while the remainder, with the assistance of what working parties could be spared, worked steadily on the extension of the buried system.

---

The general policy of forward signals advocated in S.S. 148 was a great advance on anything that had previously been attempted. It was based upon the principle that on each Brigade front all efforts should be concentrated upon the establishment and maintenance of one main cable route reinforced by all available means of communication. This route was to run from the advanced Brigade headquarters to the Brigade forward station, that is, from the headquarters of the Brigadier before zero to that at which his office would be established if the attack was successful. Forward of the latter, smaller arteries would run to the various forward observation officers and to the battalion forward command posts. By means of this one main route all artillery and infantry traffic was to be passed. Should the advance be of such a depth that movement of batteries and consequent re-registration were involved, one forward observation officer from each group would be permitted to lay one line back to cable head to reduce the congestion on the artillery lines. All circuits were to be metallic and no lines were to be laid without the express permission of the infantry Brigade signal officer.

The scheme had been matured with care and was based upon the experience of the previous fighting. In theory, it looked to be perfect, but in practice several defects were found to prevent its general adoption without considerable modification. The grouping of all signal responsibility along one line, and the implied obligation to Staffs to select their new command stations along that line, was a novel feature which was destined to revolutionize forward signals in position as well as in mobile warfare. This was still further insisted upon in the successor to this first intercommunication manual and was the more easily fallen in with by the Staffs because it was from the first patent to all concerned that it was the most economical and most efficient method yet adopted. No longer did the signal officer fritter away his energies on quite unnecessary lateral spurs between the main route and the various headquarters he served. His duty was complete with the completion of the backbone of the communication system, though he often assisted the signal personnel of junior formations to lay lines from their command posts to his forward report centre. If Staffs could not comply with orders and settle down along the immediate line of advance, their signal communications would be more precarious according as their distance from the line increased. In so far as this prinicple was concerned, no fault could be found with the new policy.

In its details, however, there was much to cavil at. The decision to allow none but metallic circuits was a mistake. It was an ideal quite impossible of realization. In 1915, 1916 and 1917, one great stand-by of the forward signal officer was his laddered lines. These were earthed lines in the fullest sense of the word. Thirty, forty, fifty breaks had occurred without destroying the circuits. Often they were the only means of line communication left. The same troubles were experienced in laying and maintaining the forward line system which have already been referred to in describing the 1916 battles. At Ypres and Passchendaele, especially, lines of any description were often impossible to maintain. Behind the newly captured defences on the Passchendaele Ridge, everything had been shot away with the exception of one main road which an army of men laboured to preserve. What lines were left by the shells were not likely to survive the attentions of the labourers. In such circumstances, metallic circuits were impossible and the attempt to keep them through would have been a farce.*

Another feature in which the scheme as laid down in S.S. 148 failed, was the inadequate provision for artillery traffic. Nearly all the important traffic in a position battle had reference in one way or another to artillery. Normally, it was upon this arm that the General Officer commanding the formation relied for the series of situation reports which enabled him to form his mind-pictures of the progress of the action.†

One pair only was provided for the artillery on a Brigade front, and stringent regulations debarred the forward observation officers from laying other lines on their own initiative. The system broke down hopelessly in this respect and after the first attempt was

---

* At Passchendaele some Divisions laid a metallic circuit ladder consisting of two parallel pairs of twisted "D8" cable (different colours for each leg) about 500 yards apart. Other linemen then laid the rungs of the ladder with about 200 yards between each, joining the corresponding colours of the cable. This much facilitated patrol work and repairs. It is, however, a doubtful question whether this policy would often be justified. Overhearing during intense battles is not very likely to be dangerous ; while, if circumstances are such as to render laddered lines necessary, earthing is likely to be caused by frequent breaks in the cable.

† In this connection an interesting example of the use of the signal pair of the 1917 buries is reported. This pair was reserved for signal traffic only. During the earlier stages of the battles this line was sometimes used on many Corps fronts to collect from local signal offices the gist of the information in the possession of their headquarters. This was concentrated, divested of irrelevant detail, and conveyed to the General Staff to whom it often formed a most valuable supplementary source of information.

modified in one of two ways. In some cases, the artillery ignored the Brigade forward centre and each forward observation officer laid lines of his own to buried cable head and endeavoured to maintain them as best he could. In others, an extra forward station was improvised and the two systems ran parallel to each other down the length of the Brigade area. Of the two, the latter method was, of course, the better organized and therefore the most successful. When the two systems were connected by lateral junctions in front and in rear, a strong line system resulted which was very efficient and amply sufficient for the needs of the infantry Brigades and their allied artillery formations. In yet other cases, the need was met more simply by the addition of a third line or pair to the main route. By this means and by the allowance of a certain amount of latitude to unfavourably situated artillery F.O.O's, a close approximation to the original plan was worked with success.

As regards the detail of the Brigade routes, it was soon realized that the fullest latitude must be allowed to the discretion of individual commanders. No situation resembled any other in its entirety. A scheme devised for the crater-pitted, mud-strewn flats of Flanders was quite unsuited to the hilly and wooded country further south and *vice versa*. A system devised for a hurried advance over a comparatively broad zone, must be decisively and quickly modified if the attack failed and the intended lines were telescoped to one-half or one-third the length for which the original organization was intended. This was, indeed, one of the serious faults of the new system. There was a tendency to crowd so many means along one route and to allow for so many relay posts in case of an unexpected depth of advance, that resources were severely strained to find the necessary personnel. Signal officers became seriously concerned as to the advisability of persisting with so many alternative methods of signalling. Towards the end of the year there was a disposition to rely upon lines and visual or on lines and wireless only, instead of dividing up the available men between all three means.

The Brigade signal section of one officer and 24 N.C.O.'s and men could not man the proposed forward route. The difficulty was overcome by calling upon the battalions for visual signallers and runners, and upon the Division and the Corps for wireless and power buzzer operators and linemen.

Later on, with further training, battalion signallers were also to operate the forward wireless sets, but this stage had not yet come within the realm of practical politics.

The main feature of the Brigade signal system during the position battles of 1917 was thus the single chain of stations somewhere along the middle of the area of operations. Along this line were cables—metallic if possible, but usually earthed—runner relay posts, pigeon, aeroplane, and visual stations, wireless, and power buzzer-amplifier stations. The number of stations varied, of course—within the limits possible to the Signal personnel available—according as the advance was shallow or deep.* Protection was attempted, and posts were usually selected in the best available shelter. In the south they were frequently sited in dug-outs, connecting possibly with above ground machine-gun emplacements. In the north, use was made of some of the " pill-boxes " which were the characteristic feature of the German defence system in the low-lying swampy country where deep dug-outs were impossible. The occupation of such sites agreed very well with the general scheme of the advance,

* To avoid the necessity of reference to an out-of-date book, the composition of the Brigade forward party as laid down in S.S. 148 is given below :—

### Detachment " A."

*Personnel* :—

| | |
|---|---|
| Earth induction set | 3 signallers |
| Aeroplane signal station | 3 signallers |
| Visual station | 1 N.C.O., 2 signallers |
| Runner station | 2 runners per attacking battalion |
| Telephone station | 3 signallers (one from party found by Div. Artillery personnel) |
| Pigeon station | 2 pigeoneers |

*Equipment* :—
Two signalling lamps ; 4 folding signal shutters ; 2 telescopes, signalling ; power buzzer and amplifier ; 2 "D3" telephones or fuller-phones ; 2 4-plus-3 buzzer exchanges ; "D" twin or twisted cable on reels in ¼-mile lengths ; signalling flags ; light pistols ; S.O.S. rockets ; ground signal sheets, strips, and ground signal panel ; 4 pigeons.
(This detachment will be accompanied by two battalion intelligence officers in addition to the one for code work, each with two snipers or observers.)

### Detachment " B."

*Personnel* :—
1 N.C.O. signaller
2 linemen
4 runners
2 additional runners and 2 linemen for each relay post between the end of the buried cable and the forward station. (One of the above linemen will be detailed from the party found by Divisional artillery personnel.)

*Equipment* :—
One "D3" telephone ; "D" twin or twisted cable on reels in ¼-mile lengths as may be necessary for 2 circuits from head of buried line to forward station. (One additional "D3" telephone and ¼-mile cable for each relay post.)
(From the above detail the type of signal route aimed at is easily reconstructed and it will be seen that its principal feature is the multiplicity of means employed.)

for they were usually favourably situated with regard to possible command posts.

It was in such a central combined system that the universality of training aimed at by the Signal Service was of superlative use. In many cases, when part of the complement of a forward station or relay post had been disabled or killed, the station would have been rendered useless but for the presence of men who could make shift to use signalling apparatus for which they were not specially trained. Many an orderly rendered useful service in repairing lines, many a lineman took his turn at the key and proved a serviceable substitute for a wounded operator. The fact that forward parties were on some occasions involved in the fighting has already been emphasized. S.S. 148 laid down the principle that " The Brigade forward party must move forward soon enough to escape the hostile barrage, but must avoid becoming involved in the fighting. Usually it should follow the last wave of the attacking infantry." Here, again, individual discretion was necessary. Mopping-up was oftentimes a lengthy operation and it was not always possible to proceed according to schedule. Many signal officers decided to hold back the forward party until the first objective had been reached.

The composition of the forward parties also varied greatly according to the situation. As a general rule, the principles laid down held good and signal commanders soon learnt how best to vary them to suit particular sets of circumstances. For instance, if the attack were not pressed home, the collection of the whole of the forward party on a shortened line of communication could only lead to congestion and unnecessary casualties. Arrangements must be made for the speedy evacuation of a proportion of the men to positions further to the rear where they could be of more use and in less danger. Every advance, and almost every formation taking part in an advance, presented its own special features. The experience of each battle was collated and utilized as a means of further improving the general policy. S.S. 191 was the crystallization of the experience of 1917, just as S.S. 148, on which the policy of 1917 was based, was the outcome of the earlier experiences of 1916.

---

There remains the consideration of the individual means of forward signalling : lines, visual, power buzzer and amplifier, loop wireless sets, pigeons and runners, etc. In some we shall see little change from the methods already described in the previous year, while others became of much greater importance in 1917. All were of considerable value except, perhaps, the loop wireless sets, which were new and in the use of which few signallers had yet been trained.

Forward lines remained unchanged to any great extent during

1917. They were laid on a more systematic plan, the main object of the Brigade forward parties being the establishment of two metallic (?) circuits between the Brigade forward station and cable head. Here, once more, is seen the rather academic nature of the first intercommunication manual. It was definitely laid down that the circuits should be metallic. It was also definitely ordered that detachment " A " of the forward party should proceed forward to the appointed spot, establish a signal office, and then commence to lay back two circuits to meet detachment " B " which was laying forward from cable head. Both of these instructions were impracticable. The inadvisability of the use of metallic circuits has already been referred to ; the folly of attempting to lay back towards cable head was amply demonstrated on many occasions. In the event, the policy followed was to lay earthed lines forward, either to the site selected or, if this was not recognisable or not accessible, to a suitable spot as near as possible to the site ordered in operation orders. The spot selected was then marked conspicuously with a blue and white pennant or other mark. If distances were long, the lines were looped in at fairly frequent intervals to other friendly dug-outs or shelter points of one description or another. Here the runner relay posts were set up and these also were conspicuously marked.

These earthed lines were replaced by metallic circuits as soon as shelling permitted, but this was not always possible. It depended primarily on the weight of our own artillery and the depth of our advance, and these two factors varied, of course, with every attack. Good examples of this variation were afforded in the third Battle of Ypres. After the success of the first attack, and the capture of the ridges, the British artillery for a time dominated the position and poured such a devastating hail of fire upon the enemy's lines that his retaliation was comparatively ineffective. Work became possible by day for the first time in this sector and a good cable system was completed forward of buried cable head. This was the more fortunate as it was some time before it proved possible to advance the buried cable head into the captured territory. This favourable position lasted for two or three days, when the attack was completely held up by the malign results of the heavy rain which characterized the beginning of August in this sector. The shell-torn ground became quite impassable. The enemy guns from their new positions on comparatively untouched ground once more began to assert a local superiority. They were reinforced daily, as the enemy realized the gravity of the threat to his defences. The maintenance of ground lines became almost impossible. Lines were blown to bits almost as soon as they were laid. Even laddered cable could not survive the storm of shell. To add to the troubles of the signal units the ground was flooded by the choked and overflowing streams. The shell-holes which pitted the greater part of the country were filled with foul gas-saturated water from 2 to 15 ft. deep. The pill-boxes in which the signal offices and relay posts had been set up had not escaped the attention of our own artillery. They were now subjected to an equally fierce bombardment by the enemy and many of them were shot to pieces, overset, or crumbling under the repeated impact of the heavy shells. It was in these circumstances that methods of signalling which did not involve lines or human passage scored most freely. The power buzzer with its short earth leads, the wireless set with its inconspicuous and easily-erected aerial, the pigeon with its free flight through untainted air, all played a significant part in bridging the gap between the different headquarters whose cement roofs stood out above the rain-soaked, mud-drenched country.

In the battles of 1917, as in those of the two previous years, there was a constant struggle for mastery between " air " and " ground " signalling. In normal circumstances in stationary or slow-moving warfare, " ground " signalling was quickest and most reliable. When conditions became abnormal or movement rapid, the situation was often reversed and " air " signalling established a momentary superiority. In fact, just as in Arctic exploration, the difference between "winter" and "summer" sledging can be best tested by whether a man is most happy pulling hard in the traces of his sledge or lying at ease in his sleeping bag, so in position warfare, the normality or abnormality of the conditions could often be accurately gauged by the relative efficiency of these two classes of signal methods. " Air " signalling of all descriptions, whether pigeons, wireless, or visual were employed, involved a loss of time and a lack of reliability which was only compensated by a gain in invulnerability and a decrease in the loss of life involved.

To return to the general consideration of the forward lines of the 1917 offensives, the characteristics peculiar to these battles were more in the way of special organization to improve maintenance of lines than in methods of laying. On some occasions lines were pushed forward through underground saps until the enemy's barrage was passed. Breakdown parties were often utilized right forward along the Divisional routes, the men making their headquarters at or near a Brigade signal office. At other times, when buries were impossible to any great extent, and the situation was fairly stable, special efforts were made to obtain small working parties and to bury short lengths of the routes. Instances of such local buries were those laid over the Pilkem Ridges during the Ypres battle—one on each Brigade front. The work was most unpleasant. It had to be done in a great hurry by night and under heavy shelling and the casualties in the working parties were heavy.

Laddered lines were, however, still the normal expression of signal ingenuity, when shelling was heavy. The use of three parallel cables,

15 yards apart and laddered at intervals of 50 yards, was common and such lines were kept through in spite of as many as 75 breaks in two or three thousand yards.

Another innovation adopted by some Divisions was the appointment of an officer to control all forward lines. The breakdown parties and the maintenance personnel acted under his orders and careful organization often resulted in the fairly continuous maintenance of lines right up to the artillery observation posts in front. The amount of traffic dealt with on such an improvised system during one of the later offensives is shown by the figures of a Division in the Passchendaele fighting. On zero day, besides continuous telephone calls, 1,010 urgent operation messages passed over the Divisional lines. Imagine a complete interruption of communication for 24 hours, and it can be seen that a break-down of the Signal Service would have made all the difference between success and failure. Such a break-down, however, never occurred. Always alternative methods worked to a greater or less extent.

Methods of laying lines were much as in the Somme offensive. It was seldom that the country to be traversed was clear enough to permit of cable wagons being used even in the deepest of the advances. Most lines were laid by hand or at best from a light cable cart or from a horse-drawn or man-drawn barrow. Man pack cable-laying apparatus had been designed and issued and was extremely useful. Brigade sections which had had their pack horses withdrawn did not greatly miss these animals now, though in the later battles at Cambrai and during the March retreat their loss was to be severely felt.

---

When lines were continually broken, as often happened forward of cable head, other means were employed. Other means must, indeed, always be available from Divisional headquarters forward and especially on a Brigade forward signal route. The least technical of the means employed were runners, pigeons, and messenger dogs; slightly more technical were visual, aeroplane signalling, Very lights and S.O.S. rockets. Most technical of all, and therefore the source of most trouble to the unspecialized forward personnel, were the wireless and earth induction sets.

Of these three groups, the first and second presented few special features of interest this year except as regards their organization along the main forward route.

Signalling to aeroplanes did not occupy nearly as prominent place as in the Somme offensive. The methods employed were again the ground sheet, the ground panel and the aeroplane dropping ground. The panel was cumbersome and slow and still unpopular; the latter was the most popular method and the most efficient. By this means valuable information was brought back by the aeroplane observers and a series of *précis* of the situation delivered regularly to the General Staff at Division and Corps. Signalling to kite balloons and aeroplanes by visual was again tried without success. Visual, generally, was much employed, but all other methods paled to insignificance beside the efficiency of the Lucas lamp. Flags were little used, discs were used only by very forward units, and by these less than in 1916, other types of lamps than the Lucas were practically obsolescent, and were superseded as fast as the Lucas lamps came to hand. Very lights and rockets were laid down as part of the equipment of the normal Brigade forward party and were specially useful for the purpose of notifying sudden emergencies and for showing up the position of the front line and of particular posts. They were used also, as in the previous year, for acknowledging the receipt of D.D.D.D. visual messages.

One special feature of the use of visual was the greater prevalence of two-way working. This was made possible by the smothering of enemy observation stations by the British artillery fire and by the depth of the advances. Another innovation was the use of the pill-boxes in the Ypres district as the sites of visual stations. These little fortresses had deep embrasures and doors which still further decreased the dispersion of the rays of the Lucas lamps. Two-way working in the very face of the enemy was possible in many cases by judicious use of suitable posts.

Pigeons, messenger dogs and runners are a separate group of methods of signalling all involving the element of life. In all three cases, but of course much more in the last, sentiment must enter to some extent into the question of their use. In the case of the two former, it took the shape of a tendency to make pets of what should strictly have been treated as mechanical means of conveying messages. In the case of the third, the human element introduced a variety of complications, both good and bad.

The use of pigeons for forward signalling had undergone little change in the last year. The service itself had undergone a most vital change through its decentralization. All forward signal officers recognized this as the dawn of a new era of usefulness to the pigeon.

No longer would all arrangements have to be made with a remote and inaccessible officer at G.H.Q. whose duties necessarily involved many and repeated journeys to all parts of the French and British fronts. His responsibilities were largely delegated to pigeon officers at the Army and the Corps, and, in many cases, Divisions now had their own lofts allotted to them by the Corps. The roundabout nature of the itinerary of pigeon messages was thus decreased and the " times " improved in like measure. General supervision was still exercised by the O.C. Carrier Pigeon Service at G.H.Q., who acted as adviser to the D.D. Signals of the Armies and the A.D. Signals of the Corps in all matters appertaining to the organization of their own pigeon services.

The value of pigeons had been so demonstrated during stationary warfare that the service had reached very important figures. In one Corps alone, in the Second Army offensive of June, 1917, 532 birds were issued on a single day and 92 operation messages received back. The approximate number of pigeons in use during the offensive on the Somme in 1917 was 12,000 birds.

Times were also much improved, averaging 25 minutes for a message from the front line to the formation headquarters for which it was intended. The speed of the pigeon remained constant, but delivery was hastened by constant attention to the minutest points of organization of the forward service and particularly of the means of despatching the message from the loft to headquarters.

Casualties to pigeons were comparatively high during the battles and in the German offensive on the Belgian coast a mobile loft was hit by a shell and destroyed. At the battle of Messines, also, quite ten per cent. of the birds in action were killed, over 50 being destroyed by a shell which made a direct hit upon a distributing station. On the other hand, their value was demonstrated again and again and the demand was still in excess of the supply. Several hundred messages were passed by this means in every battle, and a reflection of the efficiency and utility of the service was seen in July, 1917, when a further increase of establishment to 120 horse-drawn lofts and six motor mobile lofts was authorized.

Novel features of the employment of the birds in this year were their use by artillery officers for observation purposes, and by the crews of tanks. An unusual incident of training occurred when, in preparation for a coast offensive which never materialized, motor despatch boats were allotted for training a proportion of the birds out to sea.

The pigeon service at this period of the war had far outstripped the forward wireless service in its practical utility. No better example of the mutability of the fortunes of the various branches of the Signal Service can, however, be seen, than the reversal in the importance of these two methods of signalling which took place in the following year.

The use of messenger dogs in the British Army is an interesting instance of the evolution of an entirely new method of forward signalling to meet a particular type of warfare. In September, 1917, definite information was received from German prisoners of the utilization of these animals for message-carrying purposes, and it was rather earlier than this—in the Messines offensive—that the first experiments with " liaison dogs," as they were then called, was carried out by an artillery commander. These initial ventures were so successful that the project was taken up officially and a War Dog School was formed at Shoeburyness under an officer who had long made a hobby and business of training dogs for war purposes and who was an acknowledged expert on this subject. At first the employment of the dogs was permitted to depend upon the will of the individual units who expressed a desire to have them as an extra means of communication, but this haphazard organization could not long survive. The relations between the human and the canine species, though very gratifying from the point of view of civilization, were too amicable for the best results to be obtained without great insistence upon dog discipline. The tendency to make pets of the animals, and the lack of appreciation both of their capabilities and of their limitations, much decreased the value of the dogs as reliable means of *liaison*. Orders were therefore issued in November, 1917, for the centralization of the messenger dog service under the O.C. Carrier Pigeon Service as the senior representative of the most nearly allied branch of the Signal Service. The messenger dogs already with units in the field were withdrawn to a central kennel at Etaples, re-sorted and re-trained. Sectional kennels were then formed at certain Corps headquarters and the messenger dog service re-started on a regular basis.

Reports as to the utility of the dogs varied considerably in tenor during the next few months ; but they were sufficiently successful to permit of the retention of the service. The animals were speedy— averaging in one Division a mile in seven minutes—but their eyes were badly affected by gas and they were reported as somewhat unreliable under heavy shelling. On the other hand, they frequently did valuable service in situations where runners would have been exposed to great risk. They had one or two advantages over pigeons ; they could be used at night, and their training to a new area took one week only as opposed to the three or four weeks necessary to habituate pigeons to a new district. Training was carried out both at home and abroad. At home, the dogs were given a thorough training at the Shoeburyness War Dog School. Here they were accustomed to the noise and smoke of gunfire, and certain conscientious objectors were sorted out and consigned to a handy lethal chamber. On arrival in France, however, it was found—as was often the case, too, with hastily trained Signal Service personnel—that they had forgotten most of what they knew. The Central kennel at Etaples was therefore surrounded with bomb pits and the explosion of the bombs carefully synchronized with the feeding of the dogs, in order to associate the noise with the greatest of their daily pleasures. Thorough training in message-carrying was also carried out at both places, and the new service was in full working order by the spring of 1918. Its usefulness was, however, seriously curtailed by the general aspect of the war in this year. The exploitation of the messenger dog to its full extent is reserved for the intercommunication service in future wars, if position warfare should recur before the present signal prac:ice has been altered out of all recognition.

Runners, again, as in 1916, were the last resource of the forward commander and his signal officer.   Their use was limited by the need for the economy of personnel, by the heavy casualties amongst their ranks, and by the slowness of this method of conveying information. Forward of battalion headquarters, however, runners—and possibly visual—were the only reliable means of signalling in anything approaching moving warfare.   In the very forward areas, runners held their own throughout, and they often formed a valuable adjunct to the Brigade forward route.   Whenever feasible, other means were employed and the signal officer who was reduced to the use of runners only, was compelled to confess to himself that for the time being.he was a failure.   His main preoccupation in such a situation was to organize some alternative means ard take as many of his runners as possible off the route as quickly as he could substitute them by some other means of conveying the information.

When defining the principal advances in signal practice during the battles of 1917, prominence was given to the success which attended the use of the power buzzer and amplifier stations and to two fresh developments of army wireless—the initial attempts to use special " forward " sets, and the use of continuous wave wireless with the artillery.   Even yet, forward wireless had not gained its rightful place as an essential means of communication, though in many situations the wireless stations had dealt with traffic of vital importance. Month after month, propaganda work had been zealously carried on, and the education of the Signal Service in the use and management of forward wireless sets had been steadily pursued.   The decentralization policy, coming as it did at a critical period in the history of signals, much improved the chances of wireless making good.   It occurred too late to have its full effect upon the position battles of this year, but was destined to act as a potent influence for the popularisation of this form of signalling.   Its complete effect was seen in 1918 when, at the time of the March German offensive, wireless in the Divisions was at last in a position to utilize to the full every opportunity given to it.   Then, and only then, was seen the wisdom of the policy persisted in in spite of every obstacle.

Meanwhile, in 1917, two principal developments marked the progress of wireless telegraphy.   The first was the invention of special " forward " sets to supersede the trench set in work for which the latter was not fitted.   The British field wireless set (trench set, spark, 50 watts) was eminently fitted for its normal work as a station for work at Brigade headquarters or Divisional headquarters. In stationary warfare, when time and labour were available, it had often been used with good effect in special situations well forward of either. It could not, however, be called a " mobile " set in the strict sense of the word. It required a party of at least three men to carry it forward, and the accumulators used with it were bulky, easily damaged, and required frequent renewal.

The set could not be used with any likelihood of great success as a subsidiary part of the Brigade forward route in a sustained offensive. In addition, its aerial was fairly conspicuous and limited its use in exposed positions near an ill-defined front line. A conspicuous wireless set was a special mark for enemy attention and as such was anything but popular with headquarter staffs. There was a distinct element of nervousness in their attitude towards it and this was strengthened by the spread of rumours as to the extreme accuracy with which the enemy could locate such a set by means of directional apparatus. Something much less obvious both to the enemy and to our own Staff was required. This need was met by the invention of the " loop " wireless set.*

The essential advantages of the new sets were their lightness and compactness, inconspicuous aerials, and short wave lengths. They were designed to work on one or two low fixed wave lengths (65 and 80 metres) far below those in use by the Royal Flying Corps, the trench sets, or the direction finding sets. They were made in four distinct parts, a front transmitter and receiver and a rear transmitter and receiver. Special canvas " carriers " were issued with the sets and much improved their portability. The front sets were intended for erection well forward—possibly even within direct view of the enemy —and had " ground " aerials for the receiver and a small brass loop fixed to a bayonet for the transmitting aerial. This set could be erected and worked entirely under shelter, except for the projecting ends of the ground aerials which were invisible at a distance of a few yards. The rear set, on the other hand, had a low horizontal aerial supported on tripods. This was less inconspicuous, but much more efficient than the forward aerials. The general range of the sets was from 2,000 to 3,000 yards so that they were well adapted for use between the main stations along the Brigade forward route and also between battalion forward command posts and the Brigade forward station.

Three considerations reduced the practical value of the sets. The first was a certain " individuality " about the earlier sets which was

* Known officially as the " W/T set, forward, spark, 20 watts, B, front and rear." A full technical description of this set was issued as " Technical Instruction No. 4, November, 1917."

Q

the cause of a rather disconcerting uncertainty as to their efficiency. The second was an unduly great dependence upon favourable circumstances and surroundings for their success. The third and deciding factor was a shortage of supply which prevented the universal training of forward signallers in the use of the sets until the opportunity for their employment was almost past. Even in 1917, individual signal units—notably those of the Canadian and Australian Corps, often more hospitable to fresh departures in signalling than the Imperial troops—made conspicuous successes with the new sets. On individual occasions they were the only means of signal communication between forward units for as long as 24 hours at a time. For a short time in the summer of 1918 they almost completely ousted the power buzzer and amplifier sets from the position these had won as a result of their brilliant successes in the 1917 battles. Then, however, mobile warfare set in and the loop sets, in company with other innovations of the position warfare period, were relegated to the bottom of the transport wagons and to relative obscurity.*

The trench wireless set itself underwent little change during this year. Slight technical alterations resulted in a more robust and efficient set, but in its essentials it remained unchanged, awaiting its opportunity in the future. For a short time, these sets achieved a certain popularity with the artillery who were beginning to turn their attention to wireless for observation purposes. From this position, however, spark wireless was quickly driven by its half-brother, continuous wave wireless, which was just beginning a rapid and extraordinary career as applied to Army purposes.

Its great advantages over spark wireless were an extreme selectivity, an extraordinary efficiency which gave altogether disproportionate ranges for the same power, and, bound up with the latter trait, a consequent inconspicuousness of aerial which was a particularly great asset at forward observation posts.

These advantages were, however, for some time, counter-balanced by equally great disadvantages, though fortunately disadvantages which could be gradually overcome. The sets were extremely delicate, so delicate in fact that until 1917 none had been evolved which were capable of surviving the exigeant conditions of service in the field. The work also was technical in the highest degree, for the most simple sets required delicate and careful adjustment. On the early stations, the C.W. operator needed to be considerably more than a good manipulator of the key. There were literally dozens of ways in which the sets might go wrong, and some of these faults, at least, he must be capable of diagnosing and repairing. These earlier sets were gradually improved upon, and then C.W. wireless came further and further within the sphere of practical politics,

---

* A few Divisions used these sets throughout the advance in 1918.

though until the Armistice its use in the forward area was practically confined to the artillery.*

In June, 1917, two continuous wave wireless sets were in constant communication between a Corps H.A. headquarters at Ecorves and a Corps observation post at Bailleul—a distance of 12,000 yards. The forward aerial was 3 ft. in height and 25 yards in length ; the height of the rear aerial at such a distance from the front line is, of course, immaterial. For some time when telephone communication was unsatisfactory, the stations were working continuously and handled from 50 to 60 messages daily. This was a landmark in the history of Army wireless but it was soon paralleled by similar exploits in other Corps and other Armies. For a time, some Armies reported satisfactorily on the new wireless, others unfavourably ; it was largely a question of the personality and technical bias of the wireless officer with the Army. Continuous wave wireless had, however, come to stay, and in December, 1917, orders were sent home for 882 sets, chiefly for the use of the artillery. At the same time, consideration was being given to the use of similar sets for anti-aircraft signal communication in which, as already indicated, direct communication was essential. Sound-ranging sections also put in a claim, and, indeed, there sprang up at once several ways in which this type of signalling might become of·paramount importance.

Probably the most striking success of all the alternative methods of communication in 1917 fell to the lot of the previously despised power buzzer and amplifier. The first suggestion of the utilization of earth induction telegraphy is found in the early experiments which were conducted at the Signal Service Training Centre at about the time in 1915† when the overhearing problem first became acute. Signals were transmitted through the earth by means of buzzers and were picked up on an ordinary telephone receiver connected to widely separated earths. The first practical apparatus used in the British' Army was contrived at Vermelles in the area held by the dismounted cavalry Division in January, 1916. Here, two French earth conduction transmitters were installed in the forward trenches. They were hand-driven alternators giving a high note which was picked up in special listening sets which had just been introduced, also borrowed from the French Army. These represented the first type of power buzzer, but they were not persisted with for several reasons. They were unwieldy and there was difficulty in working them in

* This was a matter of policy. After the Armistice, continuous wave wireless commenced to be used for general intercommunication purposes in the lower formations.

† Experiments in earth induction telegraphy were also carried out by the 163rd Brigade R.F.A. while training in England in July, 1915. The experiments resulted in good communication over distances of 1,000 to 2,000 yards and were referred to France by F.W.4a.

the confined space of the forward dug-outs ; but, above all, they were unfavourably reported upon on account of the likelihood of their being overheard.   The overhearing problem was so acute at the time that all means of signalling which frankly depended upon overhearing for their success could not be expected to find favour.

It was, perhaps, natural that the French should take a prominent part in the development of this type of signalling.   Their engineers were the inventors of the original valve listening set.   It was on their front that intensive warfare reached its first great climax in the battles at Vimy and at Verdun.   Their idea of forward signals also differed considerably from the British, their system being directed much more towards getting back information from the front line and less towards the conveyance forward of orders and instructions.   In other words, the Staff, dealing with a fully-trained army of long standing, felt they could afford to leave more discretion to the forward commanders than could the Staff of the less mature British armies.   One-way working from front to rear, therefore, presented many more attractions to the French Signal Service than to the British.

It was from the French, also, that the next step in the development of earth induction telegraphy came.   This was the introduction to the British Army of the French " Parleur," which was the earlier equivalent of the British power buzzer.   The possibilities of this large buzzer, worked by accumulators and with short earth leads, 100 to 150 yards in length, were at once seen and in 1916 it was generally adopted throughout our own Army.   A proportion of the available listening sets were set aside to receive the messages sent by this means from selected forward spots and in the battles on the Somme and the Ancre these instruments gave valuable, if inconsistent, results.   They were on the whole unfavourably reported upon, however, for several reasons.   The buzzers themselves were fairly robust instruments, but the accumulators needed a certain amound of care and had to be carried in an upright position.   The signallet stumbling along in the dusk across shell-pitted, wire-infester country, frequently arrived at his destination with his power buzzer in order, but with accumulators quite dry, having distributed the acid between his clothes, his other equipment, and the ground over which he had passed.

In addition, geological considerations intimately affected the efficiency of the sets.   Earth conductivity varied with geological strata, with the physiographic relief of the country, and with the amount of shelling to which the ground had been exposed.   No two situations were alike.   Carefully co-ordinated experiments were necessary before general rules for the use of the sets could be issued. Again, the earths, although less vulnerable than lines, were still vulnerable to a certain extent, even when they were laid in trenches.

Finally, the British staffs and British officers generally had an ineradicable dislike to one-way signalling and would only use it as a last resource, while the signaller himself, sitting at his key and tapping out " S.O.S. K23 c4, 5 " or some equivalent shibboleth, felt no conviction that his message was getting through. Only occasionally did the shriek and whine of friendly shells, passing overhead, point the moral of his message and give him pleasing proof of his value in the military machine.

The winter of 1916–1917 was, therefore, devoted to experiment with the new apparatus. In December, 1916, an order was issued by certain armies that ten first-class signallers in every Brigade should be withdrawn from infantry and trained with the power buzzer. At the same time, the protection of the stations was improved and it was found that the best results were obtained if the forward earths were buried to a depth of 6 ft. This could easily be accomplished with comparatively little labour by an army accustomed to burying cable on a large scale, and, with the power buzzer established in a deep dug-out and the earths buried 6 ft. deep, the station was practically shell-proof. Another expression of the same policy showed itself in the increase in length of the rear earths to 300 or 350 yards, thus making possible the use of still shorter bases—60 or 70 yards—for the forward station.

The difficulty of one-way working was also overcome to some extent by the invention of special amplifier sets and their provision in large quantities. The opening of the 1917 campaigns thus found the earth induction set in a much stronger position than it had held in the previous year.

This was soon reflected in the reports of signal officers and of regimental officers, too. Again and again, it was recorded that, when all other communication had gone, power buzzer and amplifier sets had bridged the gap until better conditions returned. Most of the occasions were for a few hours only and the number of messages handled was of course relatively small. At Bullecourt, however, in May, 1917, during the attacks on the Hindenburg line, the classical instance occurred which illustrated at its best the value of this means of signalling under favourable circumstances. For several days, the shelling had been so intense that no ground or air communication was possible between the Australians in the Hindenburg line east of Bullecourt and their supports. Wireless aerials would not stand up ; lines were blasted off the face of the earth, runners left the trenches only to be blown to pieces, the supply of pigeons could not be maintained. Deep down in the tunnels and caverns beneath the line, however, were installed two power buzzers and amplifiers. With their bases securely hidden in the tunnels and with the sets themselves under many feet of headcover, they remained inviolate. For several days after the line was occupied these sets kept up con-

stant communication with other sets further to the rear, and gave
warning of several impending counter-attacks which were successfully
repulsed. At the same time, lateral communication with the 7th
Division to the west of Bullecourt was kept up, though the village
itself was at that time in the enemy possession. It was a striking
instance of the triumph of a highly specialized form of intercommunication in the peculiar situation for which it was designed.

After this and other less dramatic but useful successes, the power
buzzer achieved some degree of popularity and was used to a great
extent as part of the normal intercommunication system in position
warfare. In 1918 it was further improved by the issue of a combined
set which made the two-way station more compact and portable.
During this year, however, the " forward " wireless sets replaced it
in the affections of many units, including the Australian Divisions
with which it had scored its most notable success. With the passing
of position warfare the earth induction set became so much lumber
to be carried with the signal companies, but in its day it had been
of vital use on many occasions and had well justified the time, money,
and labour spent on its evolution, and the personnel employed in
working it.

CHAPTER XIII.

# THE SURPRISE BATTLE OF CAMBRAI AND THE WINTER OF 1917–1918.

## SYNOPSIS.

First Battle of Cambrai.—Signals in the Surprise Attack.—Cavalry Line System in Addition to Command and Artillery System.—Use of Area Personnel.— " Camouflage " Line System of Poled and Trench Multicore Cable.—Effect of Tanks on the Line System.—Precautions to Ensure Secrecy.—Testing with Galvanometers and Fullerphones.—Alternative Methods.—Problems Caused by the Depth of the Advance.—Cavalry Signals.—Decreased Telephone Facilities.—Congested Transport Prevents Line Stores from Getting Forward.—Twisted Cable in Mobilization Equipment.—Cable Dumps.—Visual : Two-way Working.—Wireless.—Other Methods of Forward Signalling.—Brigade and Battalion Signals.—Use of Enemy's Lines.— Pigeons and Runners.—Stabilisation of the Situation.—Consolidation of the Signal System.—The German Counter Attack.—S.S. 191, like S.S. 148, Ignores Possibility of a Retreat.—Emergency Divisional Route Saves the Situation.—W/T Very Useful. —Signal Personnel Engaged in Fighting.—Guards Division Counter-Attack.— Lessons of the Battle.—History of Tank Signals.—Evolution of Tank Wireless.— A.D. Signals, Tank Corps.—Trench Warfare Again.—Increase of Enemy Bombing Causes Modification of Rear Routes and Signal Offices.—Second Great Re-organization of the A.S.S.—No. 5 Section of a Divisional Signal Company.—Strength of Signal Service and Economy of Personnel.—Army Conference Considers Possibility of Retrenchment.

The action in November, 1917, now known as the battle of Cambrai, although not carried out on as large a scale as the summer offensives and not an unqualified success, had several features of particular interest from the point of view of the Army Signal Service. It was in the nature of a surprise attack long thought out by the attacking side, and it was this feature of the battle which gave to the signal preparation for the action and the signal communication during the attack a character altogether unusual. The principal characteristic of the assault was an entire absence of artillery preparation, the wire cutting, usually assigned to the latter, being carried out by the organized advance of large bodies of tanks in the wake of which the infantry were to follow. In the main, everything went as originally planned, and the striking Divisions came within an ace of breaking through the German defences and permitting the cavalry to pass through and operate along the enemy's lines of communication.

In considering the signals of the battle of Cambrai, therefore, three problems which were presented to the Signal Service for solution require particular attention. These three were :—(1) The preparation of a " secret " system of intercommunication before the battle; (2) Tank signals and the effect of the tanks on line communication ; (3) The unusual speed and depth of the advance, some Brigades moving forward five miles in a few hours.

Undoubtedly the characteristic feature of the signal preparations for the battle was the laying down of a complete system of overground lines to accommodate the extra formations and units which it was proposed to move into the area immediately before the date fixed for the commencement of the action. The attack was carried out by seven Divisions in line, while two others on the left flank were engaged in subsidiary attempts to breach the Hindenburg line. If the initial assault was successful, the cavalry were to pass through the infantry Divisions resting upon their objectives and raid the enemy's communications on a huge scale.

Preparations involved the erection or laying of 13,000 miles of wire in rather less than a month. It was clear that the most careful organization was necessary, if the line system was to be ready by November 20th, the date fixed for the attack. The difficulties of the Signal Service were also increased by the necessity for strict secrecy which would naturally prevent the thorough testing of the new lines according to common practice and would also hinder the use of the circuits by the newly-arrived units prior to zero hour.

A complete system with one main forward route for each Division in the line was planned on the principles laid down in the new Staff Manual for Intercommunication in the Field (S.S. 191). Owing to the necessity for secrecy and the need for hurry, however, buried cable was prohibited and some other means had to be devised. Safety had to be sacrificed to speed and secrecy, and it was decided to rely entirely upon poled cable in the rear areas. In those areas so far forward as to invite enemy observation, the main aerial routes disappeared, being split in half and continued as trench cable to two cable-heads on each Divisional front.

For the building of the system the personnel available consisted of the Corps signal companies and attached cable and airline sections with the exception of men already employed on the maintenance of the existing system. In addition, were certain area parties supplied by the Army signal company and such small parties as could be spared by the signal companies of the Divisions in the line and those which would later be called upon to take up their battle positions in the area. Each small Divisional party was under a senior officer— usually the second in command of the signal company or the Divisional artillery captain—and formed the nucleus of the party working on what was to become their own system. The exceptional importance and urgency of the work was fully realized, and both Army, Corps and Divisional personnel worked long hours during the day, while at night special parties tested each portion of the system that had been laid during the previous day.

For the rear portion of the system lead-covered cables were used, and the routes were poled as far forward as possible. One obstacle to the quick building of the rear routes consisted in the fact that the paper-core cables were too heavy to be carried in lengths of more than 200 yards, and a large amount of work which could only be carried out by skilled jointers was thus required. Forward, where trench cable had to be resorted to, armoured cables were used and a portion of these were laid in existing open traffic-proof ditches one foot deep. Other portions were laid along the bottom of communication trenches and yet others along the ground. The latter was camouflaged as much as possible by taking advantage of hedges, ditches and tracks, and does not seem to have attracted any undue attention from the enemy. It was, however, cut on many occasions by the normal enemy shelling and the necessity for re-laying damaged sections made it very difficult to complete the forward position of the system in the time allotted. Another great difficulty was the damage done by the tanks proceeding to their hiding places during the last few nights before zero, and from their hiding places to the rallying point immediately before the attack was to begin.

This difficulty had been anticipated to some extent, but for two reasons the action taken was not altogether successful. The special crossing places of poled cable were not made high enough to clear supply tanks or tanks loaded with fascines for crossing moats and streams.* In addition, through lack of *liaison* between Tanks and Signal Service, the former often failed to use the crossing places provided for them. This was in part due to lack of information as to the existence and location of these local buries and overhead crossings, partly due to tanks getting lost and wandering about the country indiscriminately during the night, partly also to a failure to take into consideration the limitations of the 1917 tanks. Whatever the reason, however, the result was very serious. Poled cable of normal height was caught up in the upper works of the tanks and scattered broadcast over the country. Poles were snapped and cables torn apart. Ground cables were churned into the earth and the insulation ripped off them for many yards. If the lines were not completely interrupted, they were rendered useless for speaking and could only be used with difficulty for buzzing. In one case, even, a tank was propelled straight over a Divisional cable head, crushing in the inefficient shelter which had been the best that could be provided in the short time available, and destroying the connecting frame inside.

Where damage occurred during the initial concentration of the tanks in the area, it was, of course, possible to remedy it, though much extra strain was thrown upon the signal personnel responsible for the perfection of the system. Such breaks were, however, recurrent throughout the operations and the damage done by the tanks during the forming-up period immediately preceding zero hour and during the battle itself, was much more serious and, indeed, often irreparable.

---

* A height of 15 ft. was required for the former and 20 ft. for the latter. As may be imagined, the building of a large number of crossings on this scale in the forward area presented difficulties almost impossible to overcome. Local buries were a possible solution of the difficulty, but time was not available in this instance.

Thus, the first great lesson of the surprise battle which involved the use of massed tanks was the necessity for closer *liaison* between the Signal Service and the Tank Corps. The lesson was driven well home to a distracted Signal Service during the next ten days and it needed no repetition. The result was seen in certain recommendations made for the modification of the Tank Corps signal units.

The new line system was to be superimposed upon the old one and a feature of the preparations on which great stress was laid, both by the Intelligence Staff and the Signal Service, was that all forward traffic right up to the opening of the battle must be carried on over the lines of the old system. It was, of course, impossible to keep traffic down entirely to normal, and the original Divisions in the line reported their " operations " telegrams as rising from a normal average of between 500 and 700 to 1,600 and even 2,000 messages in the 24 hours. Every effort was made to keep down the number of messages, however, and the above total is not excessive when it is realized that no less than four Divisions were accommodated on the lines of one, and that, in addition, the essential portion of the work of many extra units was also included.

In order to ensure secrecy, the offensive signal system was divided into two distinct parts, the boundary line being the recognized limit of enemy overhearing—3,000 yards behind the front line. At this position, all the more forward routes were disconnected and, while the rear portion was taken into use immediately upon its completion, the forward part beyond this line was not employed at all until " Z " day. New units arriving in the area were allotted their lines but not allowed to connect until just before zero. The use of telephones forward of Brigade headquarters was absolutely forbidden except for artillery observation, and observers were instructed to take their telephones up with them and to remove them immediately their observation was completed.

In the meantime, it was necessary that some special means of testing the forward system should be devised. It was out of the question that it should be left untested. Not only must a thorough initial test be made immediately the cables were laid, but the tests must be frequent and repeated. Breaks were constantly occurring both in the rear and the forward portions. Tanks, shells, and the normal traffic of a congested area, played havoc with the lines night after night. Shells continued their work in the daytime also. It was equally out of the question that the system should be tested by the normal means—lineman's telephone and buzzer. That would at once betray to the enemy the presence of a greatly reinforced line system opposite to this portion of his lines. A knowledge of the presence of the lines would not only nullify the precautions taken to restrict their use, but would convert those very precautions into a further source of suspicion.

To realize the danger of this, it is only necessary to refer back to one or two examples already given in this narrative, of deductions made by our own Intelligence Staff—and even by the personnel of listening posts—from similar indiscretions on the part of the enemy.

A suitable compromise was, however, effected and the whole of the forward line system was tested, each section as it was completed, by means of galvanometers and fullerphones used with the minimum possible battery power. Both these instruments involved the use of small direct line currents only, and there was, therefore, no danger of giving anything away. A final test was carried out before the lines were taken into use on " Y-Z " night and proved that the work of both construction and maintenance parties had been conscientious and thorough in the extreme. Very few pairs existed which were not through. Any notable exceptions to the rule could be traced to specific damage to the routes at the last moment by shells, traffic, or tanks. Zero day broke to show a completed system with ample circuits for the essential needs of all Divisions, the cavalry, and other formations and units normally foreign to the area.

The demands of the tanks and artillery could be catered for upon an adequate scale and the system resembled that for an ordinary position warfare battle, with two significant exceptions. It was composed practically entirely of overground lines and was, therefore, particularly vulnerable. It was of somewhat slender dimensions and, therefore, it involved the elimination of many of the less important subscribers usually accommodated upon the Divisional and Corps telephone exchanges. The R.F.C., Casualty Clearing Stations, and anti-aircraft organizations, all had their intercommunication considerably reduced. Such officers as the C.R.E., D.A.D.O.S., and A.D.M.S. of Divisions, and all purely administrative units except those immediately concerned with the supply of rations and ammunition, were forced off the main telephone system and were obliged to make shift temporarily with less facilities. In other words, an approximation to mobile warfare conditions had been brought about by an entirely different set of circumstances. Later on in the battle, telephone facilities were to be still further cut down, this time by semi-mobile warfare itself.

The relative vulnerability of the battle line system made the provision of alternative communication more necessary than ever before. Efforts were made to duplicate the lines as far back as Divisional headquarters with chains of visual stations and with wireless. Visual schemes were formulated by Divisions and co-ordinated by Corps. Wireless sets were used as far as possible to reinforce the signal system between Divisional and Brigade headquarters and forward of this a good system of power buzzer and amplifier communication was planned. At the same time, arrangements were made to replace the rear cables as early as possible with airline routes, though these could not be erected before " Z " day for fear of arousing enemy suspicion. Forward dumps of airline stores of all descriptions were made and cable dumps from which Divisions might be fed in case of a far-reaching advance were also a marked feature of the very thorough signal preparations.

By the morning of November 20th, the day fixed for the attack, the whole pre-arranged scheme of signal communications was completed. Already tanks were playing havoc with the forward lines while proceeding to their rallying points, but this was a development which could not be entirely countered under the circumstances of the action. Circuits were everywhere tested through and the signal staff of the attacking Divisions had taken over. All units and formations who had been allotted a place on the main system were connected up and awaiting the raising of the interdict of silence. For the first time, signal secrecy and silence had been organized on a huge scale with decisive success and the result showed that little if any knowledge of the forthcoming attack had leaked through to the enemy. Certainly signal restrictions had been so efficiently supervised and so loyally carried out that indiscretions had been practically eliminated. The signal preparations for the battle of Cambrai, indeed, had proved that such indiscreet use of buzzer and telephone as had been prevalent in the British Army for so long, was so unnecessary as to border upon the criminal. They also proved conclusively that Staffs could do efficient work with less telephone facilities than they had been accustomed to have given them. This was to be seen still more decisively in the battle itself, for after a deep advance, speaking on many of the long cable lines became practically impossible. Message traffic increased till it averaged between 1,200 and 1,500 messages a day in single Divisions, but telephone conversation was far less common than in the position warfare of the previous summer. The effect of this lesson was not lost. It was to be further emphasized in the spring, and both experiences had a distinct bearing on a development of Staff methods which made for greater efficiency with still less telephone communication in the summer and autumn offensives of the advance in 1918.

At zero hour on November 20th, the barrage opened, and, preceded by battalions of tanks, the British infantry advanced to the attack. From the first, the result was never in doubt, and, on almost the whole front affected, the enemy resistance was quickly overcome and his defences captured. By 1030 hours, the Hindenburg reserve line had been overrun, the general advance to the final objectives had begun, and the cavalry was moving up behind the infantry. By the end of the day, the advance had reached a depth of four and a half miles over a wide front.

The signal units with the Corps and the attacking Divisions were faced on this day with a problem quite different from those of the position battles of the previous summer. Enemy resistance had been short and his guns had been captured or forced to withdraw early in the day. It was no longer a case of achieving as good a signal system as was possible under heavy retaliatory fire. Cable wagons could be used freely and there were no restrictions on the use of poled cable beyond that of the difficulty of transport of the supplies required. This situation, however, satisfactory as it was, presented special problems for solution, the main difficulties being the supply of cable to the Divisions in the line and the damage done to the line system by the tanks. To this must also be added a considerable amount of destruction of the same system by the cavalry in their advance towards the front line and still more in their subsequent withdrawal.

It was the first occasion on which an attempt had been made to utilize cavalry on a large scale since the battle of Loos in 1915. For their use, a separate line system had been reserved. This consisted of two forward routes, one laid by the cavalry Corps themselves, the other carried out by Third Army. The former consisted of four pairs of poled twisted " D5 " cable and this gave satisfactory service during the short time it was required. The second was laid from a tank but was experimental in its nature and was never through satisfactorily. The only novel feature of the cavalry signal communications as compared with those of the infantry Divisions was, of course, the use of wireless sets of higher power and greater range than the trench sets usual in forward work. The pack wireless stations with the cavalry Divisions and the Crossley lorry set with the cavalry Corps headquarters were in constant communication throughout the operations and imparted a distinctly novel tone to the sound of the operations as heard by the Intelligence stations. After the failure of the mounted action and the withdrawal of the main body of the cavalry, such formations and units as took part in the later fighting played the rôle of dismounted troops and were accommodated with signals of the ordinary type used by the infantry Divisions.

During the initial advance, lines were extended from cable head by cable wagon, extra transport being used to carry forward the light hop-poles which were necessary if the system was to be at all safe. One poled cable route of two or three pairs was carried forward on each Brigade front and little difficulty was found in laying these initial lines.

Two troubles soon made themselves felt, however, and between them effectually prevented any large amount of telephone traffic between the Divisions and Brigades in these first two or three days of the offensive. The poled cable was strongly built and, as in the preparatory system, special crossings were made which were intended to be tank-proof. The tanks, however, paid little attention to these crossings and their lateral movements across the front from flank to flank when carrying out a " rally " were so frequent that the lines were carried away and torn to pieces almost as fast as they were laid. It was impossible to build lines which would be tank-proof throughout their length. When a tank ran into a poled route or even a ground cable line, it meant—not the destruction of the short section actually run into or over—but the dislocation of the whole line and often the complete tearing away of several hundred yards. Until the tanks ceased their movements or kept strictly to the special crossing places made for them, telephone communication was intermittent at best and often impossible.

The movements of large bodies of cavalry across the open country which characterises the Cambrai district was also destructive of any routes but those suspended well above the height of a mounted man. The height of the routes was, of course, dependent on the means of suspension and it was only in the few places where trees afforded opportunity of keeping the lines well up that this trouble could be avoided. For the first two or three days, until the situation settled down, all the available linemen and cable detachments were engaged in continual attempts to replace lines which had thus been swept away. It was not until the tanks ceased to take part in the fighting on a large scale and the cavalry had retired out of the area of conflict, that the Division-Brigade routes could be relied upon.

Another difficulty which confronted the Divisional signal company was a direct result of the narrow frontage held by Divisions and the depth of the advance. The authorized scale of equipment of the cable sections and No. 1 section of a Divisional Signal Company had recently been altered from single to twisted " D5 " cable. This alteration had been caused by the prevalence of metallic circuits which was one of the principal precautions against enemy overhearing. It incidentally decreased the cable carried by each cable wagon from ten miles to five miles of route and this had an unfortunate effect on the present occasion. The cable detachment endeavouring to advance with the Brigade to which it had been attached had to lay at least two pairs if the route was to approach in any degree to the ideals of position warfare. His available cable supply permitted the erection of two miles of such route. For any further extension fresh supplies were required, and it was almost impossible to get forward supplies along the few congested roads, each crowded with the transport of one or two Divisions, and closed for several hours in each day for necessary repairs. Thus, one of the most important lessons learnt by the Signal Service in this action was the necessity for dumps of a good type of light cable—twisted " D3 " for choice—well forward in the fighting area. Another lesson, based on the same experiences, was the advisability of a certain measure of priority being given to signal transport engaged in feeding the forward detachments and sections with cable and other essential supplies.

At the same time, some doubt was thrown on the newly-adopted policy of replacing single by twisted cable on the cable wagons. These were essentially likely to be used in fairly far-reaching advances only. Under such circumstances the maximum length of cable line was required and overhearing precautions were less necessary.*

One other result of the long twisted cables was that they made speaking very faint and often impossible. It was this fact which caused an unusual proportion of the Staff work to be sent over the lines as message traffic. Conversation was difficult and the energy expended upon it could usually be used to better advantage in the framing of orders and instructions in the form of messages which were dealt with by sounder, fullerphone, or in the last resort by buzzer. The overhead lines were pushed ahead by Corps and Army as rapidly as possible, but here, again, congestion along the roads prevented a good speed being maintained.

The trouble with the Divisional line routes had, of course, the effect of much increasing the importance of the subsidiary methods of communication. Visual schemes were in existence with well sited stations right back to the immediate neighbourhood of Divisional headquarters. The country in general was open and eminently suited for the employment of visual on a large scale. Only in such places as were heavily wooded, was it impossible to use this method of signalling over long distances. The disorganization and demoralization of the enemy once more made two-way working possible. The principal limit to the use of visual, where lines were not working, was often set by the disinclination of regimental commanders and Staffs to make full use of the stations provided.

The same drawback operated most seriously against the achievement of a full measure of success with the excellent chain of wireless communication that was also a feature of the signal system of most Divisions. Wireless was, indeed, used to a greater extent than ever before and was perhaps the main means of bridging the gap between Divisions and Brigades during the frequent intervals when the cable was down. A comparison of the totals of messages passing over an uninterrupted line system, with those dealt with by wireless stations keeping communication between the same headquarters when the lines were down, is most instructive. Some allowance must be made for the more cumbersome procedure of the latter method, but the totals of messages sent are even then ridiculously out of proportion. It was very rarely that the wireless sets, even on such favourable occasions as the present, were worked to full capacity, while it was seldom indeed that the signal office did not contain a pile of urgent

---

* In the advances of the summer and autumn of 1918, twisted " D3 " wound on ordinary cable wagon drums was used by some Divisions with great success. The advantages of twisted cable were retained and the length which could be carried on a single drum was rather more than in the case of single " D5 " cable.

messages awaiting the attention of the Morse operators even when the line system was working at its best. Wireless stations reported doing 16 and 20 messages a day and this was a great improvement on their record during previous operations. The waiving of field cipher regulations, however, would have much increased their usefulness. Officers would not bother to encipher messages, and if the wireless staff had to do so themselves it enormously decreased the speed of working of the stations. The relaxation of cipher and code regulations was clearly pointed to if this means of signalling was to be of full use in future mobile operations. In this action, its importance had been clearly demonstrated, while, at the same time, its usefulness had been crippled.

Power buzzers were useful during the initial stages of the attack, but the phase when they were valuable was a very short one. In an attack with a depth of $4\frac{1}{2}$ miles their range was hopelessly outdistanced. Later, when the advance was slowed down, they could not be obtained from the Brigades to which they had originally been allotted. In some cases they could not be traced at all. The provision of accumulators also had not been organized on a sufficient scale. Another lesson of the Cambrai advance was that this must be arranged under Divisional auspices, if these instruments were to be of use during the fleeting phases of the action when the situation was momentarily favourable to them.

Of the various message-carrying agencies, motor cyclists, mounted orderlies, and runners, were all employed between Division and Brigade during the Cambrai operations. The roads were so congested and in such bad repair that the motor cyclists in some Divisions were of little use forward of Divisional headquarters. Mounted orderlies had been allotted to the Divisions, but not in sufficient numbers, and extra men had to be borrowed from the cavalry. In at least one Division a chain of runners was organized on the forward route between Brigade headquarters and Advanced Divisional headquarters and under the peculiar circumstances of the action this unusual step was a success.

Forward of Brigade headquarters, the enemy's line system was utilized to some extent to give line communication, but this again was much hindered by the action of our own troops. The system was much damaged by our own barrage and still more by the tanks which accompanied the advancing troops. In spite of this, however, lines were improvised, partly of our own field cable and partly of German cable, though the efforts of the forward parties were neutralized to a great extent by well-meaning infantry officers and men who cut British and German cables alike, in the effort to prevent information passing forward to the enemy. The cutting of British field cables might have been prevented by an organized attempt to familiarize the infantry with the types of cable in use by the British Signal Service, these being easily distinguished from the German field cables by anyone who gave them more than a cursory glance. The armoured cables of the two Armies were more alike, but even these could have been distinguished in great measure by the insulation tape wrapped round the outside of the German types. As it was, however, all cables were alike to an infantry intent only on doing as much damage as possible to the enemy circuits. Not only were they cut, but, with praiseworthy but annoying thoroughness, the severed ends were dragged and tangled into snarls which defied the British linemen.

Yet another lesson learnt during this most instructive battle was that enemy airline should not be interfered with at all by uninformed personnel, since it is extremely unlikely that the preliminary shelling has left a single wire continuous. Enemy cable, if touched at all, should be cut and left in position, so that the least work would be required should our own Signal Service desire to reconstruct portions of the enemy cable routes.

Where enemy lines could not be used, circuits of twisted or single "D2" cable were laid by the British forward parties but these lines were not immune from the attentions of cavalry and tanks and were much more exposed to damage from enemy shells than the rearward lines. Altogether, from the 20th to the 23rd—when the situation stiffened a good deal—forward intercommunication was mainly by runner, other subsidiary means being much less in evidence than usual.

All available wireless was concentrated upon the Divisional-Brigade routes, power buzzers and amplifiers had gone astray in some cases and been left behind in others, messenger dogs were out of the question in such mobile warfare, and pigeons were of less use than was usually the case.

There were two reasons which acted against the usual efficiency of the forward pigeon service : (1) The secrecy and short period of preparation prevented the concentration of lofts in the neighbourhood in good time to train the birds to their new area, and this decreased the available supply of birds ; (2) the failure of forward units to return pigeon baskets, and the congestion of the forward roads, practically confined the effective use of pigeons to the earlier days of the battle.

The initial advance of the 20th and 21st of November was followed by a period of exploitation when local attacks with special limited objectives were carried out in the attempt to widen the salient occupied by the British troops. Increasing enemy resistance had slowed down the advance to a pace normal to previous position battles. The elimination of the cavalry and the comparative quiescence of the tanks combined with the increasing intensity of the artillery fire to give an aspect to the later stages of the battle which caused a resemblance to the battles of Arras and Ypres. Buried cable on a

R

large scale was not possible, and all efforts of the Signal Service were directed towards the consolidation of the existing poled and ground cable system and to the perfection of the alternative schemes of intercommunication. A useful variation of the normal forward Divisional system at this stage of the battle was a lateral connection between the forward end of the two Brigade forward routes so that Divisions were working upon loops of ground or poled cable. This doubled the security of the forward line communication for, while breaks in one " leg " or other of the loop were common, it was seldom that simultaneous breaks on both sides of either Brigade effected a complete severance of line communication.

During the 27th and 28th of November, the situation remained unchanged with maintenance increasing in difficulty under a gradually swelling volume of enemy fire. On November 29th, the enemy gunfire increased to the hurricane bombardment which preceded the great counter-attacks to the north and south of the salient which had been bitten deep into his line. The attack to the north presents few features of special interest from the point of view of the Signal Service. What little progress the enemy made was strictly local in its effects and signal communication was as good as could be expected over an overground system of lines under heavy artillery fire. Incessant activity of the maintenance parties secured at least intermittent line communication. Wireless, power buzzer and visual all helped to reinforce this.

To the south, however, the situation was much more grave, and at one time it looked as if retreat might become general and far-reaching. Here, the Signal Service was faced with new experiences and suffered heavy casualties. Following a whirlwind bombardment, masses of the enemy surprised the British front line posts and, passing over them in their stride and without serious interruption to the speed of their advance, penetrated deeply and rapidly toward Divisional headquarters. S.S. 148, and its successor S.S. 191, did not legislate for a retreat and the signal practice to meet the new conditions had to be improvised. Forward lines were cut in all directions, and at one time the fate of the Brigade and Divisional headquarters of more than one Division was in doubt. The forward signal system was perforce abandoned to the Germans and the rear system was largely destroyed with one significant exception.

The exception which proved the salvation of the situation was a two-pair emergency route of armoured cable which had been laid through Gouzeaucourt by a Division as an alternative to the multicore cable route provided for it by the Corps. This route providentially remained uncut throughout the operations and became the main channel of communication for no less than three Divisions. It was over this cable—at that time partly in the area occupied by the advancing German infantry—that the messages passed which apprised the Corps of the urgency of the situation and resulted eventually in the counter-attack by the Guards Division which restored the situation. On no single occasion during the whole war, was the value of an alternative route demonstrated in such a striking manner. The line passed in and out of German hands, but was overlooked by the enemy and remained through for two critical days.

By the date of the German counter-attack the pigeon service had been largely reconstituted, but the 29th was misty and birds were much hampered in their flight by the fog. Many were away for several hours and the situation was complicated on the most critical portion of the front by the necessity of withdrawing a loft to prevent its capture by the enemy who had already overrun the headquarters of one Division. Visual was also interfered with to a great extent by the same mist, and the weather conditions on part of the front included a snowfall which made it difficult to locate breaks in the lines.

The alternative method which was most useful of all was wireless. The aerials of Brigade stations were shot away, but were re-erected again and again and urgent messages dealt with in considerable numbers. In the emergency, code and cipher regulations were to a great extent swept away. Extra wireless stations were rushed up to the supposed locality of missing Brigades and by this means the signal system was largely reconstructed without the use of lines, which were, however, laid as soon as correct locations were obtained

One interesting aspect of the situation as it affected signals was the absorption of a large proportion of signal personnel into the fighting line where they shared the fortunes of their infantry comrades. A particular instance which is deserving of record is that of a forward wireless station serving a battalion headquarters which was surrounded by the enemy. One of the operators remained in the dug-out to destroy the apparatus, the remaining two took their rifles and helped to man an adjoining trench. One was killed and one was captured. The third man, having thoroughly destroyed his station, joined the infantry and retreated with them fighting a rearguard action for 24 hours. He remained with them until the company was relieved, when he proceeded to join the signal company to which he belonged. It was such emergencies, occurring from time to time, which gave Signal Service personnel an opportunity of showing that they possessed the same qualities in action as the men of other fighting branches of the Army. The maintaining of lines under shell fire, the reckless riding of motor cycles over crowded slippery roads, the manning of insufficiently protected visual stations or signal offices, all called for courage of a high order. None had, however, the same effect of drawing the Signal Service nearer in sympathy to the infantry as such isolated instances when the wearers of the blue and white armbands threw aside their technical instruments and took up rifle and bomb to do their share of direct damage to a triumphant enemy. It is to the credit of the Signal Service that similar instances can be quoted whenever opportunity for such action occurred. It is equally to its credit that so few instances are recorded of unnecessary fighting by forward signal parties during an advance.

The experiences of the Guards Divisional signal company in the counter-attack which restored the situation, merely emphasized the lessons already learnt in the earlier phases of the battle. Special attention had been paid to mobility. All surplus stores and exchanges, many magneto telephones, all power buzzers and amplifiers, and all sounders but two, had been left behind before the company took over the signal office from which the signal system of the advance was extended. Here is seen the result of the experience of the previous few days. For almost the first time since the beginning of position warfare a signal company went into action stripped for battle. The result was a skeleton but highly efficient system in which none but essential needs were accommodated. The only difficulty proved to be in the moving of personnel for advanced signal offices. The men were actually taken forward in the 30-cwt. lorry. Had the roads been too bad to permit the lorry to be used, G.S. wagons would have had to be employed and the establishment of the signal offices would have lagged behind the general advance. The best solution was pointed out as the addition of a box car to the signal company. A further problem which was indicated as likely to arise in the event of an extended advance was the impossibility under present circumstances of keeping touch between Divisional artillery headquarters and the artillery Brigades. This had been met in some Divisions by the attachment of a cable detachment from No. 1 section for artillery use only. The place of this detachment in the Divisional scheme of communication was sometimes supplied by the attachment of a cable detachment from the Corps. This was the method usually adopted in the advances of the following year.

A review of signal practice during the Cambrai battle shows at once that, even if the greatest interest the operations held for the Signal Service was the secrecy and thoroughness of the preparations, yet their greatest importance lay in the lessons drawn from the near approximation to mobile warfare, both in the advance and the retreat. It was, indeed, singularly fortunate, bearing in mind the type of the two decisive phases of the war in 1918, that the Signal Service should have had such an opportunity of studying both problems on a comparatively small scale as regards space, time, and degree of decision. Many adjustments were made as the result of the relatively small action described in the foregoing pages. In particular, one of the principal outcomes of the battle was a report which embodied in its main outlines practically the entire policy which was later to be adopted by the forward signal units during the advance in October, 1918.

Little has yet been said of the special signal system which was rendered necessary by the evolution of the Tank organization which played a prominent part at Cambrai and at all the subsequent British offensives. The growth of Tank signals is, perhaps, best outlined in the present connection, since the use of tanks was the outstanding feature of the battle as originally planned. In many ways, forward Tank signals were necessarily experimental. Tank wireless, indeed, was in the nature of an " experiment inside an experiment." It was, therefore, liable to constant adjustment and change, and doomed to many initial failures in the early days of its development.

The development of the Tank signal organization and practice divides naturally into two distinct parts. One system was required for intercommunication purposes between the headquarters of the major Tank formations and units. The other, and more specialized (and therefore more interesting) system was that required to keep touch between the fighting tanks, the supply tanks, and the infantry and forward artillery, with which they worked.

The question of special signal communication for tanks first arose after their initial use in the battles of the Somme in 1916. In these early operations, tanks were only partially successful and, amongst other things, the need for a greater degree of intercommunication was proved. As the result of the experience of these battles the first provisional establishment of signal stores was proposed in December, 1916, when the Director of Signals put forward the suggestion that each battalion should be given two trench telephones and each company one trench telephone, and that tank battalion headquarters should be provided with a five-line magneto exchange. To work this primitive system it was proposed to attach four signallers to each company and eight to the battalion. In January, 1917, with the formation of a headquarters and the brigading of the tanks as Brigades of the Heavy Branch, M.G. Corps, a further establishment was proposed of one sergeant and six telephonists for headquarters and for each Tank Brigade. The Army Signal Service was still to provide and maintain all lines.

With the rapid extension of the use of these machines and the formation of the Tank Corps in 1917, it soon became clear that the original establishments were hopelessly inadequate and that Tank signal units must be formed on a scale commensurate with the growing importance and independence of this arm. The whole question was reconsidered by the Signal Directorate and as a result the formation of special Tank Corps signal units was approved in principle and recommended. The final form taken by this reform was a headquarters signal company at Tank Corps headquarters and Tank Brigade signal companies with all Brigades. The Tank Brigade signal company was planned somewhat on the lines of a Divisional signal company and possessed a headquarters with four sections for dealing with each of the battalions of the Brigade.

As the essence of the employment of Tanks lay in their sudden concentration wherever offensives were to take place, it was impossible to allot to them any recognised system of lines in each Army. Their needs were, however, accommodated on the general command and administrative systems of Armies, Corps and Divisions according to the temporary location of the Brigades. These lines were usually in the maintenance of the formation to whose system they belonged and in consequence only a small proportion of the new Tank signal establishments consisted of linemen. By far the greater proportion of the rear units consisted of operators, and of a pool of wireless operators and telegraph operators " B " who were held in readiness to man the wireless stations which were the mainstay of the Tank signal system during operations. Another feature of Tank signal units which was also directly dependent upon the particular conditions to be met was the unusually large proportion of instrument repairers contained in the establishment. Signalling instruments are of delicate constitution and not well adapted to withstand without injury the rough usage inevitable in the interior of a wildly-gyrating machine whose chief title to fame is a disregard for obstacles and unevennesses in its path. Breakages were, therefore, unusually numerous and an efficient staff of instrument repairers was required to minimise damage as much as possible.

The reorganization which brought the establishments of tank signals to their final form was also marked by the appointment of an A.D. Signals Tank Corps, to supervise and co-ordinate the whole. The desirability of a central signal authority with high rank and considerable power had been shown by the lack of efficient *liaison* between the Tank Corps and the Signal Service in the battle of Cambrai. The destruction of lines by wandering Tanks during that action did incalculable harm to an otherwise efficient signal system. The future employment of Tanks on a large scale was assured by their success on this occasion, and efficient measures had to be taken at once to prevent similar disasters in the future.

This was done by mutual arrangement. Improvements in methods of laying lines, earlier dispositions and a better system of dissemination of information about available crossings, voluntary restriction by the Tank Corps of lateral movement of Tanks in the area between the F.O.O.'s and Brigade headquarters, all assisted to remove a dangerous menace to intercommunication in battle. The appointment of A.D. Signals, Tank Corps, made certain of efficient *liaison* in future. The multiplication of crossings, the use of slack ground cable or cable laid in open shallow trenches, and special arrangements for maintenance during actions in which Tanks were employed, again minimised the danger to a still greater extent. The success of the precautions taken is witnessed by the fact that these machines never again caused a wholesale disruption of the signal system of any of the higher formations.

In some respects the evolution of Tank signal methods lay along the lines already familiar from a study of the general evolution of stationary warfare signal practice. The exceptions of interest were all concerned with the solving of intercommunication problems during the actual fighting. In the training area, communication was normally by telephone and telegraph, the lines serving the higher formations being allotted from the ordinary signal system, those serving the lower units being laid as required by the Tank signal personnel.*

It was in battle that some special signal system was needed. By their very nature the Tanks, to be of any use, must have their place in the forefront of the action. They advanced to the attack and fought under circumstances where the protection afforded by their armour alone enabled them to survive. The ideal signalling apparatus was therefore that which could be operated from within the Tank itself.

In the early days of 1916, forward Tank signals were conspicuous by their absence rather than by their efficiency. A simple visual code and the use of red, green and white discs displayed on the side of the Tank were the first primitive means employed. The infantry accompanying them replied to their signals and indicated their own wishes by gesture with rifles or with helmets held on the end of their bayonets. These methods were later reinforced by the Aldis lamps which gave very good results but which could not be answered by the forward troops without attracting enemy attention. A later innovation was the use of Tanks fitted with ploughs for burying cable. The parts of the discarded mechanical excavators and cable ploughs were borrowed from the Signal Service for experimental purposes.

The use of pigeons from Tanks was first attempted on a large scale in the offensives in the summer of 1917. They were so successful that in future operations all Tanks were supplied with these birds. Their employment from Tanks, however, does not involve any novel features other than a special organization to ensure that the higher Tank formations secured their own messages in good time. This was arranged by the employment of Tank Corps despatch riders at the lofts. The prevalence of grease and oil in the interior of the Tank and the shaking experienced by the birds were the greatest obstacles to the new departure, but they were successfully surmounted, and good averages both as regards messages and items were achieved.

---

* An alternative system of intercommunication was provided by the installation of wireless stations at all the major Tank formation head-quarters. Much traffic was normally dealt with by these stations, which were erected in barns, bell-tents, etc., convenient to the head-quarter offices.

In June, 1917, a distinct departure in Tank signal practice was initiated by the experimental use of special signal Tanks with wireless, visual and pigeons. A variety of experiments with wireless followed and, in October of the same year, continuous wave stations were employed in battle. Old out-of-date Tanks of the Somme period were first fitted out as " wireless " Tanks and these were sufficiently successful to secure for continuous wave wireless a permanent place in Tank signal organization.

The next step was the use of Tanks as carriers for wireless stations which were set down at suitable places in " No Man's Land." Later, when this method had not proved altogether satisfactory, wireless aerials were fitted to modern Tanks. Special short masts were devised which could be lowered on a swivel when railway journeys were undertaken. The sets themselves were carried within the Tank and a small dynamo fitted to the engine provided the electrical power. Wireless sets were used in the battle of Cambrai with good effect. They were of the ordinary type in use with the artillery and were carried forward by fighting tanks. They proved to be too immobile when they had been set down by the Tank and in addition suffered from the disadvantage common to all forward wireless, the fact that it was necessary for the officers and men with the stations to solicit messages. What messages they did receive were, however, despatched promptly. In this action and the actions of the following summer, continuous wave wireless with the Tank Corps justified itself to such an extent that, in August, 1918, 288 C.W. sets Mark III. and 96 120 watt sets were asked for for the Tank Corps alone.

The last development in Tank signals occurred in July, 1918, when experiments with wireless telephones were carried out successfully both between Tank and Tank in the field and between Tank and contact aeroplane. Had the war continued into the next year, wireless telephony would doubtless have played a prominent part in this as in some other departments of army signals.

---

The battle of Cambrai was followed by a short lull which lasted through the winter months of 1917-1918, to be succeeded on March 21st by the German offensive which once more entirely changed the aspect of the war. This period, otherwise quiescent, was marked by a great increase of enemy bombing and long-range shelling which gave considerable food for thought to the officers responsible for the signal communications in rear of Divisional headquarters.

The general tendency in 1917 had been to continue the grid system of buries to the rear with a chessboard system of heavy semi-permanent and permanent airline routes. This policy was already giving a characteristic appearance to those portions of the front where the situation had been more fluid and reconstruction of communications had been made necessary by the advance of the Armies. · Now, however, the system had to be modified considerably by this new factor which was bulking more and more largely in the minds of signal officers.

In the summer of 1917 a great extension of enemy long-range shelling in the rear portions of Divisional areas first made itself felt. This was accentuated by a disposition evinced by his artillery to search out Divisional headquarters and to pay special attention to the main nodal points of the line system. This situation was countered, as has been shown, by the rearward extension of the buried system to the neighbourhood of Divisional headquarters. In Divisions where the situation did not permit of this, nearly every day was marked by the destruction of one or other poled cable or airline route by a direct hit from a shell or the blast from a projectile falling in the immediate vicinity. Signal camps and signal offices also began to suffer, and casualties to signal personnel in rear areas increased considerably. In the autumn of 1917, the enemy bombing squadrons commenced to single out Divisional headquarters for special attention and, after considerable damage had been caused, the order was issued that sufficient bomb-proof shelters must be constructed to house all ranks.

About this time, however, it became evident that the enemy's attention was not going to be confined to Divisional areas. His long-range guns commenced work on the Corps communication system and on Corps headquarters, while his long-distance bombing squadrons began the first of the raids which were destined throughout 1918 to add a distinct element of uncertainty to life in the back areas generally. The effect on the rear signal system was at once evident. The system had been built up entirely with regard to two considerations; economy of personnel and stores, and convenience to subscribers. Heavy main routes were the rule and these were usually carried through, or terminated in, camps and towns, where billeting accommodation was plentiful and where, therefore, the administrative units had their headquarters. These were naturally the spots raided by the enemy airmen, and the lives of the operators housed in unprotected signal offices became harassed and anxious. Communication was often interrupted by the destruction of whole routes or of heavy junction poles in towns and villages. Signal offices were not safe, and at any time a wholesale catastrophe might paralyse the administrative services of the whole army.

Breakdown parties, who had until now been accustomed to judge the amount of their work by the state of the weather, were kept in a continual state of activity. In the past, wholesale damage had been done by storms of unusual fury or even by heavy accumulations of rime, hoarfrost, or snow, upon the wires. These visitations were, however, rare occurrences ; the visits of the enemy bombing machines depended solely on the state of the moon and took place many times each month.  Signs were not wanting, either, that they would shortly become independent of this controlling factor and be of nightly occurrence in fine weather.

The situation needed to be taken in hand at once and a policy was outlined which aimed at four ideals.  These were, (1) the adequate protection of signal offices, (2) the burying of leads in and out of signal offices for considerable lengths, (3) the diversion of routes round towns, and (4) the substitution of lighter parallel routes 150 yards or more apart for the heavier routes which had been the rule until this date.

The protection of the personnel in signal offices was achieved in several ways.  In tents, hutted camps, or other temporary buildings, splinter-proof walls three feet high were raised all round the billet to give protection against the spreading splinters of the bombs. In the case of brick and stone buildings of considerable strength, additional protection was achieved by building up windows with sandbags, and sometimes, also, by the deposit of extra layers of earth and cement upon the roof of the signal office.  Basements were utilized whenever possible and, where suitable cellars existed, signal offices were always established downstairs in preference to the better-lighted and more airy rooms on the ground floor.

In important offices the problem of the protection of intercommunication facilities and instruments ranked only second to that of protection of personnel, and, during those periods in 1918 when stationary warfare conditions held sway, Army signal offices were sometimes duplicated in heavily protected dug-outs.  The wiring of these was ingeniously arranged in every way as a duplicate of the signal office above stairs and, in the event of a raid, the whole of the essential circuits could be switched through to the subterranean signal office by one movement.  Dislocation of traffic was thus limited to a period of minutes only.  Similarly, at G.H.Q., a duplicate signal office was built in the ramparts of Montreuil, and on completion the office staff moved in and the old office was abandoned.

The protection of the permanent routes was assisted by an order that future routes would not exceed 28 wires, thus making necessary two or three separate routes for all the superior formations.  By this means alternative circuits were assured, the principle aimed at being to make it impossible for one bomb to sever entirely the vital communications of any formation without registering a direct hit on the signal office itself.  Large junction poles were a great source of danger and were done away with whenever possible, their place being taken by protected dug-outs into which the lines were led by cable buried for 200 yards on either side.  In the same way, buried multicore cable of one description or another was used to terminate the routes, which were also in many cases rearranged so as to deceive any enemy desiring to use them as a clue to the location of the signal office into which they ran. Diversions round all main towns were also contemplated and in urgent cases were carried out, cases in point being those round St. Pol and Amiens. These caused the Lines of Communication signal units a great deal of heavy extra work in 1917 and 1918.

Finally, special arrangements were made for maintenance with a view to reducing the dislocation caused by catastrophic interruptions as much as possible. The maintenance personnel was increased in number and redistributed. Special lengths of two-pair interruption cable 150 yards long were prepared to put through emergency circuits, and a re-echo of the experience of 1914 is heard in the instructions that in future the most important circuits should be given positions upon the top arms.

---

The period between the first great reorganization and the retreat in March, 1918, was marked by two main changes in organization. The first was the reorganization which took place as a direct result of the position battles of 1917, the second was the formation of a special section of the Divisional signal company to deal with the intercommunication of the machine-gun battalion which now formed an integral portion of each Division.

At the time of the first great reorganization, the Director of Army Signals was given to understand that no further great increase to the Signal Service could be permitted. Any future reorganization which involved an increase in one unit must be compensated for by a decrease in another. When, therefore, the position battles of the summer of 1917 and, in particular, the operations which ended in the capture of Passchendaele, betrayed clearly an absence of flexibility in the position warfare signal service, the necessary adjustment had to be made by a redistribution of personnel amongst the signal units. The great need was more constructive power on active fronts, and it was decided that this would have to be made good at the expense of the formations in the more quiescent areas.

A review of signal units showed one direction, only, in which a considerable saving might be affected without loss of efficiency. The question of the loss of man-power due to the horses of the cable section has already been referred to in connection with No. 1 Section of the Divisional signal company, and the reasons which turned the scale against a radical reorganization of these sections have been discussed. The need for mobility was not, however, of such paramount importance in the case of construction and maintenance personnel attached to Corps and Armies. At any rate, it was quite evident that under present circumstances and, indeed, under any circumstances that could be foreseen, certain of the cable sections could be spared. At the same time, a review of the establishments of both airline and cable sections showed ways in which the individual units might be slightly reduced in strength.

It was therefore decided to attempt a considerable increase in the number of airline sections—the most mobile construction signal unit in country where motor transport could be used—at the expense both of the number of cable sections and the strength of the individual airline and cable sections.

A table showing the strength of the Signal Service on September 1st, 1917, at the time when the question of this reorganization first came under consideration is given below.

TABLE V

| Unit. | Number. | Estab. | Total. | Total. |
|---|---|---|---|---|
| G.H.Q. | ⎫ | | | |
| " L " Signal Battn. | ⎬ | 3,665 | 3,665 | 3,665 |
| Pigeon Service | | | | |
| Signal Depot | ⎭ | | | |
| Cavalry Corps Signals | | 899 | 899 | 899. |
| Tank Corps Signals | | 436 | 436 | 436. |
| Army Signals H.Q. | (5) | 274 | 1,370 | |
| Airline Sections | (15) | 61 | 915 | |
| Cable Sections | (15) | 38 | 570 | |
| Area Signal Detachments | (40) | 16 | 640 | |
| A.F.A. Bde. Sig. Sub-sections | (47) | 20 | 940 | |
| Extra for Corps above 3 | | | 50 | |
| Construction Company | (5) | 117 | 585 | |
| Light Rly. Sig. Sections | (5) | 41 | 205 | |
| Intelligence W/T Groups | (6) | 47 | 282 | 5,557 |
| Corps Signals H.Q. | (20) | 140 | 2,800 | |
| Airline Sections | (20) | 61 | 1,220 | |
| Cable Sections | (64) | 38 | 2,432 | |
| Corps H.A. Sections | (20) | 37 | 740 | |
| H.A. Group Sub-sections | (90) | 27 | 2,430 | |
| Extra for Divisions above 3 | | | 154 | 9,776 |
| Divisional Signals | (62) | 289 | 17,918 | 17,918 |

Grand total (including attached), 38,251.

It will be seen that at that date 79 cable sections and 35 airline sections were distributed between five Armies and 20 Corps. On the new basis it was decided to give to each Army and each Corps the two cable sections which would suffice for their needs and to abolish the remaining 29. The men thus produced by the abolition of these units, together with those found by the slight reduction of the individual establishments,* were then pooled and formed into airline sections on the new establishment, thus increasing the number of the latter from 35 to 63. The new airline sections were then re-allotted to formations, each Army taking three and each Corps

* For the changes in the individual cable and airline sections see the Comparative Establishments and Trades in Appendices I and III.

two. The remaining eight were kept in reserve as a G.H.Q. pool for employment as considered requisite from time to time.*

By means of this reorganization about half of the constructive power of the signal units with the Expeditionary Force could be moved about without upsetting the situation on the quiet fronts, and the value of the reconstruction was to be very clearly perceived during the campaigns of the last year of the war.

A study of the foregoing rearrangement will show at once that a saving of a considerable number of officers was effected, but this was to a certain extent offset by the creation of certain specialist officers which had now become a matter of great importance. It was the saving incidental to the reconstitution of the signal units which permitted of the appointment of an officer in each Army as D.A.D. Signals, of a second wireless officer for each Corps, and of a subaltern for each heavy artillery section. The urgency of all these modifications was incontestable and they were all approved. In addition, the new reorganization included the grouping of Army signal units under the Army signal company and the appointment of one of the officers of that company as Adjutant to assist the O.C. company in his administrative duties.

The final result of the above redistribution is shown in the following comparative table of the increases and decreases involved.

TABLE VI.

| Decrease. | Increase. |
|---|---|
| 4 officers | 25 box cars |
| 794 other ranks | 25 3-ton lorries |
| 362 horses | 16 bicycles |
| 145 cable and limbered wagons | |
| 26 30-cwt. lorries | |
| 29 motor cycles | |

At the same time, a review was made of other signal units and it was seen that certain small economies in men and horses could be made which resulted in a net saving of a further 104 men and 124 horses.† It was found necessary, however, to add certain tradesmen to G.H.Q. and Army signal companies,‡ while the field artillery

* On a quiet front one airline section only was left to a Corps. This gave a very large pool for the Director of Signals to move about as he liked. The use of this pool in March and April, 1918, much eased the situation.

† The individual savings were :—
    (a) Two sappers or pioneers from each Area Signal Detachment.
    (b) One shoeing and carriage smith corporal from each Corps Signal Company.
    (c) One farrier serjeant from each Army Signal Company.
    (d) Two horses from each Divisional Signal Company.

‡ Additions were :—
    (a) G.H.Q. Signal Company, 28 sappers and pioneers.
    (b) Army Signal Company, 37 sappers and pioneers.

signal sub-sections to which no transport had been allotted and which
had been greatly handicapped by this fact, were accommodated with
a limbered G.S. wagon and the necessary horses and drivers.

Other amendments carried out at the same time were the addition
of a box car to the Divisional signal company, and the substitution
of the 30-cwt lorry at present on the establishment of that unit by
a 3-ton lorry  The latter had been made necessary mainly by the
great increase in the wireless equipment of a Division which could
no longer be carried in the P.E.L.* lorry as had formerly been the
case.

. The second reorganization referred to in an earlier paragraph—
that of the Divisional signal company to improve machine-gun
signals—involved a small addition only to each signal company,
though the total increase of establishment was not inconsiderable.
The additional men were, however, offset in great measure by a
reduction of the signallers already with the machine-gun battalion.
The machine-gun signal system in a Division was comparable with
that of an infantry Brigade and the old state of affairs when all lines
were run by the M.G. Corps personnel was not satisfactory.  The new
section of one officer and 20 other ranks was needed, if the machine-
gun communications were to become incorporated in the Divisional
system.  Certainly much greater economy both of material and of
personnel might be expected from such an amalgamation.

In the event, the new scheme was not always successful.  It
depended very much on the personality of the machine-gun signal
officer who had been transferred to the Signal Service as part of the
reform ; upon the relations of the latter with his commanding officer,
and upon the extent of his willingness to identify himself with the
signal company to which he now belonged.  There is no doubt that
the absorption of the machine-gun signals was an unqualified blessing
to the efficiency of the signal system generally, but the unfavourable
reports of various officers should be given due prominence in an
unbiassed examination of the result of the change.  Certainly, the
additional personnel was of great value to the O.C. Divisional signals
in the forthcoming mobile warfare.  Equally certainly, in individual
cases, the machine-gun battalion was not so well served under the
new conditions.  Weighing both sides of the question, however, the
balance was strongly in favour of the reform.†

The period during which these reorganizations took effect was also
a period of thorough revision of all existing establishments throughout
the Expeditionary Force with a view to economy of man-power.
The British Armies in France had reached their maximum size and

* P E.L. (Portable Electric Light).
† Detail of the machine-gun section (No. 5 Section of a Divisional
Signal Company) is given in Appendix I to this volume in the 1918
column.

the available manhood of the Empire was insufficient to replace casualties and keep up the strength of the fighting forces on the various fronts. The situation had been relieved to a great extent by the entry of America into the fray, but was still grave, and every effort was made to keep the administrative services within reasonable bounds and to free more men for the infantry. The Signal Service shared in the careful scrutiny given to these services and in August, 1917, an Army signal conference had been appointed to consider ways and means of reducing the signal facilities given to the Armies in the field. With the D.D. Signals of an Army as President, an officer of the Adjutant General's Staff and an officer appointed by the Director of Signals as the other members of the conference, the interests of the Signal Service were safeguarded, while the man-power question was yet given due weight in a dispassionate examination of the facts.

The conference passed in review the whole question of signals in relation to the Staff. Signal communication was discussed under three heads :—(1) The delivery of written messages to the addressee (D.R.L.S., orderly, runner, etc.) ; (2) the reproduction of the written message for the addressee (phonogram, telegram, fullerphone, visual, wireless, etc.) ; and (3) methods where no record is kept (telephone). The advantages of the three methods were tabulated : the slow speed but accuracy of the first, the rapidity and relative accuracy of the second, the supreme rapidity but relative inaccuracy of the third, where, however, the latter quality is offset to a great extent by the freedom of discussion made possible. It was decided that the first method was needed to carry all matter too urgent for post but not exceptionally urgent, that the second was equally needed for all very urgent traffic, and that the third should be reserved exclusively for conversations between staff officers. This left the situation very much as it was before the conference was held. An examination of lists of officers who were connected as subscribers to the telephone system showed no way in which economy could be achieved. The policy of giving as few direct lines as possible was confirmed and emphasized. In effect, the conference was unable to suggest any radical decreases of establishment as justifiable or desirable. The result was to vindicate once and for all the conservative policy as regards increases of establishment which had been pursued consistently by the Signal Directorate, who had always subordinated the interests of the Signal Service to those of the Army as a whole.

Scrutiny of signal establishments was not confined to those of the Armies, but was exercised also on the units working the Lines of Communication signal system. Here, also, no case could be made out for decreases of establishment, but the recommendation was made that still further women telegraphists and switchboard operators should be employed. The employment of women on out-door services was deprecated by the Deputy Director of Signals, at any rate until considerable further savings should have been made in the home signal establishments which appeared to be unduly swollen in comparison with those of the Signal Service overseas.

Indeed, the substitution of the indoor tradesmen on the L. of C. by women was itself not easily completed, since the terms of service offered did not attract women with suitable qualifications and educational attainments. The employment of native labour on the L. of C. and even as drivers with the Divisional signal companies, was advocated by the Signal Service itself and might have taken place had stationary warfare been much further prolonged. The employment of Boy Scouts as orderlies in rear offices had been recommended twice by the Director of Signals but refused by the home authorities. The use of women further forward than on the Lines of Communication was rendered impossible by lack of suitable accommodation and for other reasons.

The final outcome of the struggle waged by the advocates of expansion and reduction was thus to leave the Signal Service much as it was before, if anything slightly increased.

# CHAPTER XIV.

## SIGNALS IN RETREAT.

### SYNOPSIS.

The General Situation in March, 1918.—Buried Cable Absent or Incomplete on the Critical Front.—Poled Cable and Airline Between Divisions and Brigades.— Visual and Wireless Relied Upon to a Great Extent.—Too Little Attention Paid to the Signal System of the Rear Defence Lines.—The Opening of the Attack.— Fog prevents Observation and Visual Signalling.—Line System Destroyed within a Few Minutes.—Two Main Phases of the Retreat.—The Fighting Retreat through Prepared Defences.—Arras and the North.—Safe Buries and No Retreat.—The Situation South of Arras.—Excellent German Long-Range Artillery Preparation.— Loss of Forward Signalling Apparatus and Signallers.—Importance of Wireless and P.B. and A.; Visual and Message-carrying Agencies in the First Phase.—Formation of a Rear Emergency Carrier-pigeon Service.—The Second Phase: The General Retreat.—Extent of the Withdrawal.—Characteristics of the Retreat.—General Signal Policy.—The Divisional Route.—A Contrast in Staff Methods and the Effect on Signals.—The Need for Concentration of Headquarters.—Chief Difficulties Encountered.—Hurried Movements.—Laterals.—Congestion of Traffic.—Supply.— Filling Up at Dumps.—Destruction of Routes.—Lessons Learnt during the Retreat. —Line Signalling in Retreat.—Permanent Lines and Ground Cables.—Effect of Tanks, Traffic and Horse Lines.—Cables Used.—Instruments Used.—Emergency " Grid " of Ground Cable.—Wireless.—Practice in Stepping Up Required.—Supply of Accumulators.—Interception.—Rise in Importance of Wireless.—Visual.— Differences in Procedure.—Message-carrying Agencies.—Battalion Communication.— Loss of Stores.—The Lys Retreat.—The 9th Corps in the Marne Retreat.—Signal Personnel in the Fighting Line.—Carey's Force.—The Retreat Reflected in Rear Signals.—Special Instructions for Future Similar Emergencies.—Special Training for Mobile Warfare.

THE campaigning season of 1918 found the Allied Armies resting on the line which had been the boundary of their gains of the 1917 offensives and awaiting the expected German attacks which would be the logical outcome of the general war situation. The collapse of Russia during the autumn of 1917, and the immense reserves which Germany was thereby enabled to transfer from the Eastern to the Western front, precluded the Allied Command from entertaining the thought of a sustained offensive on a large scale, and at the same time made certain of a great attack on the part of the Germans. The first three months of the year were, therefore, spent in attempts to consolidate the defence system on the entire British and French front. On the front held by the British Army the situation had been still further complicated by the fact that 28 miles had been recently taken over from the French.

From all points of view the situation was not too favourable. The losses sustained in the offensives of the previous year, combined with the importance of retaining all ground gained in the north, made it impossible to hold the southern portion of the long front in any strength. Divisions were widely spaced and Divisional areas

S

were in some cases as much as 7,000 yards broad.* A severe strain was thus thrown upon the whole Army, and the Signal Service was not exempt from the ill effects of a dangerous situation.

The very success of the battles of 1917 had carried the forward formations far in advance of the safe buried cable systems to the west of the Somme battle area. Behind the armies—in the event of a retreat—were the battlefields themselves where cross-country traffic was practically impossible.

Across this devastated area signal communication was by a few main routes strung out along the roads over which the materials for their construction had been transported with difficulty. These routes, even in the quiescent times which preceded the main attack, were already suffering severely from the attentions of the enemy's long-range guns and from his long-distance bombing planes. Yet these troubles were but a foretaste of what was to come.

In the battle zone itself frantic efforts were being made to improve the signal communication of the three main defence lines. Here, however, the Signal Service was much hampered, both by the competition of other branches of the Army for the use of the available infantry working parties, and by the shortage of cable. The latter difficulty was almost masked by the former. Labour was required for the perfection of defences, for the building of light railways, for the digging of water mains, for a thousand other purposes. Buried cable routes advanced very slowly, indeed, and in the majority of cases had only reached Brigade headquarters by March 21st, the fateful date when the opening of a fresh campaign ushered in a new variety of experience for the Army generally.

Forward of Brigade, in many cases, only a few pairs could be hastily put through. In other cases, the forward portion only had been completed, and the bury stopped several hundred yards in front of Brigade headquarters and was continued backwards by poled cable or open wire routes. In yet other cases, and this applied especially to the portion just taken over from the French, no bury was available at all. It was only in the neighbourhood of Arras and further to the north, where the advances had not been of such depth and where the signal situation had been more stable, that a safe buried cable system enabled the signal officer to look forward to the future with comparative confidence.

Everywhere south of this the buried system was, at best, partial and, at worst, absent altogether. When it was incomplete or missing, the line system was partly of ground or poled cable, partly of open wire routes which frequently reached as far forward as Brigade headquarters.† Between Brigade and Divisional head-

* One Division was holding a front 10,500 yards in width.
† In one or two cases airline was carried forward as far as battalion headquarters.

quarters, strangely enough, the area which had previously been *par excellence*, the natural habitat of the bury, was almost everywhere spanned by these comparatively inefficient substitutes.

Previous experience had been sufficiently decisive to make all signal personnel absolutely certain that, when the attack came, the first thing that would happen would be the failure of line communication all along the front. No one, however, could have foreseen the completeness with which that prophecy would come true. The work of the German artillery was to be far in advance of anything it had previously achieved.

It was quite clear that more reliance than had usually been the case must be placed upon alternative means of communication. Comprehensive visual schemes were arranged right throughout the length and breadth of the unusually large Divisional sectors. The wireless chain was made as complete as the available apparatus would permit. The third week in March saw the latter preparations as complete as was possible, but the immaturity of the buried cable system left in the signal officers' minds an uneasy feeling which was to be justified only too completely by events.

Every available means of communication had been made use of to the utmost, but a relatively insecure system was the best result attained, and this was to be made even more inadequate than it might have been by the extremely unfavourable weather conditions. There is, perhaps, one direction—though one direction only—in which the signal preparation can be subjected to legitimate criticism after the event. If anything, it appears that too much attention had been paid to the forward communications in the outpost zone which was intended to be lightly held and which, it was anticipated, would be overrun by the enemy in any persistent attack. The communications of this zone—visual, runners, forward wireless, and even telephone, were very thorough and left neither time nor material to ensure a like thorough system in the second and third lines of defence where it was to be expected that the main stand of a sorely-pressed Army would be made. In the event, this proved to be a serious weakness in the signal dispositions, but it cannot be criticized too harshly under the circumstances. All previous experience had gone to show that forward signals were of paramount importance. In previous battles, also, the presence of a safe buried system had been the rule, and a reasonable amount of communication in rear of Brigade headquarters in stationary warfare had become, under these conditions, almost a matter of course. It was an unfortunate concatenation of circumstances which caused the balance of importance to shift from front to rear at the very time that the incompleteness of the buried cable system rendered the rear communications peculiarly vulnerable.

The enemy bombardment commenced at 5 a.m. on March 21st,

and the whole British front from Arras to its southern limit on the Oise river was subjected to a shell storm which exceeded all previous experience. For four hours shells of every size, containing high explosive and every variety of deadly or disabling gas, were poured upon the thin line of British forward troops. At the same time the areas as far as 15,000 yards behind the front line were searched by high velocity guns firing by the map on all important head-quarters, cross-roads, battery positions, strong points, etc., that had been previously registered by the enemy. British and German lines alike were shrouded in a dense ground mist which made observation impossible. Thickened by the smoke and dust from the bombard-ment, the fog soon became impenetrable, and all preparation to meet the imminent attack had to be made by guess work. Within the first few minutes practically all the forward open routes were out of action, whole sections being blown away in some cases.

Within a few minutes of the commencement of the bombardment, a thoroughly complete—though recognizedly unsafe—signal system had been reduced to a partial haphazard medley of such ground cable as had survived, such wireless stations as had escaped extinction, and a few power buzzer and amplifier stations in strong points and at formation headquarters. Many of the visual stations had been flattened out of existence by direct hits during the earliest stages of the bombardment. The remainder were ready to work, but rendered quite useless by the ground mist, reinforced as it was by the smoke from the shells, the dust raised by the bombardment, and the large quantities of gas which were a marked feature of the shelling. It was on this half-destroyed system that forward signal officers had to rely for intercommunication during the forthcoming attack ; it was over various arteries of this system that the first reports from the infantry began to come back, as the garrisons of post after post dis-covered the presence of the German infantry, often to find them-selves completely surrounded before they could signal back for assistance.

In the struggle which followed, and which continued until the 3rd and 5th British Armies had been pressed back upon their final defence positions covering Amiens, there are two main phases to be dis-tinguished as far as the Signal Service is concerned. The first of these was the initial fighting in the prepared positions of the 1st, 2nd and 3rd defence systems : the second was the hurried retreat, with occasional pauses and with continual rearguard actions, which ended at the position finally taken up before Amiens and behind the Somme. Following upon the two main phases, again, came an entirely different but less interesting period when the situation had been stabilized and the retreat was stopped. Here, position warfare once more set in and a fresh signal system was built up which resembled those of the previous periods of position warfare with a few modifications due partly to the evolution of new methods and partly to the after-effects of the previous retreat.

A general review of signal practice in the first and most intense phase of the March battle again shows that this in its turn presented two distinct aspects. Signal practice differed markedly on the front to the south of Arras from that opposite Arras itself and to the north, which was outside the scope of the original attack. The latter— being of least interest and less intimately associated with the second or semi-mobile phase of the retreat—may be referred to shortly first.

On March 21st, the British line opposite Arras was subjected to a certain amount of bombardment, but no attack took place. It was not until the success of the attack further to the south seemed assured, that the German higher command decided to extend the area affected by the attack, and fresh Divisions were launched against the troops manning the Arras and Vimy defences.

The problem facing the local signal officer was here relatively easy. The difference in his favour lay mainly in the fact that this area had only been slightly affected by the advances of the summer and autumn of 1917 and had not been affected at all by the German retreat that took place in March of that year. Arras was alike a valued possession and a desired objective of attack. Its importance and its nearness to the line were potent causes both of the strengthening of the British defences and of a like consolidation of the German lines so that the enemy might not be forced back from a position whence it seemed to him likely that he might successfully envelop the town. The defences round Arras had thus been for both sides a bastion on which the opposing lines had pivoted, and were destined to pivot once again, in the fluctuating fortunes of the long years of war.

The buried cable which underlay the town and penetrated the caves and tunnels of the defences was still within the sphere where its common everyday use was practicable and, indeed, essential. It had, therefore, been kept in good order and formed a secure basis for a safe signal system which presented none of the anomalies of those of the Corps and Divisions further to the south.

Once more the attacks on Arras failed and in the recoil our outpost lines were re-established, or even in places pushed further forward than before. The history of the signals of this portion of the action would only be a repetition of the story of signal practice in the position warfare of 1917. It is better to pass on to the consideration of the more difficult problems and more interesting lessons which were being solved and learnt in the south, where by this time the retreat had become general.

South of Arras, the opening phase of the battle was marked by an almost complete destruction of Division-Brigade signal communications, while those between Division and Corps were interrupted over a considerable portion of the front. A characteristic of the short but furious preparation had been the exceedingly efficient work of the German long-range artillery who were shooting by the map on all the main communication features and likely concentration areas as far back as Corps headquarters. The practice made was truly extraordinary and numerous examples could be cited from the experience of the Signal Service alone. On several occasions direct hits were secured on junction poles ; main telegraph routes were brought down wholesale in blocks several hundred yards long ; Divisional signal offices were " bracketed," or even struck by shells and the personnel forced to take refuge in dug-outs ; the roads up which supplies had to pass were rendered impassable by direct hits or destroyed transport, or were blocked by the ruins of houses.

During the remainder of the 21st, while the British infantry, supported by the artillery as well as was possible without adequate observation or signal communication, were endeavouring to retain their hold upon the second and third lines of defence, the rear telegraph and telephone system had gone to pieces almost beyond repair. The sole surviving remnants were ground cable hastily run out by cable detachments, or patched up circuits on those permanent routes which were less thoroughly destroyed.

One or two circuits were kept through intermittently on the front of the majority of Divisions, but even with six men spread out on each mile of route it was found impossible to expect communication between Division and Brigade for more than half of the time.

Forward of Brigade headquarters, the signal situation depended largely upon the presence of absence of buries. Where buries were in existence, working was continuous even over routes the test points of which had been overrun by the enemy. Where buries were absent, the ground and trench cable had shared the fate of the lines further back, and intercommunication between the various isolated posts of the first defence system was either non-existent or was carried on by means of alternative methods of signalling which did not need lines.

As the British forces were gradually forced back off their forward defences or surrounded and isolated in strong points and separate trenches, the various signal dug-outs were also ceded to the enemy and gradually the whole forward signal system passed into their hands. Where possible, instruments, terminal boards, and exchanges were destroyed, but a great deal of undamaged material must have been captured. It may be said that, forward of battalion headquarters, practically no signalling apparatus was saved, while a large number of signallers, both of the battalions and batteries, and of the Brigade forward parties, were involved in the debâcle and were either killed or captured.

The comparative failure of the line system once more—as in the Cambrai battle, though here for a different reason—caused the various alternative means of intercommunication to assume a greater importance than usual. In this particular case, also, the range of means which could be employed with any hope of success was still further restricted by the dense fog which made visual completely out of the question until well on in the afternoon. During the critical hours of the morning of the 21st, power buzzer forward of Brigades, and wireless between Brigades and Divisions were the mainstay of the intercommunication system. Until 8.30 p.m., many hours after they had been surrounded, wireless and power buzzer messages were received from isolated strongholds which were invested by the enemy. Such messages afforded valuable information to the higher command as to the situation in the forward positions which were still holding out. Prisoners since repatriated have told how the wireless sets, by enabling them to keep touch with their more fortunate comrades, put heart into defenders who felt they were in a hopeless position and encouraged them to fight to the last. The stubborn resistance of these isolated parties did much to embarrass the German advance and thus to steady the retreat of the shattered Divisions endeavouring to withstand the impetuous rush of immensely superior forces. Anything which encouraged their *morale* and helped them to hold out was of vital importance and, from this point of view alone, the work of the forward wireless stations was of incalculable value.

Further to the rear, such wireless sets as survived, though their aerials were shot away again and again, formed in nearly all cases a valuable auxiliary method of communication and, in many Divisions, were the sole reliable link with the Brigades until the second phase of the battle commenced. Not only did the stations in the battle zone itself do good work, but the personnel of stations on the flanks came to the rescue of their more hard-pressed comrades and assisted to dispose of urgent messages when touch could not be obtained directly to the rear. Already wireless was proving itself invaluable. In the days which were to come its importance was to be demonstrated to a still greater extent.

It was not until the afternoon that visual became possible, but when the mist rose it was used to a great extent. Many of the forward visual stations had been destroyed by direct hits during the bombardment, but between Brigade and Division in the second and third line positions heliograph was used with success and the Lucas lamp proved its usefulness again and again.

It was the first time that visual had been given a great opportunity on the Divisional-Brigade line of communication and in this and the succeeding days long distance work was somewhat hampered by the reduction that had taken place in the number of heliographs issued to forward troops. Their place was, however, fairly successfully filled by the Lucas lamp which proved an efficient substitute over most of the distances involved. Bearing in mind the usual European

climate with its large proportion of overcast weather, there is no doubt
that, in spite of such isolated cases as the present, the withdrawal
of the heliograph was more than justified by the saving in transport
effected and by the greater simplicity rendered possible in the training
of reinforcements.

Message-carrying agencies played a less important part than usual
in the phase at present under consideration. In the early hours, the
fog was so dense that runners could not be used with great success,
while the attack was so overwhelming that the whole available rifle
strength of the front line troops was required to reinforce the firing
line. Later, as the various posts realized that they were cut off,
parties were told off to cut their way through the investing enemy
troops and carry news of their comrades who were remaining to fight
to the death at their posts. In some cases, the survivors of such
parties made their way through the enveloping Germans ; in others,
isolated runners succeeded in finding their way to the rear formation
headquarters. More often, the first news of the success of the German
attack received by the higher command was given by the advance of
bodies of the enemy on the headquarters themselves.

Between Divisions and Brigades motor cyclists did good work
under great difficulties. Men were blown off their machines by the
blast of shells falling near them and resumed their journeys immediately they had righted their cycles. Cases occurred of motor cyclists
and machines being buried, dug out, and then carrying on as if nothing
had happened. During the next few days the motor cyclist despatch
rider was to experience a few short but crowded hours which recalled
the early days of 1914. He was once more to be, on occasion, the
sole means of intercommunication.* The descendants of the men
who made good in the retreat of 1914 proved now that they could
worthily uphold the traditions which had heretofore been the only
reminder of a glorious past which seemed to have been replaced
permanently by a humdrum routine.

The pigeon service was perhaps more thoroughly disorganized by
the fresh turn taken by the war than any other branch of the Signal
Service. As the retreat gained in depth and accelerated in velocity,
the so-called mobile lofts proved to be relatively very immobile. In
many cases, the necessary horses to carry out their removal were not
available, while in others congestion along the roads prevented the
early retirements of motor lofts. In all, 40 horse-drawn and motor
mobile lofts fell into the enemy's hands. Of these, most had been
destroyed by fire and the majority of the birds they contained had

* It was due to the activities of the motor cyclist despatch riders
that a considerable proportion of the heavy guns in action on the
southern front were saved from capture. No other means of warning
the battery commanders existed, but messages were sent through by
D.R. in time to permit of the early withdrawal of the guns.

been killed. In no single case during the present retreat was a mobile loft captured complete with its birds.

The credit for the relative smallness of the losses is due to the head of the carrier pigeon service, who had foreseen the emergency. Twelve months before the events which momentarily crippled the forward organization on this front, orders had been issued for the destruction of lofts and birds in the very circumstances which had now arisen. These orders were conscientiously carried out by the N.C.O.'s in charge of the lofts, and the enemy can have reaped little advantage from those stations that did fall into his hands.

During the first few hours of the battle, many pigeons were released with S.O.S. messages, but the results were considerably more patchy than usual. In the most favourable cases, birds homed quickly, were received at their lofts as in normal times, and the messages were despatched by hand or phone to the headquarters to which the loft was attached. In some cases, where the telephone lines were down, corporals in charge of pigeon lofts acted on their own initiative and improvised a bicycle service between the loft and the headquarters until one or other was forced to withdraw. In less favourable circumstances, there were several stages of a complicated process where things might go wrong. Sometimes the birds were lost in the fog, and in one or two Divisions, though many birds were despatched, no single one reached the loft. In other cases, the loft had been destroyed by shell-fire, evacuated, or burned, before the arrival of birds which had been retained by their holders as an emergency means of communication. In yet others, the messages were received in safety at the loft, but the pigeon corporal was unable to find a headquarters which had precipitately retired.

At times, carrier pigeons once more proved to be a useful supplementary method of communication, but on the whole their success was less complete than usual, while the loss of birds was so heavy that the service was crippled to a certain extent. Immediate steps were taken to secure more birds and reorganize, but it was some little time before the effect of these fresh efforts could make itself felt. In the meantime, both from the new aspect assumed by the fighting, and from the shortage of birds, the pigeon was largely to drop out of place as a regular means of forward intercommunication on the critical front.

An interesting result of the success of the German offensive was seen in the organization of a two-way pigeon service by both French and British Signal Services between Paris, the French G.Q.G., the British G.H.Q., and the headquarters of the various French Armies. Although never actually brought into use, the service was organized and worked effectively. Had the German success carried the enemy far across the Marne and driven a wedge between the British and French Armies, the presence of this auxiliary pigeon service would have been invaluable. As it is, it is of interest to observe that in their practice flights, birds flying between G.H.Q. at Montreuil and the allied headquarters in Paris were flying part of the way over territory in German occupation.

The main lesson learnt by the pigeon service in the German retreat was that, although the majority of the lofts should be as close as possible to Divisional headquarters, some should be kept further back towards the limit of the birds' flight. In the event of a successful advance by the enemy, these lofts would remain safe throughout the fighting in the rear defence systems. Once a retreat becomes general, the pigeon naturally drops out as a means of intercommunication, and is not missed to any great extent. During the hard battling through rear defence zones, however, their services would be particularly valuable and future pigeon service organizers might well bear this in mind.

With the penetration of the third defence system, the second phase of the retreat was ushered in. Hurled out of their last prepared positions, the British Armies were forced to withdraw behind the line of the Somme, where a fresh attempt was made to stem the German flood of invasion. The withdrawal was successfully accomplished, but the enemy pressed hard upon the heels of the retreating British infantry and the Somme line was penetrated almost as soon as it was taken up. A further retreat to an " Army " line along the Roye-Albert road was then undertaken and, after a short pause, this line was turned at its northern extremity where the Somme runs east and west. The final stage of the retreat ended with the British Armies holding the outer Amiens defences and a line running south from there. Here the situation was more stable and the final stages of the 1918 battle of the Somme were waged with varying fortune, but without decisive result, along this last hastily-prepared defence zone. It was here that on April 5th the first stage of the great German offensive was stayed and normal trench warfare resumed its sway.

The greatest depth of the retreat was from 20 to 25 miles, and the fortunes of the Divisions engaged varied with their distance from the pivot point to the east of Arras. One Division established five headquarters in five miles in six days, another as many as 14 headquarters in 16 miles in three days. The experience of others varied within these limits. Signal practice of course was largely dependent upon the depth and speed of the retreat. There were, however, in this second phase of the battle, certain definite features which were characteristic of the warfare and which were faithfully reflected in the type of signal system adopted.

The first phase of the battle had been characterized by insufficient preparation, by overwhelming shell-fire, and by intensive fighting in well-prepared positions. The result had been a modified position warfare signal system whose success was only partial. In the second phase now under consideration, on the other hand, the characteristics were negligible shell-fire and comparatively rapid retrograde movement, varied by occasional rearguard actions of fiercer intensity when an approximation to position warfare once more set in.

The characteristics of the signal system differed accordingly and the general policy adopted under force of circumstances was that of the central route down the Divisional front. The success of the signal communication of different formations varied considerably and was even more a reflection of the methods of the General Staff than of the efficiency of the signal officer. The shortcomings of a demoralized staff were at once apparent in the inefficiency of the system. In the one case where a Corps headquarters vanished suddenly to reappear in a French area, no communications existed between the Corps and its Divisions, because lines were not available on the French system. In another case, where a Corps handled the unprecedented number of 13 Divisions, line communication was never lost between Division and Corps, because the retreat was conducted on a well-considered policy.* Divisions moved to new headquarters as ordered by the Corps and found at least one metallic circuit waiting for them on arrival. Corps airline sections and cable sections were employed with forethought and skill to serve the needs of subordinate formations. Not only was line communication available, but it was reinforced and assisted by a wireless chain which was of the greatest help.

On no previous occasion was the effect of Staff methods on signals and signals on Staff methods more clearly seen. When the Corps controlled the route followed by Divisions and Divisions that followed by their Brigades, the subordinate formations fell back along permanent lines which had been reconstructed and put through for their use, or, better still, along the uprights of a " grid " of cables which would give them communication to rear and flank alike. When Divisions were left to retire at their own sweet will and Brigadiers followed the routes that most appealed to their fancy, the signal officer was faced with an impossible problem and his cable and wireless detachments were tired out by attempts to run lines to places where he guessed the Staff might be.

On more than one occasion a wireless or cable party was exposed to imminent risk of capture through proceeding in the course of their duty to lay a line to or erect a station at a place where the Staff of a Brigade had been directed to take up their headquarters but to which they had not gone. On one occasion, a wireless officer who had billeted himself and erected his station was aroused from sleep by

* Only one case of complete interruption of communication in this Corps is recorded. In this case the Division with which touch was lost was working under another Division at the time.

the tidings that the enemy were entering the village, and he escaped with his detachment by minutes only.

Another lesson learnt early in the retreat was the necessity of grouping artillery and infantry Brigades on the same route and at the same "communication centres." Where this policy was not followed, bad shooting inevitably resulted and the troops of the rear-guard were sometimes exposed to the shells of their own artillery through the impossibility of quickly communicating range corrections. When artillery and infantry Brigades worked in close *liaison* along one central route, there was no difficulty in improvising circuits or laying cables. Communication by line was good and the retreat well-ordered.

The chief difficulties in a hurried retreat were the number of moves of headquarters, the provision of lateral lines, the congestion of traffic, and the replenishment of cable and stores. The first of these was inevitable to a great extent, but the trouble could be minimised by careful attention to organization, by co-ordination from Corps head-quarters, and by the exercise of forethought. Movements of Corps headquarters twice in one day appear unnecessary, but such movements occurred. Divisions moved more frequently than they need have done, and lack of instruction as to direction of retreat resulted on more than one occasion in a swinging movement which brought the lines of communication, and consequently the main signal route, right across the exposed flank of the Division.

The question of the provision of lateral lines was difficult, and, under the circumstances of the retreat, often impossible of solution. Information from the flank was frequently of more importance than from the rear, yet it was usually not available. This could have been overcome only by the exercise of co-ordination by the higher command. If individual Divisions had been kept advised of the direction in which their neighbours were retreating, the problem in keeping intermittent lateral signal communication would have presented little difficulty to the signal companies.*

Congestion of traffic much affected the movements of the cable detachments and it may be laid down as an axiom that fast cable in such a retreat will not normally exceed a speed of one mile an hour. Roads crowded with retreating transport and with first line transport bringing up supplies, presented an almost insuperable obstacle to the harassed leaders of the cable detachments. Cross-country journeys were almost impossible—certainly impossible to a six-horsed team in the devastated Somme area across which the greater portion of the retreat took place. The arrival of an enemy bombing plane was even hailed on one occasion as an opportune incident. Bombs

---

* For example, W/T between Divisions and between Corps, W/T or visual between Brigades, visual between battalions.

were dropped and the road was cleared of traffic by a helpful combination of anxious drivers and unmanageable horses. The cable detachment was able to make unexpected progress and the occurrence was recorded in the report of its commander as an unmixed blessing.

The question of supply also bristled with difficulties when the zone formerly occupied by the Armies in their battle positions was left behind. As the cable and airline sections retreated through towns and villages which had formerly contained signal headquarters and stores, they filled up in turn with cable and other essentials. Single cable was taken in preference to twisted, for once again earthed lines had come to the fore and the importance of length of lines overrode any consideration of enemy overhearing. As the Divisions retreated off the Corps areas, however, the cable dumps became few and far between and the greatest economy had to be exercised. A cable famine was well in sight, and, indeed, in some Divisions, in existence, by the time the Amiens line was reached.

As far as possible Army lines were utilized by Corps, then by Divisions, and finally by Brigades and Battalions. Line communication was never attempted forward of battalion and only by about half of the formations forward of brigade. Finally, as the area was ceded to the enemy, Divisional personnel were instructed to complete the destruction of those circuits which the Corps linemen had left intact for their use. Here a distinct difficulty was encountered. Divisional signal companies were equipped neither with tools nor with explosives for destroying permanent routes. The best that could be done was to cut the wires and, whenever time permitted, this was carried out.

The different measure of success achieved by different formations very clearly pointed the principal lessons of the retreat as regards signal policy. The main principles laid down in S.S. 191 for an advance held good equally for a retreat. The direction taken should be controlled by the highest formation concerned. The movements of headquarters should be decided as early as possible and thoroughly advertised to superior, subordinate and lateral formations. Divisions Brigades, and battalions should be bunched as much as possible along one main Corps route.* If this is not practicable, work should be concentrated along one route in each Division. In order to ensure efficient *liaison* between Artillery and Infantry headquarters, it proved essential that they should camp together or within easy reach of each other by orderly. This was difficult to insist upon, as the tendency

---

* At one stage in a subsequent retreat, four Divisions were grouped together and were accommodated upon the Corps line system along which they were retreating. Everything would have worked very well, but unfortunately the Corps " lines " officer was not upon the spot. There was no one to allot the lines and the fourth Division found no circuit available for it at all.

was for the artillery Group or Brigade commander to live amongst his guns. It was, however, important, and was perhaps the most essential of all the lessons learnt.

Apart from general questions of signal policy it is interesting to review the effect of the retreat on each of the different means of signalling employed. First and foremost in rank of importance, as usual, was a line system modified considerably by the reversion to semi-mobile warfare. The measure of line communication achieved depended upon the utilization of the existing permanent routes and the use of the cable wagons. A certain amount of cross country work was still carried out by hand or by the use of one-horsed carts improvised from a hand barrow carried in the front half of a limber. By far the greater proportion of the main line system, however, was made up either of improvised circuits along the permanent lines, or of ground cable laid from the wagons of the cable sections.

The permanent routes within nine miles of the original front line had been much destroyed, but beyond this distance less damage had been done. The enemy's long-range guns could not be moved forward quickly and his bombing planes had such a large area to cover that a great proportion of the routes escaped. The troubles that arose in the utilization of the system by the subordinate formations were usually of a technical nature. Permanent records had not been kept at all test-poles and test-boxes and the confusion left in the offices after their hurried evacuation made it difficult to test out individual pairs. In addition, the Divisional linemen were not used to dealing with heavy routes and it was often found to be less trouble to lay fresh cables than to utilize the partially damaged permanent routes. In some cases the topmost circuits were reconstructed. In other cases, the whole of 12 or more pairs would be bunched and used as a single conductor. The permanent routes were, however, used to a much greater extent by the retreating Corps. Corps linemen knew more about these lines and were better able to sort out an office previously unknown to them. A Corps looking after 13 Divisions, seven Divisional Artilleries, and five Brigades of R.G.A., could not afford to lay cable to all its units. Both airline sections were fully employed testing out the circuits required, while the two cable sections ran short spurs from the nearest test-poles on the permanent lines to the proposed headquarters to which the formations were instructed to retreat. The task of the signal units was simplified to some extent by the adoption of a system of advanced exchanges for groups of Divisions and Brigades of R.G.A. For making stray connections, motor cyclist linemen were found invaluable and the judicious use of two or three of these men saved an immense amount of time and labour to the remainder of the maintenance personnel.

Within the Divisions, on the other hand, the cable wagon was the main means of establishing intercommunication. It was discovered that ground cable could be maintained in all cases except under barrage fire. Intercommunication by cable was the rule between Divisions and Brigades, and, with a little more organization, could have been used to a greater extent than it was between Brigades and Battalions. Speedy and unexpected moves and poor Staff work often resulted in interruptions of considerable duration, but when the situation had again cleared and the strayed Brigades or Divisions had been once more located, the cable wagons quickly reconstructed the Division—Brigade line system.

On occasions short lengths of cable were laid at a canter, but, as already mentioned, one mile an hour was a good average. Cable detachments worked devotedly and spent themselves to the utmost in the endeavour to give good and continuous service. Here, again, success varied with the method of employment, and cases occurred where Divisions relegated their cable detachments to the rear early in the retreat with drastic consequences to their intercommunication system. Others used them too recklessly in the first few days of rapid retreat and found they had no cable left to create a line system for their next stand. An old lesson was re-learnt when it was found that it was not advisable to lay lines at all when movement was fast unless a halt of 24 hours was likely. Judicious employment was essential to the success of the cable detachments, but in the majority of cases good results were obtained.

The cable parties were often much hampered in their work by lack of reliable information. Cases occurred constantly of a thousand or more yards of cable being laid, of orders being rescinded, and the cable dragged back and again " pulled " out in a different direction. Every such case added an unnecessary increment to a fatigue which was cumulative in its effect. Lines were laid under long-range infantry fire and under machine-gun fire, and many casualties occurred among the personnel of the sections. No department of the Signal Service did better work in these critical days than the cable sections and none justified to a greater extent the training in mobile warfare which had been carried out as part of the normal routine in every " resting " period.

Tanks and traffic were a source of damage to the lines and efficient *liaison* with the former was of course impossible. It was not possible under the circumstances to prepare "tank" crossings, and they would have been of little use, had they been built, since their presence could not have been notified in time. The use of ground, rather than poled cable overcame this trouble to a great extent, and, for the rest, it had to be accepted as one of the evils of the situation. The establishment of horse-lines along the main route of retreat was also a fruitful source of trouble, but this also could not be avoided.

The cables in general use were single " D5 " and " D1," though " D3," " D2," and twisted " D5 " were also used to some extent.

The need for the reinstalment of single cable in the equipment of the cable wagons was proved, and this reform was carried out immediately after the situation settled down.

In the rear of Brigades, ringing telephone with superimposed sounder represented the last word in efficient communication. Where lines were not well balanced, telephones were used for the transmission of phonograms as well as for speech. Forward of Brigades, message traffic was by fullerphone or by the ubiquitous "D3" telephone, which was still the last resort of the Signal officer in difficult situations. The large exchanges which had come into use during position warfare proved to be a nuisance in the mobile fighting which had now set in, and a strong recommendation for smaller exchanges was one result of the new phase. Many units made up small offices for use in temporary communication centres and in some cases the instruments of these were rigidly fixed to a table for facility of transport.

In effect, the possibility of good line communication even in a rapid retreat was demonstrated as surely as was the danger of the telephone habit which had gained so great a hold upon the Staff. The ideal line system during a retreat was shown to be a slender "grid" of ground cable laid out by the Corps cable sections along a carefully thought-out route and taken over by Divisions which were falling back in orderly manner by fore-ordained stages through headquarters selected by the Corps. One or two circuits only would be available for each Division, but these should suffice to carry all essential communication. As in the lesser retreats in the Cambrai sector, it was amply proved that the greater proportion of telephone conversation was unnecessary and might well be replaced by concise operation messages, carefully worded to prevent possibility of misconception.*

It was quite possible to maintain such a skeleton network in spite of shelling and traffic, but a heavy line system was out of the question. When the situation stabilized, as it did, first on the Army line and then upon the G.H.Q. reserve line in front of Amiens, the line system could be extended forward and reinforced in the rear. This was actually achieved on the front of most Divisions and a good example is afforded by the system of one Division, in particular, on the Army line.

In this Division, signal touch was maintained for three days by ground cable to each battalion in the line. Five minutes before the time when retreat became essential, orders were given to all battalion commanders over the telephone, the lines were disconnected, and the offices removed. The Division continued its march to the rear, with communication by D.R., and orderly. On arrival at the G.H.Q. line, the line system was once more built up and remained in existence until it was replaced by the normal buried system of position warfare.

* An interesting reversion to pre-war practice.

In spite of the comparative success with which line communication was kept up, wireless telegraphy again became an essential method of signalling. The two factors which still limited its usefulness were jamming—both from our own and from enemy stations—and the necessity for cipher or code.* Interference by enemy stations was very pronounced and, indeed, the Germans appeared to be relying principally upon their wireless stations for forward work. Jamming from neighbouring British stations was also serious, but was remedied to a great extent by strict control from Corps and Army headquarters. Where this control was not enforced, the system broke down ; where it was properly exercised, on the other hand, wireless proved invaluable.† The figures of wireless traffic during these few days had never been approached before. Stations of individual Divisions were dealing with as many as 100 to 120 tactical messages a day and this result was achieved in spite of the partial survival of cipher regulations. These latter were, however, swept away to a great extent, as they always were in anything approaching mobile warfare. Where they were rigidly insisted upon by a punctilious Staff, the wireless stations of the formation were, of course, crippled in their activities and their value was much reduced.

The mobility of the situation affected the Corps and Army stations for the first time and the need for practice in stepping-up procedure as far back as Army headquarters was at once seen. The stations of the higher formations were not habituated to mobile warfare and their absence from the scene of activity for periods of varying length invalidated the whole system to a certain extent.‡

A great advance in tactical organization was made by the issue of Wilson sets as local directing stations for Divisions, and, where this was done, much improvement in the Divisional scheme at once took place. In some Divisions, the question of transport was overcome by the use of the car of O.C. Signals for the transport of the Divisional directing station, and of pack horses for the stations

* Instances of confusion of cipher occurred. On one occasion an " urgent operation " message was delayed for several hours owing to the use of an Army code-word for an inter-Army message.

† In one Army the wireless officer and most of the personnel were sent to man the trenches, with consequent breakdown of the intercommunication system. This afforded an excellent example of the advisability of retaining technical personnel on their accustomed duties even in moments of the gravest emergency.

‡ For the first time, wireless became an essential means of intercommunication between an Army headquarters and G.H.Q. Soon after midnight of the first day of the retreat 5th Army headquarters lost touch by wire, and communication was re-established by wireless. Owing to the fact that the 5th Army wireless stations had been refitted for interception work, messages had to be transmitted through the medium of 3rd Army wireless station.

T

with Brigades. In the majority of cases, however, the Brigade stations were moved about by hand and it was only by herculean efforts on the part of the personnel of the stations that they were kept in action at all.

The available "loop" sets were very useful, and, as one of the lessons of the battles, a much more general issue of these forward sets was advocated. They were frequently invaluable for maintaining touch between Brigade and battalion headquarters and the transport problem was less serious where such light stations were concerned. The supply of accumulators to sets of all types was one of the difficulties which had to be overcome and the absence of the signal box car authorized, but not yet issued to Divisions, was especially felt in this connection. Many officers solved the problem by devoting a limber to this duty ; in other cases recourse was had to small dumps of accumulators left in well-marked spots along the line of retreat. By one means or another, most Divisions managed to arrange for a sufficient supply, and the wireless sets were in use during the greater part of the retirement, while power buzzers and amplifiers made their transitory appearance whenever the situation became more stable.

In many cases, the wireless stations fulfilled a valuable rôle by intercepting messages from all neighbouring formations and providing a *précis* for the digestion of the General Staff. On one occasion, at least, a German concentration was broken up through the interception of the orders by a station in the area affected. The message was translated at once and conveyed to the Staff, who ordered artillery fire to be directed upon the concentration area with the result that the attack never developed.

It was in keeping touch with flank formations that wireless, from its very nature, was most useful. Lateral lines were often impossible, but the portable wireless stations could establish touch, as well to right and left, as to the rear. It was to this method of signalling more than to any other that the Staff looked for information as to what their neighbours were doing. So long as the flank wireless stations were in commission there was little fear of a break-through taking place to right or left without information reaching the Divisional Commander in time to permit him to organize a defensive flank or to hasten his retreat.

Casualties to sets were very numerous, especially when attempts were being made to hold up the German advance on a definite line. At one time, one Division had every set out of action with injuries caused by enemy shell fire. During the second phase of the retreat, casualties to wireless personnel were not so common as those among the cable detachments. Many instances of individual bravery were recorded, however, and the personnel behaved well and rose fully to the exigencies of the situation. The one great chance of justifying wireless appeared to have arisen and few opportunities were lost.

Army wireless telegraphy came out of the March retreat holding an entirely different place in the opinion of the signal officer and the General Staff from that which it occupied before the battle.

It was now recognised that in mobile warfare this method of signalling had to be reckoned with as an essential means of communication. The formation without its wireless sets was nearly as crippled as that without the means of creating a line system. The time was soon coming when wireless was to prove its use equally well in the advance. When that had been done it had risen to its legitimate place in army economy as an essential means of signalling. Its early struggles for recognition had been justified by the result.

With the exception of the early hours of the morning during the first day or two of the retreat, conditions for visual were good and this means of signalling was extensively used. Forward of battalion headquarters it formed, as usual, the only alternative to runners. In rear of battalion headquarters it was frequently used to establish communication between the more erratic Brigade and Divisional headquarters. As in the case of wireless, the chief opportunity for visual arose when there was lack of co-ordination between retreating formations. A well co-ordinated retreat could be accommodated on an improvised line system ; formations retreating at random could only obtain touch through the medium of their wireless sets, or by utilizing favourable opportunities for the establishment of visual stations. For lateral communication, especially, visual was invaluable. In the rear areas the Lucas lamp was the main means used, with the heliograph as substitute on isolated occasions. Forward, flags were used a great deal, but the folding shutter attached to a bayonet fixed on the end of the signaller's rifle was the favourite method. Pocket electric torches were again used with success over short distances.

In one Division, visual was the sole means available between Division and Brigade for three days, and 50 messages a day were disposed of by the visual stations. This was exceptional, however, and implied a breakdown in other methods of intercommunication. One difficulty experienced as a result of the general use of visual was the exposure of certain small differences in the procedure used by different units. This could be traced directly to imperfections and ambiguities in the Training Manual of Signalling which had led instructors at different schools of training to adopt their own interpretation of the obscure points. In a normal chain of visual signalling where the units of a Division worked usually among themselves, these peculiarities had not been particularly noticeable, but the general use of visual for lateral signalling at once betrayed them and pointed out the necessity for a more precisely worded manual.

The employment of message-carrying agencies was perhaps most marked by the rise in importance of the motor cyclist despatch rider and the elimination of the pigeon. Motor cyclists were all worked exceptionally hard and were often called upon to carry out portions of their journeys under rifle or machine-gun fire. Frequently the location of the units they were bound for was uncertain, but considerable ingenuity was displayed in unearthing headquarters. Many despatch riders did valuable reconnaissance work in addition to their normal duties. The men worked with little rest and less food and in the more hurried hours of the retreat were of vital importance. They were reinforced where possible by mounted orderlies but the latter were too few to be of maximum use.

In some formations, both motor cyclists and mounted orderlies were worked with a lack of discrimination which resulted in undue fatigue and sometimes in the delay of urgent despatches. Despatch riders were sometimes used to find subordinate units who should have notified their whereabouts to the nearest signal office. Here the importance of the paragraphs in Section 20 of S.S. 191 were strongly emphasized. Unless units gave their assistance in establishing a system of orderlies between themselves and the signal office during the halt for the night, it was impossible for the Signal Service to undertake delivery of more than a few of the more urgent messages. The supply of signal orderlies was totally inadequate for the purpose, for these men were only intended for the delivery of messages to the offices of the local formation Staff. This lesson, also, should have been learnt from the mobile fighting in 1914, but the command of the majority of units had altered entirely since those days.

Forward of battalion headquarters, the experiences of the retreat all pointed towards the formation of one main chain of intercommunication on each battalion front. Here, as further to the rear, the main lesson learned was the need for economy of personnel and for concentration along one predetermined route. Thus, and thus only, could fairly uninterrupted intercommunication be achieved. It was seen that, if this system of concentration was adopted in position warfare, then transition to mobile conditions was easy and could be carried out with the least loss of material and expenditure of man-power. The same policy should be carried out successively back to Brigade, Division, and to Corps. When open warfare supervened, the concentration of all efforts on one single Divisional route would then be easily accomplished.

The vital importance of the axiom, " *One formation, one signal route* " cannot be overestimated, for this principle, well carried out, provides the acme of signal communication of forces on the move. The application of signal methods in an advance to the situations of a retreat is not too obvious, but the resemblance which *should* exist between the signal systems in both types of warfare cannot be too strongly insisted upon. A comparison of a series of diagrams of signal systems in the retreats of the summer and the advance of the autumn of 1918 would show this very well. A comparison of similar diagrams of the hypothetical systems the signal officers concerned would now employ in similar situations in the light of their experience of that year would probably illustrate my point immeasurably better. It is unfortunate that financial considerations will not permit of the inclusion of such series in the present volume.

---

The loss of stores which accompanied the retreat was to be deplored, but was inevitable. It had been foreseen to a great extent, but circumstances were such that it could not have been avoided. Preparations for a withdrawal were to be deprecated on many grounds, and particularly on account of the effect they were bound to have upon the *morale* of the troops concerned. The loss of trench signal stores was the lesser of two evils and was necessarily acquiesced in. Actually, much of the Army signal equipment was saved, being thrown hastily unto railway trucks and despatched back to Abbeville. The stores that remained were largely used by the subordinate formations in their retreat and were the one factor which made possible the maintenance of the line system. Large quantities, again, were destroyed by the last signal units to pass them; more still were annihilated by our own and the enemy artillery. Considerable amounts did, however, pass into the enemy's hands intact, and evidence of this was afforded during the advances of the following autumn, by the amount of British field cable being used by the Germans. The effect of the loss and destruction of signal stores was severely felt in the ensuing summer, but, on the whole, the situation might have been much worse.

---

On April 5th, the German offensive on the Somme front came to an end and the exhausted troops were left to recover themselves while the scene of action shifted quickly to the north. On April 7th, a bombardment, which rivalled in intensity that of March 21st, broke out along the whole front from Lens to Armentières. The attack which followed presented in its main features a marked resemblance to the advance in March, but was not on anything like so important a scale. Only 42 as opposed to 73 German Divisions were engaged : the front was much shorter, and the advance in no case exceeded a depth of ten miles. The action also was slower and the advances more spasmodic, except upon the front held by the Portuguese Corps. It was here that the pigeon service lost a fixed loft, that at Lacouture being captured complete with birds.

Thick fog was, once more, a characteristic of the calm weather of the day of the initial attack. All the elements were again favourable to a surprise and the enemy made appreciable progress on the first day of the battle. In the days which followed, many of the tired

Divisions just recovering from their experiences on the Somme were thrown in to stem the onrush of the German hordes. The signal companies were thus given an opportunity of putting into practice the experience they had gained in the previous battle and a very efficient signal system was usually the result. In its main features it followed the lines indicated earlier in this chapter. (pp. 257—275).

The same isolated instances of power buzzer-amplifier communication to surrounded strong points was again recorded. The station at La Basse Ville, in particular, was still working when the rear station was forced to withdraw out of range. The less general nature of the retreat enabled twisted cable to be used in preference to single cable. Pigeons were of greater use, and in one case a service of birds was kept up, although the loft to which they worked was within 500 yards of the front line. It was found, however, that pigeons were inclined to be shell-shy when alighting in heavily shelled areas.

Wireless, on account of the slight nature of the withdrawal, still suffered under cipher restrictions and operators who had become used to sending " in clear " messages during the great retreat were betrayed into indiscretions in consequence of that experience, and in some cases disciplinary action was necessary. The first work carried out on the line system was the replacement of airline by cable. In front, the buries were giving good service, and when the retreat carried the Divisions off them, the ground cable once more formed a good basis for a reliable intercommunication system. The principle of the Divisional route was by now firmly established and the chief lesson of the short Lys battle was confirmation of the fact that correct deductions had been drawn from the experience of the previous month.

---

The failure to penetrate the northern portion of the British front brought to a close the enemy offensives against the British Armies, but on May 27th the 9th Corps was involved in a very similar battle, where 28 German Divisions were hurled against the 6th French Army in their positions on the line of the Aisne.

The report of the A.D. Signals on the signal practice in this battle, where a solitary British Corps was isolated amidst French formations, contains several paragraphs of peculiar interest. Comment was made particularly on the weakness of the French system of arbitrarily fixing the dug-outs of the buried cable system and then leading in to headquarters with poled cables. When the initial bombardment opened, all these aerial connections were blown to scraps and much valuable personnel was lost in attempts to replace them. The buries themselves remained through, but full use could not be made of them because of the frequent interruptions in the leading-in cables.

The waste of material and labour in installing a telephone system forward of battalion headquarters was also once more emphasised.

The network of cables which had been built up with much care and trouble was blown away in a few minutes. During quiet times such a system could be dispensed with ; during a battle of any intensity it was worse than useless.

One feature of the battle was the absence for several days of rear intercommunication except by despatch rider. Owing to the peculiar disposition of the Army headquarters, all the main rear routes ran for many miles parallel with the front that the enemy were attacking. Moreover, practically all the routes were concentrated at one point in a town which was an obvious target for the enemy's heavy artillery. The result was that, for a long period after the first few hours of the battle, the Corps was practically isolated. It was not until the headquarters of formations had retreated on to an excellent system of locality telephone exchanges in the rear areas that the absence of shelling, which here as in previous retreats distinguished the mobile phase of the battle, permitted of general telephone communication to the rear.

Forward of Corps headquarters, the communication to Divisions and Corps H.A. depended entirely upon hop-pole routes and these served excellently until the mobile phase of the retreat set in. Then, again, recourse was had to ground cable laid by the Corps along the routes by which the Divisions were directed to retreat. As in the Lys retreat, in which this Corps played a prominent part, each Corps airline section was divided up into three improvised detachments which were used for laying cable. By means of these detachments three main cable routes were laid which were looped in at intervals to nodal points and were used throughout by the retreating Divisions.

As in the previous battles, the necessity for more lateral communication was seen. The retreat was very hurried and signal touch from front to rear was all that could be maintained. Alternative methods were useful, but were only very partially successful. Wireless was used during the early hours of the battle, but the destruction of numerous stations and the capture of others soon practically eliminated this means of signalling. Pigeons also were of great use during the first few hours of the retreat, but when the withdrawal became more hurried, all lofts were evacuated or destroyed.

The withdrawal was so hasty and equipment was so scarce that visual was of little use. Aeroplane *liaison* was, however, better than it had ever been before. The Divisional dropping grounds were used continually and almost all the messages contained information of value. Motor cyclists once more came into their own and the observation was made that the attachment of a *liaison* officer to collate the incidental information collected by these men might have been extremely valuable to the higher command.

The casualties of the signal units, already decimated by the previous fighting, were once more very high. The following table which gives the establishments of the units and the percentage of casualties suffered by each in these few days of fighting will give some idea of the wastage which the Signal Service as a whole had suffered during each of the three retreats referred to.*

## TABLE VII.

*Percentage Casualties of Signal Units of the 9th Corps During the Aisne Retreat.*

| Unit. | | Casualties. | | Establishment. | | Percentage. |
|---|---|---|---|---|---|---|
| | | Officers. | Men. | Officers. | Men. | |
| 50th Div Sig. Co. | .. | 6 | 110 | | | 41% |
| 25th Div. Sig. Co. | .. | — | 10 | 11 | 272 | 4% |
| 21st Div..Sig. Co. | .. | — | 22 | | | 8% |
| 8th Div. Sig. Co. | .. | 3 | 90 | | | 33% |
| 9th Corps Sig. Co. | .. | — | 25 | 1 | 97 | 26% |

The signal units were in urgent need of a prolonged period of rest to enable them to refit and to absorb the partially trained reinforcements who now formed some considerable portion of the strength of the forward sections. This they were to have when a new period of stationary warfare enabled them to prepare for the victory that was to crown the efforts of the Allies.

One aspect of the recent fighting about which little has been said is the absorption into the firing line of signal personnel which took place to an unparalleled extent during the retreat. The fighting formations were strained to the uttermost to cope with the emergencies which arose one after another. In order to man reserve lines of trenches, officers were deputed to collect stragglers and non-combatants of every grade, arm them as best they could, and line them up to stop the enemy rush. In the early stages of the Lys battle, for instance, one battery alone lost 15 orderlies conveying important messages in less than one hour, and it seemed farcical to attempt to keep up intercommunication by runner at all. Signal personnel apart from orderlies were usually exempt from such forlorn hopes by virtue of the distinguishing blue and white band which vouched for their importance at their legitimate work. There were, however, exceptions to the rule, and there may arrive a time in any battle when the technical value of the signaller is outweighed by his potential value as a rifleman or bomber.

It should be remembered, however, that he is a signaller first and an infantry soldier only a long way afterwards. His technical training has fitted him for specific duties for which the ordinary infantryman has not been trained : while his technical duties have not fitted him for employment as a marksman and have made him totally

* Figures in *Table* VII. are exclusive of attached men. The proportion of casualties in two units'was unusually high. This is explained partly by capture of forward personnel and partly by the fact that the Brigade Signal sections became involved in the fighting.

unused to the bayonet. He is also likely to know nothing of the intricacies and ways of bombs.

It is very seldom that a justifiable case can be made out for the deliberate employment of Signal Service personnel in the firing line. When such a case is made out, however, or, when the signaller is caught up in the rush and hurry of a rapid retreat, experience has shown that he will rise to the occasion and fight with a resolution and intelligence which will help to make up for his lack of skill.

Examples of the use of Signal Service personnel as infantry occurred on all three retreats, and in the Aisne battle, especially, the Brigade sections of more than one Division acted as riflemen through a strenuous action. The classical instance occurred, however, in the retreat from the Somme when a mixed force of details which contained a proportion of signallers, wireless operators, linemen and telegraph operators, was hastily organized and thrown into the reserve line of trenches before Amiens.* For five days, from March 29th to April 2nd, these amateur infantrymen held their position under intermittent bombardment from artillery and low-flying aeroplanes.

---

As a general rule, the special effects of the retreats on the dispositions of the Signal Service stopped short at the final positions taken up by the headquarters of the Armies involved. A certain amount of telescoping of the routes between Army headquarters and G.H.Q. naturally occurred, and emergency measures were prepared for a general removal of the dumps and Depôts which were threatened by the German advance.

Perhaps the most interesting result of the situation was the closing of the school at Abbeville, the men and material being held in readiness for use as reinforcements to the Corps engaged in the fighting. The increased importance of wireless in particular made imperative the need for the immediate replacement of losses both of personnel and instruments. An innovation which should be noticed as part of the emergency signal system, was the establishment of a C.W. motor wireless section at Abbeville, to act as an alternative means of intercommunication between the O.C. Troops, Abbeville district, and G.H.Q., where similar sets had been installed.†

Two sequels to the retreat also deserve mention. The first of these was the issue of elaborate instructions for the destruction of signal stores and communications in the event of another serious retirement. All instruments and stores were to be destroyed. Test-boxes

---

* Fifth Army Signal Company provided a complete company, with officers and transport, all volunteers.

† A similar set was also sent to Second Army with whom French troops were operating in order to provide direct communication between this Army headquarters and Marshal Foch's headquarters.

on buried routes were to be blown up. All open routes were to be broken down as Corps headquarters retreated past them, with the exception of the two upper wires. As the routes became spare, further damage was to be done. Stays were to be cut, poles—especially junction poles—cut or blown down, and terminal poles and roof standards were to be thoroughly smashed. When destruction was not possible, hidden faults were to be introduced with a view to making a hurried use of the routes by the enemy impossible. Fortunately these precautions were never required by ourselves, although similar instructions were very thoroughly carried out by the enemy in his retreat in the autumn of the same year.

A further direct result of the experiences of the retreat was the special training ordered for all forward signal units during the next few months of quiet. One cable detachment was kept continually at cable wagon exercise whenever possible. Wireless personnel were practised at quick installation of stations and at packing trials. Divisional and Brigade visual personnel were exercised as much as possible on moving station schemes. Half an hour's physical exercise per day was aimed at for the headquarter staff of signal units. Finally, route marches became a most important part of the normal routine during resting periods. By some or all of these means the physique of the signal personnel of Corps and Division was improved and the mobility of the units increased. By the time the advance commenced most signal units were able to carry out long marches and work through long and fatiguing days without being overtired. The policy of concentrating on training for mobile warfare was entirely justified by results.

The success of the Signal Service in adapting a rigid system to the mobile conditions of the retreat, was in itself a triumph, both for the organisers of the forward system and policy and for the personnel whose wholehearted devotion enabled the best results to be obtained from the dispositions made. The crystallisation of the opinion of the General Staff, whose needs signals are primarily intended to serve, is seen in the following quotation from the official despatch describing this incident of the war :—

" During the long periods of active fighting the strain placed upon the Signal Service was immense. The frequent changes of headquarters and the shifting of the line entailed constant labour, frequently attended with great danger, in the maintenance of communications ; while the exigencies of the battle on more than one occasion brought the personnel of signal units into the firing line. The Signal Service met the calls made upon it in a manner wholly admirable, and the efficient performance of its duties was of incalculable value."

# CHAPTER XV.

POSITION WARFARE IN THE SUMMER OF 1918. FINAL
CONSIDERATION OF REORGANIZATIONS DUE TO THE
GROWTH OF THE EXPEDITIONARY FORCE AND
STATIONARY WARFARE.

SYNOPSIS.

Effect of the Retreat on the New Stationary Warfare System.—Buries Back to
Corps Headquarters.—The Signal System of the G.H.Q. Reserve Line.—Shortage
of Material Produces a Relatively Slender Line System.—The Human Element in
Buried Cable.—Education of the Working Parties.—The Bury of the Future.—
General Characteristics of the 1918 Summer Signal System.—Development of
Wireless.—C.W. W/T *liaison* with the French.—Silent Days.—The Signal Service
thoroughly Efficient.—G.H.Q. and L. of C. Signals.—Traffic Statistics for 1918.—
Standardization of Stores.—Field and Armoured Cable.—The Four-plus-three
Buzzer and the Test Panel.—Signal Repair Workshops.—Air Force Signals.—Re-
organization of Divisional Signal Companies.—Revision of Signal Service Qualifi-
cations and Trades.—The Commanding Officer's Certificate.—Formation of S.D.6
and Appointment of D. Signals, G.H.Q. Home Forces.—Training American Signal
Units.—Artillery Effects on Signals in 1918.—Maintenance Difficulties.—End of
Trench Warfare.

THE signal system which sprang into existence in the short period
between the retreats of the spring and early summer of 1918, and
the advance in the autumn of the same year, while it closely resembled
previous position warfare systems, had certain characteristics which
were directly due to the withdrawals. Certain lessons had been
learnt, certain inconveniences had been caused.

Amongst the changes which were the outcome of the lessons of
the retreat, was the tendency to adapt the intercommunication
system to a much greater extent than formerly to the requirements of
the principle of " defence in depth." Not only were the rear signal
arrangements much more carefully planned, but forward signal
personnel were kept much better informed as to the routes which
existed in the rear and upon which they would have to fall back in the
event of a retreat.

One feature of the new system was the extension of the " tail "
of the buries to dug-outs well behind Divisional headquarters. This,
again, was the result of the experience of the recent battles, where it
had been conclusively shown that airline or poled cable forward of
Corps headquarters could not be expected to survive the fierce bombardments preceding any attack of considerable magnitude. Buries
which had formerly stopped at Divisional headquarters were now

usually carried well to the rear and terminated within the Corps maintenance area, sometimes at Corps headquarters itself. The extension of the buried cable still further to the rear can be seen in the laying down of elaborate systems in the G.H.Q. defence line which was an important factor in the new defence scheme. The proposed line was marked out and partially dug and behind it trenched cable routes were prepared. One such route was dug for each Divisional front of 4,000 yards, and routes were carried back for a maximum distance of 4,000 yards also. Shortage of cable permitted of the laying of ten pairs only in each trench, but, skeleton system as it was, it was a great advance on anything of the kind that had been attempted before.

Fortunately, the trend of the war did not make necessary the use of these emergency lines. Had the troops been compelled to fall back so far, however, they would have retreated upon a zone which was wired up with a six-foot buried system extending well forward to the front line trenches and to all important observation posts. There could have been no question of defence being made impossible by lack of adequate intercommunication.

The forward buried system was also affected by the same shortage of material and the result was a telegraph and telephone system which catered for essential needs only. One outcome of the loss of stores which accompanied the March retreat was a simplicity of signal communications quite unlike the former complicated position warfare system. In view of the speed with which the situation was again to dissolve, there can be no doubt that this enforced simplicity was a blessing in disguise. All officers were obliged to cut down their telephone conversation to a minimum even when the line system was in complete working order. Before the losses of cable and instruments could be made good, the autumn advances had commenced, and elaborate line communication was impossible from entirely different reasons.

It was only in those Divisions which had been holding the line at points other than those affected by the spring battles, that Staffs and commanders had not become reconciled to a decrease in signal facilities. In such cases, the necessary experience was to be gained in a few hectic days in August and September, when relations between Staff and Signal Service were strained almost to breaking point.

The two salient features in which the buries of the summer of 1918 differed from those of earlier stationary warfare days, have been emphasized in the preceding paragraphs. In all other essentials the systems were practically a replica of the late 1917 buries. Further refinements of camouflage were attempted, and protection was still considered to be a matter of supreme importance. Before passing finally from the consideration of stationary warfare signals, however, some space should be devoted to the human element in the buried cable problem which has not yet been referred to at any length.

Buried cable could only be laid down to any great extent by the systematic exploitation of the labour of large infantry working parties. The supervision of such parties had, indeed, become an important element of the normal work of the majority of the officers of the Divisional and Corps signal units. It was only to be expected that the work should be intensely disliked by the infantry. Troops in the line could not, of course, be employed. Sufficient reserves were rarely available to admit of labour battalions being specially told off for this very important but equally unpleasant task. The brunt of the work therefore fell upon the men of the infantry battalions which had been withdrawn from the line for a short spell of " rest." This practice had many disadvantages both from the point of view of the infantry-man and of the signal officer.

To the former, the work was anathema. Summoned from his rest billets he was forced to march long distances in the dark, and often in the wet, across shelled areas, to the site of the work. He then had to toil for several hours under most unpleasant conditions at a task in which he had usually not the slightest interest. The majority of the men would almost certainly have preferred a longer spell in the line with shorter but uninterrupted periods of rest. The signal officer was certainly doing work which was in the ordinary course of his duties and in which he had a proprietary and a technical interest. On the other hand, no task could have been so unpleasant to him as that of victimising unwilling infantrymen with whom he had the greatest sympathy.

The work had to be done, however, and unfortunately under the existing conditions no better means of carrying it out was available. Infantry working parties were essential if a safe intercommunication system was to be built up. No amount of thought on anybody's part could discover an alternative ; no amount of grumbling could alter the necessity for the work.

There were, however, ways by which hardship could be palliated and the interest of the working parties stimulated. One cause of frequent and most unnecessary injustice, it was, unfortunately, not within the power of the Signal Service to eliminate. It quite often happened that working parties arrived at the scene of their labours already utterly tired out. To a practised eye it was quite easy to distinguish between the ordinary " tired " malingerer and the man who really was utterly played out. Inquiry would usually show, either that the men had done a hard day's march before arriving at their work, or that the particular section of the party which was affected had been employed for several hours during the preceding day on R.E. Field Works or other heavy fatigue duties. Such men were, of course, worse than useless. They could not accomplish their task, and, if they were not used, they demoralized their neighbours by their inactivity.   If they were employed, on the other hand, it necessarily meant leaving a portion of the trench open for future completion. This, in its turn, probably entailed special attention from the enemy's artillery on the following night.   Such occurrences were, of course, the result of bad Staff work on the part of battalions or Brigades concerned.   The signal officer in charge of the work might, by the exercise of considerable judgment, minimise the effect of such an error, but it was beyond him to remedy entirely, and only to a limited extent could he prevent its recurrence.

Other troubles were, however, more easily dealt with on the spot or by careful preparation.   Otherwise indifferent or actively unwilling working parties might frequently be galvanized into activity by arranging as a matter of course to let them go at the completion of a stated task.   Measured tasks would be given to each man, and he would be informed that on the completion of the trench to a depth of 6 ft. 6 ins., the cable would be laid, and that, immediately his particular platoon had finished filling in and their work had been passed by the responsible officer, they might be marched away.   Work would be feverish until the trench was completed, and woe betide any man who through laziness or lack of skill with pick or shovel failed to complete his task within reasonable time.   By adopting such means, much more work could be obtained from a given party in a given time, but there was one essential—the promise once given must be scrupulously kept.   If, through miscalculation, too small a task had been allotted and the party finished earlier than was necessary to ensure their disappearance before the light returned, on no account should an additional task be imposed.   The experience gained should be filed for future reference and the men allowed to escape lightly.   They could then be expected to return cheerfully, in the assurance of fair play, when their turn came round again.

Another method by which much was done in some Divisions to overcome the natural antipathy of the infantry to signal working parties, was by efficient propaganda directed towards the education of the men in an appreciation of the uses of the cables they were burying.   Once a definite connection could be established in their minds between the cable trenches and such things as reliefs, artillery support, rations, etc., they were much more interested in their work and inclined to view it as a necessary evil.   Propaganda took the form of typed leaflets setting forth the why and the wherefore of buried cable, and describing as briefly as possible the method of burying and the essential features of a well-dug trench.

These were distributed in large numbers to the headquarters of each battalion in the Division with the request that they should be circulated among the infantry.   When this was thoroughly done, the hearty co-operation of infantry officers was ensured, while intelligent and willing work on the part of the men—a still more desirable result—was also often secured.

Under no circumstances could the working parties be expected to bring much enthusiasm to bear upon work which was done in what they felt should be their spare time and which was so far outside their normal province. There was, however, all the difference between the tasks which were carried out by men in a sullen spirit working under the compulsion of discipline, and those performed by men actuated by an intelligent desire to complete what they recognized to be an essential link in the chain of signal communication which helped to secure their comfort and safety.*

The buried cable systems of this particular period of the war were not destined to be thoroughly tested to any great extent. Isolated offensive and defensive actions took place on short portions of the British front, but the opening of the great autumn offensive was preceded over a great portion of the front by an enemy withdrawal which took the Divisions and the Corps off the freshly-constructed buries. At other points, the 1918 buries formed the backbone of a safe signal system which easily accommodated the traffic of the preparation period and the initiation of the offensive. Even in these cases they were in use for a few days only. The Armies marched off them in August and September, never to return.

The bury was essentially a product of position warfare, and disappeared entirely immediately the situation became mobile. The rapid development of buried cable, like that of almost every other branch of signal activity, may be attributed entirely to stationary warfare waged from and in well-prepared defence positions. It has been described in fairly detailed manner in the preceding pages, because it was of paramount importance from the spring of 1915 to the summer of 1918. Without it, line communication in trench

---

* Examples of two typical attitudes adopted by the normal infantryman towards signal fatigues are afforded by two anecdotes, both of which refer to working parties which were engaged on work for which the writer was responsible.

The purely intolerant attitude of the disgruntled worker was well expressed by the soldier who said within the hearing of the party of Sappers who were overseeing the work:—" If I were digging graves for b——y R.E'.s, mate, I'd be happy."

A rather more happy frame of mind, which could make a joke out of certainly very unpleasant work, is instanced by the second anecdote.

A Sherwood Forester working party was engaged under intermittent shellfire and continuous and soaking rain, in digging a bury in the district in front of Mount Kemmel. As the officer in charge of the working party passed two of the men they straightened up for a spell. Wiping the mingled sweat and rain from his brow one man said : " Well, Bill, in six days God made the earth. On the seventh day he made the —— Notts and Derbys to dig the whole b——y lot up again."

warfare would have been impossible except through periods of altogether sub-normal artillery activity. It will need to be kept in mind and its possibilities developed by the Signal Corps of the future. One obvious direction in which research appears urgent is the development of the mechanical excavator to replace the infantry, artillery, or pioneer working parties of the past. There is prospect of the need for machines that will bury cable to a depth of 10 or 12 feet at a reasonable speed and with reasonable quietness. Only by means of such mechanical aids will it be possible to cover the scene of warfare as far back as Army headquarters, perhaps even to the bases, with an invulnerable network of wires sufficient to serve the needs of the modern Army. It is possible that position warfare on a large scale may not recur. It is, perhaps, more likely that line communication will be difficult in the future throughout the whole area of belligerent countries unless through the medium of cables buried to a depth not contemplated even for the most forward routes, in the war of 1914–1918.*

Meanwhile, no complete substitute for main line communication behind Corps headquarters has yet been evolved, though an excellent auxiliary means is certainly available in the form of wireless telegraphy.

The effect of the loss of stores in the March retreat on the cable system of the summer was duplicated with similar result on all other means of intercommunication. The loss of visual apparatus had been especially severe. The loss of wireless apparatus, though less serious in amount, was far more difficult to make good. The chief reflection of the battles of the spring on the signal system generally, was seen, therefore, in the reduction of the intercommunication facilities, not only over the lines, but also by all alternative methods. The elaborate chains of visual stations and wireless stations characteristic of 1917 were replaced by a more skeletal arrangement. More attention was perforce paid to the siting of visual stations and to obtaining the maximum range from the wireless sets. Here, again, the greater depth of the defence zone made itself felt, as it had upon the line system. Divisional and Brigade headquarters had been taught by their experiences to keep well back and lines and other signalling chains in a Divisional area were stretched much further out from front to rear.

Means of signalling remained substantially unchanged. Message-carrying rockets made their appearance on a large scale for the first time. Messenger dogs and " loop " wireless sets were also beginning

* It is, however, possible that " shallow " splinter-proof buries may be the ultimate solution in rear of Army H. Q. The enemy is unlikely to be able to bomb the whole of the countryside and numerous shallow routes may give sufficient alternatives with less expenditure of time and labour.

Inside the dug-out.   A Wireless Operator at work.

A forward Wireless Station.

to be used to a considerable extent. The latter, indeed, were already fast displacing the power buzzer in the estimation of the infantry and were also becoming popular for use between observation posts and battery headquarters, and between battery and Brigade. It was a great convenience to forward artillery units to have some means of wireless communication which was common both to artillery and infantry. In the November battle and in the retreats, *liaison* between artillery and infantry disappeared to a great extent with the breakdown of the line system. In the future, this is likely to be met by the universal use of continuous wave wireless with all the higher formations of both arms. In the past, it has been a distinct drawback which was only partially overcome by a common means of wireless communication in the shape of the forward spark sets.*

Continuous wave wireless continued to gain ground in popularity with the artillery and its more general use in the future was foreshadowed. Difficulty in supplying the sets in large numbers prevented full use being made of this method. Complaints of shortage of sets had been particularly common during the retreats.

It was in the May battle between the Aisne and the Marne that C.W. wireless was first used for *liaison* between the French and British Corps headquarters. A C.W. set with French operators was attached to 9th Corps headquarters for the purpose of keeping touch with the French Army under which the Corps was working, and with the flank French Corps. This method of procedure was improved upon in the final advance, when the flank British Corps and Division were both issued with similar sets to enable them to keep in constant touch with their neighbours to the south.

The importance of wireless and visual in mobile warfare had been emphasized in the recent withdrawal, while, at the same time, the disinclination of the Staff and regimental officers to make the maximum use of these alternative methods of transmitting information had also been brought out. A result of both these circumstances was the more general use of a mode of training which took the form of the institution of what are best indicated by the title "silent days." Certain days in each week or month were set apart during which none but the most urgent tactical messages were permitted to be passed by telephone or telegraph. Alternative methods of signalling—and in particular wireless and visual—were to be substituted entirely for line signalling. The full effect of these days was not always seen, for there was a marked tendency in normal times to save up traffic until the period of the ban was passed and then to launch an avalanche of deferred messages upon the signal office ! They had, however, a good effect in proving to

* The use of these sets was, of course, much limited by jamming between the only two wave-lengths available.

U

officers of all grades and of all arms that the telephone and telegraph, though convenient and speedy, were not essential. A reflection of this teaching was soon seen in the advances of the autumn, when, in some Divisions, the alternative signal routes were relied upon almost entirely for hours together, and were fully used.* Many things are considered indispensable until through force of circumstances they have to be done without. The principle of the new training was to anticipate the time when line signalling should become intermittent or impossible and to familiarize the users of the Army signal system with the slower, but—under certain conditions —surer, of the means at their disposal.

Much might be said of this last trench warfare signal system, but the essential differences from former similar systems have been touched upon already. It was the ultimate expression of three years' experience of position warfare, and it completely satisfied the Staff whose needs it was intended to serve. It was slender, indeed, but it was entirely adequate to the requirements of the situation. The shortcomings of signal officers are speedily reflected in a lack of efficiency in their formations and in the attitude adopted towards them by their General Staff. The good relations uniformly maintained in the last few months of the war between the Staff of the great majority of formations and their signal officers was the greatest tribute to the efficiency of the latter.

———————

Although the signal system of this last period of stationary warfare requires little special notice, a digression should be made to permit of mention of such incidents of the development of the rear Signal Service as have perforce been neglected in the endeavour to convey a connected account of the development of forward signal practice, policy and organization.

On the Lines of Communication great increases had taken place, but with little alteration in type of work. As the Army grew, so the number of units on the Lines of Communication and the volume of the administrative traffic increased proportionately. This was met by a series of increases to " L " Signal Company, which culminated in its reorganization on a battalion basis.

The various steps of increase from the landing of the Expeditionary Force in France to the conclusion of the Armistice on November 11th, 1918, are well shown in the following table :—

* In the final advance one Division in the north existed for two or three days upon wireless alone. No other means of intercommunication was used between Division and Brigades.

## TABLE VIII.

| Date | | Establishment. | | Remarks. |
|------|---|---|---|----------|
| | | Officers. | O.R. | |
| Aug. 4th | 1914 | 5 | 268 | Original L. of C. Signal Co. |
| October, | 1915 | 25 | 1138 | Formation of Telegraph Con. Dets. and Rly. Tel. Dets. |
| March, | 1916 | 25 | 1218 | |
| June, | 1916 | 28 | 1334 | |
| November, | 1916 | 30 | 1773 | Name changed to " L " Sig. Battn. |
| November, | 1917 | 54 | 2380 | |
| August, | 1918 | 100 | 3358 | Absorption of G.H.Q. Sig. Co. |
| Nov. 11th, | 1918 | 110 | 4102 | |

The increases were a faithful reflection of the growth of the Administrative Services of the Expeditionary Force. Such changes in organisation as were made were undertaken to facilitate administration and centralise control under the Deputy Director of Army Signals. The latter, until June 1915, had his headquarters with the Inspector-General of Communications, but, after that month, was absorbed into the Directorate of Signals at G.H.Q.

The work carried out by the Lines of Communication construction personnel rivalled that of the G.P.O. at home in times of peace. The skilled personnel were recruited in the main from that department and from the maintenance and operating staff of the telegraph department of the railway companies. Main telephone and telegraph lines were constructed connecting up the ports between Havre and Dunkerque with all headquarters, and with all important centres of supply and administration within the area occupied by the British Forces. The district covered by these operations was roughly 180 miles by 120 miles. Moves of General and Army headquarters involved adjustment of the whole of this complicated system at short notice and such moves had to be foreseen and lines built beforehand to anticipate decisions of the Staff. Provision had also to be made for communication with London, Paris, Allied headquarters, the Independent Air Force and Marseilles. The anti-aircraft defence of ammunition dumps alone involved a very large amount of construction.

About 1,500 miles of main telegraph and telephone routes averaging 20 wires were constructed in the L. of C. area in addition to many miles in Army areas, as well as an immense amount of lesser connections. To this must be added the heavy maintenance work, the diversions, the fortification of signal offices and the burying of routes, made necessary by the bombing raids of 1917 and 1918. Finally, the signal communications required by the Director General of Transportation for the traffic control of the railways, entailed the putting up of many thousands of miles of wire both on existing railway lines and on new construction. These lines, also, were situated in heavily shelled and bombed areas and were particularly difficult to maintain.

Large as were the dimensions reached by the construction establishments, they were never more than equal to the demands made upon them. There was always more work on hand than could well be carried out with the personnel available, and the maintenance of an efficient Lines of Communication signal system was only accomplished by continual labour, often attended, even in the rear areas,* by the special difficulties inseparable from a state of war.

The signal traffic dealt with was very heavy, the total of the telegrams originated, transmitted and received in the L. of C. area in a single 24-hours period amounting in the latter days of the war to as high a figure as 23,000. Comparative telegraph and

* Two chief alterations in signal methods on the Lines of Communication require mention. The first was the introduction of "concentrator" working at the principal transmitting stations of the Force. Concentrator apparatus was first installed at Abbeville towards the latter end of 1916. Later, in 1918, a special type of concentrator was installed at G.H.Q., at Rouen and at Huchenneville. An automatic calling device was added later to relieve the concentrator operators of the considerable amount of work involved in calling distant stations.

This system of concentrator working undoubtedly effected a considerable saving in man-power, though it was found also to result in undesirable delay to messages in some instances.

The second innovation was the use of the telephone repeater to enable direct speech to take place over unusually long lines. The first experimental repeater was installed at Montreuil to facilitate communication between the R.A.F. headquarters at Nancy and the Air Ministry in London. This was in April, 1918.

The repeater was of the single valve type in which both lines in series are balanced against an artificial line. It was fitted inside an old switchboard panel and was placed at one end of the main switchboard. Each panel of the switchboard was provided with a special pair of cords and plugs connected to a pair of jacks on the repeater panel, and the repeater was fitted with a pair of cords to enable the operator to make connection with the pair of jacks which it was desired to use.

The artificial lines were brought into use by means of telephone keys. About ten artificial lines, several of which were duplicates, were found to be sufficient to balance all the long distance lines entering the office, including the cable circuits to London. To facilitate the work of the repeater operator in selecting the correct balance, a special colour was allotted to each artificial line, duplicates having, of course, the same colour. At the same time the peg bearing the name of each actual line on the switchboard was painted the same colour as the appropriate artificial line. The switchboard operator passing the call would then advise the repeater operator that the balances required were "two reds" or "red and blue," or whatever might be required.

After the Armistice, repeaters were installed near Namur on the Montreuil-Cologne and Wimereux-Cologne trunks. Six repeaters were also installed near Abbeville for use on the special London-Paris trunks required by the Peace Conference. These repeaters were in all cases allotted to individual lines and only one artificial line was therefore required for each repeater.

D.R.L.S. figures for L. of C. Signals, G.H.Q., Army, Corps, and Division are given in *Table* IX. The figures are approximate only, but may be taken as a fair average for any day of the last offensives of the British armies.*

TABLE IX.

| Unit. | Telegraph. | D.R.L.S. |
|---|---|---|
| L. of C. Signals .. .. | 23,000 | 2,250 |
| G.H.Q. Signals .. .. | 9,000 | 3,400 |
| Army Signals† .. .. | 10,000 | 5,000 |
| Corps Signals† .. .. | 4,500 | 3,000 |
| Divisional Signals† .. | 800 | 450 |

The control of stores from G.H.Q. has already been mentioned and there remains only the need for some reference to the attempted standardization which was always the ideal aimed at but never fully realized. The continual technical development of the Service stood in the way of a complete standardization of signal stores. Type after type of each instrument was issued as the conditions of position warfare changed or invention made some radical improvement possible. In wireless, particularly, the supply of large quantities of instruments was hampered by this fact.

It was overcome to some extent by a careful standardization of the individual parts from which the instruments were built up—condensers, inductances, switches, etc.—but it was not entirely eliminated until the end of the war had arrived. Certain instruments such as the Wilson set, the Trench Set 50 watt : the Forward Wireless Sets and the C.W. Set, Mark III, were finally adopted as the standard types of transmitters and receivers for certain definite purposes. Even these were, however, liable to minor alterations which interfered somewhat with output.

Fullerphones and trench telephones presented less difficulty and were standardized and the obsolescent types withdrawn. It was intended also to standardize the ringing 'phones used by the rear

* In discussing the traffic over the L. of C. telegraph system, some reference should be made to Press telegrams. Up to March, 1917, no press telegrams were accepted. In that month it was arranged for a total of 10,000 words to be accepted daily. The work was handed in at offices convenient to the Signal Service and was disposed of by Wheatstone direct to the C.T.O., London. It was stipulated that, in order to secure publication in the following morning's paper, the telegrams must be handed in not later than 4.45 p.m. This was necessary to ensure their arrival at the newspaper offices by 10.30 p.m., as desired by the newspapers.

Subsequently it was arranged to transmit an additional 2,000 words each morning, and in July, 1918, the total number of words was increased to 15,500. In October, 1918, it was raised again to 21,500. The maximum number of words actually transmitted in any one day was 26,489 on the 8th August, 1918.

† Figures are for one unit only.

formations and telephone switchboards, but this was not achieved in practice. To the end of the war, Divisions, Corps and Armies replaced exchanges and instruments when handing over, and the main reason for this was the absence of standardization. As has been pointed out, this interfered very much with the adoption of a standard procedure for such reliefs.

The development of signal stores during stationary warfare had been extraordinary. It would probably have been better if fewer types of burying cable had been adhered to and these turned out in larger quantities, but it was, of course, inevitable that experiment must be made in one direction and another before the final standard types were approved. It should be noted in passing that the British iron-armoured cables were not as suitable as the German types for employment as ground cable. It was found that the heat of the sun was liable to melt the insulation and cause faults. This was overcome to a great extent in the German varieties by an outer layer of insulating tape of good quality which was wrapped round the whole cable.

The production of field cable twisted by manufacturers which first became a recognised article of supply in 1917, was a great improvement upon the improvised twisted cable made in the armies. Not only was the manufactured article superior in quality, but a considerable amount of labour could be diverted to other and more legitimate works.

The instruments which were produced to meet the needs of the position warfare signal system have most of them been referred to earlier in the narrative. Undoubtedly the two principal advances in this respect were the introduction of the 4-plus-3 buzzer exchange and the standardization which was accomplished by the production of the " test panels."

The former instrument, in spite of its bulk and the constant renewal of cords rendered necessary by the rough conditions under which it was used, was a great advance on the old plug commutator board and the endless variety of makeshift " cartridge " exchanges improvised by units. Its great merit was its almost soldier-proof solidity and its immunity to the constant immersions in candle-wax, water and Machonnochie gravy to which its dug-out life exposed it.

The production of the test panel, also, was a great advance towards the standardization of instruments. Complete sets were issued to each Division and, later, to each Brigade in the line. The use of these permitted of interchange of formations taking place with the least interference with the lines and enabled neat wiring to be the rule rather than the exception in the forward signal offices. If a similar standardization of exchanges and ringing telephones can be achieved in the future, the greatest obstacle to the complete hand-over of instruments will be overcome.

One result of the great demand for signal instruments of every description and of the heavy wear and tear of these instruments, was a request put forward by the Director of Signals in February, 1917, for permission to form Signal Repair Workshops at Havre. The application for a special establishment was refused, but the workshops were built and manned from personnel who would otherwise have been held at the Signal Depôt awaiting distribution to units. In May, 1917, German prisoners of technical trades were employed as artisans in the shops, supervision being exercised by personnel from " L " Signal Battalion. From this date, the signal repair shops flourished and dealt with considerable quantities of instruments too badly damaged for repair in the army workshops. They were also successful in completing large orders for the manufacture of instruments and small stores which were not of approved pattern, but were required from time to time to meet special needs. Excellent work was done by the German prisoners who formed the bulk of the tradesmen employed, and a considerable increase to the manufacturing power of the Signal Service was achieved at a minimum cost and expenditure of British labour.

It was in 1918, during the period covered in the present chapter, that the final reorganization took place which left the Signal Service of the Royal Air Force on a satisfactory basis. Until this year, the ground communications of the Royal Flying Corps had been dealt with by G.H.Q. and Army Signals. The various wings and squadrons had been accommodated with circuits on the Army telegraph and telephone systems, and the instruments and the special exchanges —where such were necessary—were manned by R.F.C. personnel. With the formation of the Royal Air Force, however, it became evident that a Staff officer was required who would be in a position to co-ordinate the signals of the whole force and represent its special needs to the Director of Signals. The appointment of an A.D. Signals R.A.F. with a small establishment was approved in 1918.

Shortly afterwards, the formation of the Independent Air Force raised a similar question. The demands of the new service for direct communication could not possibly be accommodated on the general Army system. The aerodromes, workshops and parks of the Independent Air Force were distributed over an area measuring 100 by 120 miles. This involved very considerable construction and maintenance responsibilities. The immediate requirements of the situation were met by attaching an officer and 70 men to the force to construct a nucleus of communication, while, at the same time, an establishment consisting of A.D. Signals with a small headquarters staff, a signal construction company and two airline sections was recommended. A senior officer was appointed provisionally to act as A.D. Signals in July, and in August the new establishments were approved by the War Office. The addition to the Signal Service was seven officers and 229 men.

Divisional signal companies once more shared in the reorganizations which took place in the last year of the war. This unit still remained considerably smaller than the minimum required to meet its responsibilities in position warfare. Even in mobile warfare it was quite impossible to maintain forward wireless or visual communication with the establishment of February, 1918, without drawing upon the battalion signallers of the Brigade pool. It had long been felt that the position of affairs had been unsatisfactory in more than one way.

The battalion suffered from the loss of its best signallers, while a technical subject like wireless telegraphy demanded the whole attention of men who could only be specially trained to that work during periods of rest, and the use of whom could only be centralised permanently under the control of the Divisional wireless officer. There was also a crying need for more supervision in the infantry Brigade sections themselves. The forward system had grown continually, and it was not within the power of a solitary Brigade signal officer to act as Staff officer for signals to his Brigadier and at the same time exercise general supervision over the battalion signallers.

All these reforms were accomplished by a revision of establishments which took place in August, 1918.* An increase in the wireless section enabled the Divisional wireless officer to man all stations as far forward as battalion headquarters. The creation of a visual section to take the place of the overworked " Signallers and Despatch Riders " of the headquarters of a Divisional signal company finally disposed of the necessity for the Brigade pool. Finally, the addition of a subaltern to the Brigade section ensured efficient supervision of Brigade signals generally. The new establishment is shown in detail in the 1918 column of Appendix I. The increases to the Signal Service were partly counterpoised by considerable decreases in the signal establishments of the infantry and pioneer battalions.†

The final figures as calculated for the Expeditionary Force at that date were as follows ;—

TABLE X.

|  | Officers. | O.R. |
|---|---|---|
| Increase to Signal Service .. | 144 | 3936 |
| Decrease to Battn. Signallers |  | 3888 |
| Net increase .. | 144 | 48 |

* This re-organization did not actually take effect until after the Armistice.

† Infantry Battalion, 53 to 44.
  Pioneer Battalion, 41 to 30.

Minor amendments which took place at the same time were the addition of pack horses for the transport of the wireless stations of the infantry Brigade, a slight alteration in the transport of the cable section, and the addition of a very necessary motor cycle for the wireless officer.

It will have been noticeable that almost all the greater reorganizations had involved the forward extension of technical qualifications towards the firing line. This was a necessary corollary to the complexity of method and of technique which was the outstanding feature of position warfare signals. A review of the effect of these changes upon the qualifications of Signal Service personnel is interesting and essential to the understanding of the war development of the Army Signal Service.

The principal feature of the alterations in the nomenclature and qualifications of the signal personnel within a Division—which was the formation most affected—is shewn below in tabular form. It is not intended to be more than approximately correct, but, without going into detail, it gives a good general view of the broad effect upon the forward signal units.

TABLE XI.

*The Battalion Signal Section.*

Characterized by lack of differentiation into operator and lineman. Men trained to deal with all types of signalling used within their formation.

1914—Visual (Semaphore and Morse).
1915—As above, and Buzzer Telephone Lines.
1916—As above, and Power Buzzer, Pigeon, Fullerphone, Contact Aeroplane (*less* Semaphore).
1917—As above, and Amplifier, Forward W/T Set, Buzzer Exchanges.
1918—As above, and Message-carrying Rockets.

* *The Brigade Signal Section.*

First appearance of differentiation into operator and lineman.

1914—Signalmen  ..  ..  .. Ground Cable, "D3" Telephones
     Line Telegraphists ..  .. and Visual.

1915—Signalmen  ..  ..  .. As above, and Shallow Buried
     Line Telegraphists ..  .. Cable and Ringing Telephones.

1916—Signalmen  ..  ..  .. As above, and Deep Buried Cable.
     Line Telegraphists ..  .. Armoured Cables, P.B. and A.
                                  Fullerphone. Contact Aeroplane

1917—Pioneers  ..  ..  .. As above, and Sounder and
     Brigade Section Hands  .. Forward Wireless.

1918—Signalmen " B "  ..  ..⎫
     Field Linemen (Dismtd.) ..⎬ As above, and Message-carrying
     Pioneers  ..  ..  ..⎭ Rockets.

## The Divisional Signal Company.

Headquarters and No. 1 Section only. (Special Artillery units are not included, as it is desired to keep the comparative tables as simple as possible.)

1914—Signalmen .. .. .. Visual—Flag, Lamp and Helio.
      Telegraphists (Office) .. Ground and Poled Cable.
      Telegraphists (Line) .. Buzzer and Vibrator.

1915—Signalmen .. .. .. As above, and Visual (Disc).
      Miscellaneous Trades .. Shallow Buried Cable, Sounder.
      Telegraphists (Office) .. } Ringing Telephone, Telephone
      Telegraphists (Line) .. }   Exchanges.

1916—Signalmen .. .. .. As above, and Visual (Shutter).
      Telegraphists (Office) .. Aeroplane Signalling, Deep Buried
          Cable.
      Telegraphists (Line) .. Trench Wireless, P.B. and A.
          Fullerphone.

1917—Telegraphists (Office) .. } As above, and Forward Wireless
      Switchboard Operators .. |   and
      Wireless Operators .. .. } Permanent Line Work (Wireless
      Cable Hands .. .. |   Section formed).
      Permanent Linemen .. }

1918—Telegraph Operators " B " .. }
      Switchboard Operators .. | As above. (Specialization sets in
      Wireless Operators .. .. }   to a greater extent.)
      Signalmen " B " .. .. }

      Permanent Linemen .. }
      Field Linemen (Mounted) .. } As above.
      Field Linemen (Dismtd.) .. }

It will be seen that the tendency until 1917 was not so much towards specialisation as towards a multiplication of the technical qualifications asked of the forward signal personnel. In that year, however, it became evident that, except in the most forward units, a measure of specialization was necessary. It was quite impossible for the " miscellaneous " tradesmen to be sufficiently acquainted with all the different branches of signalling to give satisfactory service with any.

Another factor which also forced specialisation upon the Signal Service was the large proportion of casualties which occurred in this year, and the still greater increases in strength which accompanied the first great reorganization. The period of training of reinforcements had to be reduced considerably, and this could only be done by training definite proportions of the men for specific duties. The result was the division of telegraphists into telegraph operators " A " and

" B," according as they were intended for rear or forward units : of linemen into field linemen, mounted or dismounted : and of signalmen into signalmen " A," for use with artillery units, and signalmen " B " —the equivalent of the old Brigade section pioneer and the " Signaller and Despatch Rider " of the Divisional signal company.

This partial specialisation was attended with good results, and was, indeed, the only way in which any approximation could be secured between the demands of the Armies in the field and the supply of reinforcements. From 1917, onwards, visual signalling was still made the basis of all signal courses. After their preliminary training in flag drill, etc., however, the men were separated out according to the aptitude they displayed. The best signallers were picked out for training as signalmen " A " and " B," less apt recruits were trained as linemen or, if rejected even from this trade, as general duty pioneers. Men who had previously been in the Post Office or allied occupations, meanwhile, specialized as telegraph operators or linemen according to the trade they followed in civil life. To the ranks of the operators, also, were added the most promising of the non-technical recruits.

Finally, the pick of the men in training as operators were given a further course in wireless which converted them into telegraph operators " B." From the ranks of the latter, again, the keenest were selected for still further training as specialist wireless operators.

By this means the men best fitted to make the most of a technical education were given the opportunity to qualify for the more interesting and higher-paid trades, while, at the same time, the period of time spent in training the average recruit was reduced to a minimum.

The new departure involved, of course, the preparation of an entirely different set of qualification sheets and these were drawn out and issued in due course. In the meantime, however, the chief difficulties in the way of re-rating Sappers under active service conditions had been solved by the acceptance of the Commanding Officer's certificate in lieu of the special form for recording the standard tests laid down in the Corps Memorandum. This practice was continued with good results throughout the war, and a conscientious determination of commanding officers, generally, to keep up the standard of qualifications of the service almost entirely prevented its abuse.

Perhaps the most important of all the reforms in organization which took place in 1918 was the creation of a Signal Service department under the Director of Staff Duties at the War Office. The position as regards the Signal Service direction at home in January, 1918, was as follows.

In the War Office, besides F.W.9, there was a G.S.O.2 attached to the Directorate of Staff Duties who was responsible for technical advice as regards matters of signal policy as affecting the various theatres of war and at home ; there was also a captain on the Adjutant

General's Staff who dealt with all questions with regard to Signal Service officers.   In addition, an official of the Postmaster General's Staff held the appointment of Director of Signals, Home Defence, with the rank of colonel.   This officer was responsible for the provision of all circuits asked for by the various departments at home, but was not in a position to criticise demands.   The result was a certain amount of extravagance which, in view of the absence of a competent authority, could not well be stopped.   Finally, the Commandant, Signal Service Training Centre, was responsible for the training and supply of reinforcements to all theatres of war.   This officer also acted as Director of Army Signals to G.H.Q., Home Forces, but was unable to devote more than a small portion of his time to his duties in this capacity.

It had long been apparent that considerable friction and a not inconsiderable wastage was resulting from a lack of co-ordination between the signal services of the different Expeditionary Forces. The necessity for a senior officer who could make authoritative decisions as between the rival claims of these entirely separate services was as evident as that for a competent authority to control the often unjustifiable increase in the signal services of the home departments and formations.

The formation of a Directorate of Signals at the War Office bristled with difficulties and was ruled out of the question without discussion, but in February, 1918, it was proposed by the Director of Army Signals, France, that the required purpose might be served by the appointment of a senior Signal Service officer with control over a sub-department of the Directorate of Staff Duties.   After considerable discussion the proposal was approved in a modified form and the department " S.D.6 " came into existence with the primary object of giving to the Signal Service " adequate weight and representation at the War Office."   The G.S.O.1 at the head of the new department became responsible for the co-ordination of the Signal Service throughout the British Expeditionary Forces.   He dealt with questions in regard to the training of reinforcements for the Signal Service so far as such questions could be decided at the War Office.   He was given the task of keeping in touch with the various arms of the Service and making arrangements for the incorporation of a due proportion of signal personnel in each new formation or establishment created.   Finally, he was expected to take a general interest in everything that was being done by the Signal Service in all theatres of war and in the military signal communications of the Empire.

The question of the growth of home signal establishments and systems was solved at the same time by the appointment of a full-time Director of Army Signals on the Staff of G.H.Q., Home Forces, with the rank of Brigadier-General.   This officer was also charged with the duty of inspection of Army signal units at home.   The

Commandant, Signal Service Training Centre, was thus enabled to give his whole attention to the selection and training of the recruits for the Signal Service proper, and to the training of signal instructors for artillery and infantry.*

There remains to be considered the part played by the Army Signal Service in the training of the signal units of the American Expeditionary Force. As in the case of Britain, the American national army had been grafted upon an entirely insufficient *cadre* of regular soldiers. The last experiences of the people of the United States in a war of any magnitude dated back to the Civil War between the northern and southern states in the middle of the 19th century. The American Signal Corps was, however, largely composed of men whose professions in civil life were technically allied to the duties they had to perform in their new rôles. What was needed, was an experience of the actual conditions under which forward signal personnel worked in the field, and a personal knowledge of the types of instruments in use in the British forward signal units and with which they were themselves to be supplied.

On the arrival of the American formations at their training grounds in England and France, signalling instructors were attached to them to give the men insight by precept and example into modern army signal practice as modified by active service conditions. These men were carefully chosen from the ranks of British signal companies which were in rest or which had been disbanded in consequence of the general reduction of the British Expeditionary Force. At a later stage in the training of the units, selected American officers, N.C.O.'s and men, went up to the line, where they were attached to British Divisional and Brigade signal units and were given personal experience of work under field conditions. The result was that, when —in June, 1918—the American Divisions commenced to take their place here and there along the British line, the signal units were fully equal to their responsibilities. They began their battle duties with the accumulated experience of the British and French Signal Services to prevent them from falling into the various pitfalls that had beset the career of the pioneers. It was to be expected that the signal systems that resulted should combine the best points of the French and British systems and this expectation was often realized to a great extent.

* The organization of the Signal Service in France has been dealt with at some length in Chapter IX. and the present chapter. The chain of command as it finally existed is summarized and shown in graphic form in *Plate* XVIII.

During the period under review (the last pause before the final offensive that ended the war) the signal system whose salient characteristics were indicated in the earlier portion of this chapter, was built up, and a rear defence system prepared against the possibility of further reverses. Little marked change came over the face of the war along the British front until August, with the exception perhaps of still further activity on the part of artillery and bombing planes on both sides.

All possible measures to counteract the effect of the constant bombardment and raids had been taken. Efficient maintenance, careful choice of routes and diversions, minimised the time of the interruptions and the amount of the damage done. Linemen in forward areas and the personnel of the forward offices were, however, much harassed by the prevalence of gas in the German shells. Elaborrate precautions had to be taken to ensure the preservation of instruments. Men worked for hours wearing their box respirators and suffered considerable discomfort from the consequent hampering of sight and breathing. Casualties in artillery signal units were particularly high, and the troubles of the maintenance personnel were increased by the difficulty to the untrained eye and nose of ascertaining whether gas was or was not present in any particular batch of high explosive shells. The inclusion of a proportion of gas had become so common that it was advisable to wear a respirator in any bombardment of intensity in the back areas. This much increased the difficulty of maintenance of the lines. As time wore on, and the enemy realized that a combined offensive on the part of the Allies was imminent, his artillery counter preparation increased in volume and decreased in regularity of programme. It became less and less easy to anticipate the portion of the front which would be subjected to bombardment, or the time at which the bombardment would take place. By so much the more was the work of the maintenance personnel made more dangerous.

In the area dominated by Mount Kemmel, in particular, since the capture of the hill from the French in May, 1918, enemy observation was so perfect that work in daytime was quite impossible. All burying and all the normal routine of ration and ammunition delivery had to be carried out under cover of night and this condition of affairs was once more true of the whole of the Ypres salient. Formation headquarters were frequently shelled, lines were cut by direct hits from 5·9 and 8-inch shells again and again, and maintenance was only possible by carefully choosing times and by utilising every night to repair the ravages of the bombardments of the previous day.

On the northern portion of the British front during the critical days of June and July, offensive action was confined to small local attacks and raids designed to improve the position of the front line and to facilitate observation. The concentration of over 30 German

Divisions in the area was the dominant factor of the situation and all efforts were directed towards the perfection of defensive arrangements without thought of immediate attack other than raids. Further to the south, however, several position battles were fought on a larger scale.

No specially interesting departures in signal practice took place, however, until the failure of the last German attack launched on the 15th July, was followed by the great French counter-offensive on the front to the west of Rheims. The latter ushered in the allied offensive campaign which entirely altered the face of the campaign and brought stationary warfare to an end.

# CHAPTER XVI.

# SIGNALS IN THE AUTUMN ADVANCE.

SYNOPSIS.

As the last great action in which a British Corps took part during the retreat was with the French Armies upon the Marne, so, in July, 1918, the XXII Corps was thrown in on the same front to add weight to the French offensive which rolled back the German armies from the countries they had overrun during the June battle. As before, the most interesting features of the signal practice arose from the isolation of a British Corps amongst French formations. The French intercommunication service worked on lines which differed fundamentally from British practice.

They relied almost entirely upon the telephone for line communication and the chief alternative method used in the French Army was continuous wave wireless. Line telegraph and spark wireless were both disliked and used as little as possible. The latter was confined entirely to the area forward of Divisional headquarters, the former was not used at all for lateral work.

A British formation set down in the midst of a French Army was therefore obliged to modify its normal system in several particulars. In the case of the XXII Corps, in the advance from the Marne in July, rear communication was by telephone only, except for one superimposed Morse circuit back to the headquarters of the 5th French Army. Lateral *liaison* with the French Corps and Divisions was either by telephone over lines specially laid by the British signal sections, or by C.W. wireless. For the latter purpose the French Radio Service placed a high-powered C.W. set at Corps headquarters, and this set was also used for alternative communication back to Army. Continuous wave sets were alone used for wireless communication up to Divisional headquarters and, forward of this, British spark wireless sets were kept silent until half an hour after zero hour of the first day of the attack.

The working of the line system itself was modified in two ways by the circumstances peculiar to the attack. The exchange operators with the British formation had been taught a certain amount of French, but in spite of this preparation they still experienced considerable difficulty in passing calls which had to go through several French exchanges. This trouble was due to quick talking and colloquial expressions used by the French operators. It was overcome at the Corps exchanges by the attachment of a few interpreter operators who were given a local telephone on the Corps switchboards and were put through to the French exchange from which they followed up the call until the attention of the required office had been secured. They then informed the British operators who put the Staff through. Unfortunately the number of these men who were available was very few. The only source from which they could be drawn was the very small establishment of listening posts which were thrown spare by the advance. There were sufficient to supply the Corps exchanges, but the Divisions were obliged to do without and much delay resulted.

The second modification of the line system was the use by the French of cables slung on pickets three or four feet high. Seven or eight cables were used on each of these routes and it was claimed for them that they were much more immune from bombing and shelling than either open wires, ground cable, or poled cable. Our allies strongly recommended the adoption of these routes by the British Corps, and eight miles of eight-pair route was built in seven days over rough country consisting of vineyards and woods. In this time the preparation of all materials is included. The routes gave good service and the contention that they were less liable to destruction by enemy action appeared to be correct.

The supply of cable also presented much greater difficulty than usual. The Corps had brought with it a small reserve supply when it came into the area by rail. No further supplies could, however, be obtained for four days from the date of requisition, and units were obliged to rely to a much greater extent than usual upon their establishment.

As far as the conditions of the battle were concerned, it proved to be easy to maintain line communication as far forward as battalion and battery headquarters. Owing to this shortage of cable, however, only a very slender system could be built. A Brigade system consisted normally of an omnibus line to which all three battalions connected themselves by short spurs whenever their headquarters settled down. Every effort was made to save cable, but the chief source of expenditure, which could not be reduced very much, was that on lines between batteries and O.P.'s.

X

In spite of the utmost economy the reserve rapidly approached
vanishing point and it was only by borrowing some 50 miles of
twisted cable from the French that the line system was kept intact
until the arrival of the fresh stocks.  It was by such occurrences
that the necessity for organizing cable supply was driven home, and
one of the chief lessons of this battle was the recommendation that
in future cable should be supplied as regularly as ammunition.
Indeed, it was suggested that a supply of cable in railway trucks
should be attached to the ammunition train, issues being controlled
by A.D. Signals, but the supply maintained by the O.C. train and
replenished at each trip to the Base.

With the above exceptions the signal system in the Marne Battle
was like those of the later battles of the main British offensive, and
its features are best described in common with those of the latter.
The success of the French offensive opened up vistas of possible victory
which encouraged the Allied higher command in their determination
to press the enemy both on the French and British front, and
on August 8th the British armies joined battle with the German
defenders of the line in front of Amiens.   The general offensive which
followed was sustained until the German nation acknowledged defeat
by the signature of the Armistice on November 11th, 1918.

The struggle between these dates can be divided into two distinct
portions, which presented rather different problems to the Signal
Service for solution.   Until the forcing of the Hindenburg Line and
its reserve positions at the end of September, the enemy endeavoured
to defend himself in a series of strongly-built defence zones from
each of which he could only be dislodged after a position battle which
rivalled those of 1917 in intensity.   In between such battles the
situation was semi-fluid, the German rearguards retiring slowly
and methodically under the pressure of our advanced troops and
mobile artillery.    After the great battle of the Hindenburg Line
the enemy's retreat was more hurried and the only pauses occurred
at such natural lines as adapted themselves to defence without
much preparation.   The most serious of these obstacles were, of
course, the canal and river lines.   As the days wore on, the checks
became less frequent and less sustained, the British advance
accelerated, and the retreat of the enemy became more disorganised,
approximating more to a rout than a calculated retirement.   During
this last stage of the war something approaching mobile warfare set
in, and the main problem which confronted the Signal Service was
the physical difficulty of keeping up with the advancing troops.
Allied to this second phase, and even surpassing it in speed of action,
were the voluntary withdrawals to the north of the decisive front
when large tracts of country were ceded to our troops, often without
the slightest semblance of resistance.   Here, again, the chief
difficulty encountered by the Signal Service was that of adapting

an organization which had grown up under position warfare conditions to the needs of a mobile force.

The recognition of this problem as a most serious difficulty and a tribute to the way in which it was solved are contained in the following paragraph from the official despatches of January 7th, 1919 :—

" The constant movement of the line and the shifting of headquarters has again imposed an enormous strain upon all ranks of the Signal Service. The depth of our advance, and the fact that during the latter part of it the whole of the British armies were simultaneously involved, made the maintenance of signal communications most difficult. The fact that in such circumstances the needs of the armies were met reflects the highest credit upon the zeal and efficiency of all ranks."

In many respects the signal system of the advance much resembled that already described when discussing the less general advances which accompanied the battles of 1917, and particularly the battle of Cambrai. It differed in extent, however, and in the incorporation of the lessons already learnt during those actions. For the first time the area of movement affected the whole of the fighting forces as far back as G.H.Q., while—as stated in the despatches—problems were much intensified by the fact that at times the whole front was affected and it was, therefore, impossible to make up local deficiencies by reinforcements and stores from other portions of the line. The way the lessons of former offensives and of the spring retreats had been seized and turned to account was demonstrated by the success of the forward signal units in coping with the special problems due to the universality and the speed of action of a great offensive such as had never been matched in any previous battle. The principles followed were based upon the experience of 1914 and 1917 as summarised in S.S. 191, but to the concentrated wisdom of these pages had been added the lessons of the earlier battles of 1918. The result was a system of forward signals entirely adequate and at the same time speedy of construction, simple of maintenance, economical both of men and stores, and divested of all superfluities.

While the establishment of an advanced G.H.Q. from which operations were directed much increased the work of G.H.Q. Signal Company, it was within the armies again that the effects of the constant movement made itself felt with decisive effect. The comparative mobility of the operations of the spring and early summer had taught very useful lessons to Army headquarters as well as to the formations in front of it. In two respects especially had this been so. The Army advanced offices which, before the retreat, had been composed of large 60-line switchboards, had had the latter replaced by standard multiple boards, and the offices made portable in every possible way. The Army wireless station also had been taught to dismantle quickly, lose no time on the road, and re-erect as speedily on reaching the site of the new head-quarters. Both these lessons added greatly to the chances of success of the Army signal units in the autumn battles.

Movements of Army headquarters commenced to take place soon after the beginning of the advance. In some cases headquarters were situated at awkward corners of the areas they controlled, in others, sideslips took place for other reasons. In all, two or three moves took place and were attended by the usual extra work. This was, however, reduced to a minimum, as experience improved the portability of the forward offices and permitted of the crystalliza-tion of the exact form of skeleton communication system which was best suited to deal with all urgent needs and yet contained nothing superfluous.

Army headquarters, like the headquarters of the Corps, Divisions and Brigades, learnt to manage with the essential minimum of *liaison*. A typical forward system which was very successful in operation consisted of one telephone circuit each to G.H.Q., Advanced G.H.Q. and flank Armies, two to each Corps in the Army and three to the rear Army office. On all of these circuits, except one to the rear office, Morse was superimposed. At the forward office three multiple boards were set up and a carefully-pruned system of Staff phones was installed. So carefully were these forward offices stand-ardized and so exactly was the routine of installation insisted upon, that in the later moves 24 hours notice was quite sufficient to ensure that the Staff could rely on finding the above minimum of inter-communication ready for them in working order on their arrival at the new headquarters.

The circuits were carried forward on a main route which was the first care of the construction company and was built down the centre of the Army line of advance. In the earlier slower phase of the advance this route was of 24 wires, at a later stage the German permanent routes were utilized and reconstructed on a 16-wire basis. The speed of advance of the Army line system was limited by the speed of construction of these large overhead routes. When the advance was rapid it outran construction* and the only way in which the situation could be met was by rigid adherence to instructions limiting construction work to main routes only. The commanders of subordinate units could no longer be given the telegraph and telephone facilities they had formerly enjoyed. The main routes were pushed on with all possible speed but all intercommunication forward was limited to these and to such spurs of the Corps and Divisional systems or of the German permanent line system as could

---

* One Army headquarters advanced at an average speed of *six* miles a day.

be reconstructed without loss of time or the use of large quantities of labour.

It was recognized by the Signal Service, however, that as many intercommunication facilities as possible should be given to the units scattered through the Army areas, and their wants were catered for to some extent by means of " Public " telephones and a reinforced D.R.L.S. The former were installed at each signal office and were at the disposal of all officers wishing to transact legitimate and urgent army business. The latter was modified to meet the peculiar prevailing conditions. It was no longer possible to deliver to units here, there, and everywhere, but the offices of the various Area Commandants were utilized as the fixed centres to which letters could be delivered by motor cyclists. A General Routine Order was accordingly issued instructing all units not directly served by the main D.R.L.S post to send in to the office of the local Area Commandant with and for their mail. Urgent traffic was disposed of once or twice daily by circular runs to these offices and a fairly efficient *liaison* was thus maintained throughout the Army.

In such ways the Army system adapted itself to the new phase of warfare and proved far less rigid than might have been expected. The only innovation in signal practice besides the standard forward office and the adoption of the multiple boards, was the use of Wheatstone between forward and rear offices. It has been placed on record by the officers concerned that much delay might have been avoided if similar Wheatstone sets could have been issued to Corps headquarters also.

As the Armies moved forward across the broad devastated area, both signal construction companies and motor cyclist despatch riders suffered from the bad roads and the lack of bridges to span canals and rivers. Usually, only one or two possible routes were available from front to rear. Lateral roads were still less common, for Corps and Army Troops were far too busily engaged upon the routes leading forward to be able to give any attention to these side issues of traffic. The condition of the roads was very bad apart from recent deliberate destruction, while the work of the enemy engineers had been so consummately thorough that, at times, the construction companies were obliged to revert to horsed transport and cross-country detours in order to get ahead at all. At each pause in the operations, when the Army halted temporarily on a fortified or river line, signal traffic increased in volume until it even surpassed that of the more stationary signal system of the previous year. In the month of August as many as 20,000 telephone calls were recorded on the system of a single Army in a 24-hours period, while, in November, when the last advance ended with the Armistice, the same Army once more boasted 140 subscribers on its main telephone exchanges.

It was from Corps headquarters forward that the element of

mobility in the new situation became absolutely predominant in its effects. It was the A.D. Signals, Corps who in reality controlled the forward signal policy of the Divisions during these last four crowded months. The Corps system itself was modified to a considerably greater extent than that of the Army. The frequency of the moves of Corps and Divisions was rivalled by the distances covered at each move. On one occasion a Corps moved 35 miles at 24 hours' notice. This was an extreme case, but moves of 20 miles or so were not uncommon, while divisions moved every few days in bounds of five to 10 miles.

Each A.D. Signals of a Corps was faced with three distinct responsibilities. He, or his O.C. company on his behalf, must ensure the essential minimum of intercommunication between his own headquarters and the headquarters of the Divisions in the Corps : he must ensure an efficient signal system for the heavy artillery serving with his Corps ; finally, and this was perhaps the most important of all his functions, he must co-ordinate the systems of the Divisions in front of him and arrange matters so that his own line system could be carried forward in the future along one or other of the main Divisional lines of communication.*

The first two problems were largely a matter of careful organization of the personnel at his disposal. All subsidiary offices were closed down and the attention of all his outdoor personnel was concentrated upon the main routes. Similarly, indoor personnel was organized to form two main offices, the more advanced of which could again be split up to enable a stepping-up process to take place.

The principle of the maintenance of a minimum of efficient intercommunication along a central route which finally overcame the new difficulties raised by mobile warfare was not achieved without some mistakes being made. Both in Corps and Divisions the less important members of the Staff were tardy in relinquishing the telephone rights which they had come to claim as their due during stationary warfare. In this respect, some formations were worse than others, and it is noteworthy that the worst offenders in the early stages of the advance were such Corps and Divisional Staffs as had not been involved in the recent semi-mobile engagements at Cambrai, the Somme, the Lys, or the Marne.

The initial tendency to treat the engagements by which the successive German defence zones were breached as being similar to the slowly-moving battles of the position warfare period added much to the perplexities of the senior signal officers. It was, however, gradually eradicated from the minds of the Staff as action accelerated

---

* Some C.S.O'.s, Corps assisted to maintain lateral telephone communications between Divisions either *via* Corps forward exchanges or by the loan of a cable detachment to lay the necessary lines.

and moves of headquarters became more frequent and far-reaching. It was obviously impossible to build many miles of heavy routes in two or three days : it was equally evident that transportation difficulties would not permit of the forward movement of cumbersome offices. Gradually, as the situation developed, these initial obstacles to free movement died away of themselves and everyone concerned became reconciled to the idea of the speedy establishment of a minimum of signal communication as the dominant characteristic of the mobile warfare signal system.

The lines on which the new problems were solved had already been indicated in S.S. 191. With some slight modifications, the principles of this book were carried out with a success which could not have been attained by any other method. The two factors of the problem were as usual the General Staff and the Signal Service policies. By this date it was generally recognized that these were essentially interdependent and with the admission of this fact by both sides the main difficulties of the situation as regards signal communications had disappeared. Co-operation was the order of the day : by means of co-operation and forethought the duplication or alteration of signal routes was practically done away with and the element of uncertainty of direction eliminated from the situation so far as was possible.

With the small proportion of signal personnel available to serve the needs of the army, it was essential that none of the work done by the construction detachments should be wasted. Airline and cable sections had been reduced to a minimum establishment, while the number of units was no more than equal to their responsibilities. To ensure the rapid and efficient following up of the Divisions with a safe line system, the two airline sections of the Corps were fully occupied in the carrying forward of one main route. Similarly, the cable sections of Corps and Divisions were worked to the limit of their endurance in order to maintain the necessary minimum network of lines. From the first, it was clear that Brigades, Divisions, and Corps must advance, each along one main preordained route, and that these routes must be fully advertised well in advance and changed as little as possible.

It was here that a well-considered and carefully thought-out policy on the part of the General Staff proved to be the saving of the Signal Service. It had been amply demonstrated in the March retreat that, where forethought was exercised and efficient control exerted by the higher formations, good intercommunication could invariably be assured. Conversely, it had been proved again and again, that where forethought was absent and control not exercised, there chaos prevailed. The lesson had been learnt and now each Corps advanced along a definite line laid down in advance by the General Staff and changed as little as the situation would permit.

The names of the principal towns and villages near the centre line of the formation area were published in General Staff orders, and, whenever possible, these actual positions were utilized by all formations as important nodal points on their intercommunication routes. The signal route of one Division almost invariably followed the line laid down, and it was along this route that the Corps advanced its own air line, reeling up the cable as it was replaced by this more stable conductor.

The chief difficulty in the way of economy was the fact that the higher formation needed one only out of two or three routes in front of it. The others were therefore thrown spare after very little use. This was overcome by the adoption of a system of forward offices or communication centres. The advanced signal office of the Corps was kept as far up along the Corps-Divisional line of communication as possible. When the Division along whose route it was following moved forward, a Corps advanced office was again established close behind the new Divisional headquarters and spurs to Divisions to left or right of the central line of advance were thus kept as short as possible. The same principle was adopted at Division and Brigade, and the main feature of the line system of the advance was thus one main route per Corps which was made as heavy as time and personnel would permit and from which radiated smaller spurs to flank Divisions. From Divisional headquarters, again, longer lines ran to forward communication centres from which short spurs branched off to Brigades, Similar forward centres in Brigades completed the system and kept down the expenditure of cable to a minimum.*

Comparative skeleton line systems from Corps to Brigade with and without forward communication centres are shown in *Plate* XX. These are drawn to scale and give a very good idea of the saving of labour and cable effected by the adoption of the former method. Equally great advantages in the direction of ease of maintenance and greater safety are also self-evident from a comparison of the two methods.

The first problem with which A.D. Signals of a Corps was faced— the maintenance of the necessary minimum of communication between Corps and Division—was thus simplified to some extent by the presence of the main cable axis which had been laid by the Division that happened to be advancing along the Corps route. Attached to the headquarters of this Division, and following close behind it, would be a Corps cable section. It was the duty of this section to make the hastily laid Divisional lines more safe. Thus, as they passed behind Divisional headquarters, they were in a fit condition to act as the main Corps route until, in due course, they were replaced by

* *Plate* XIX. illustrates a Divisional signal system during the 1918 advance. In the particular case illustrated part of a German permanent route has been utilized. Lateral lines are omitted for the sake of simplicity.

the Corps airline. If the advance were unusually fast, it might well be that the Division might not be able to lay more than one " earthed " and one metallic circuit to serve its own needs. It was then the business of the Corps cable section to reinforce this too slender trunk line. This might be done either by laying another single cable or by adding an extra twisted pair. The minimum aimed at for the Divisional route in the slower intervals of the advance, and for Corps routes at all times, was three twisted pairs.

The route would also frequently require strengthening and (unless the lines were well slung on hedges) it was usually necessary to pole them before they could be considered safe. If the advance was slow, on the other hand, the Divisional cable detachments were themselves able to achieve a safe line. The Corps cable section could then often work in advance of Divisional headquarters, thus relieving the Divisional cable wagons of the rear portion of their work and enabling the latter to keep well ahead of Brigade headquarters. It was on these advanced Corps cable sections that the brunt of the more dangerous work in bombed and shelled areas fell, and several well-earned distinctions fell to the lot of the officers and men comprising them. Their presence forward of Divisional headquarters, also, was conducive in the highest degree to good feeling between the signal units of the Corps and its Divisions.

Where advances were speedy and movements of headquarters rapid and carried out over great distances, much trouble was experienced in speaking over the cables which usually formed a considerable proportion of the very lengthy lines between Corps and Divisional headquarters. It was not an uncommon thing to have a Corps working to its Divisions over distances of the order of 10 to 20 miles of which two-thirds might be airline and the remaining third poled or hedge cable. In such circumstances speech was almost impossible, unless the lines were very carefully built or laid. It then became more than usually important for the airline construction to be hurried on. Just as, in the Army area, the advance of the signal line system was limited by the speed of construction of the permanent routes, so, in the Corps area, the speed of advance of the lines was not always commensurate with that of the more mobile headquarters in front. The general plan was to build forward a 12-wire route to take the normal traffic of the Corps.* If movement was comparatively slow, the whole 12 wires were taken forward at once ; if rapid, four wires were pushed ahead with all possible speed by the best men of the construction detachments, while improvised parties, made up of all the

* In one Corps at least, which was working on an unusually wide front, two 16-wire routes were carried forward. This was only made possible by the attachment of an American Construction Company and a detachment of some 40 labour personnel for the rough work of digging holes, etc. Both were provided by the Army.

odds and ends of signal personnel that could be collected, followed as quickly as possible with the remaining eight wires. Everything possible was done to speed up construction. In the chief battles permanent routes were dug well forward before zero hour, pot-holes being dug and carefully camouflaged and stores laid out.

A typical record that has survived, was the building of 53,000 yards of 12-wire hop-pole route by the airline sections of one Corps in 16 days This route was put up under difficulties, for, owing to the shortage of stores, it had to be taken straight forward across the devastated country. Roads were few and far between, and the country in between the roads was impassable for wheeled vehicles. In many cases, the " carries " were as much as 1,000 to 1,500 yards over torn and shell-pitted country and the work involved was twice as much as would have been expended in building the same length of route through ordinary terrain.

In some cases the roads were so congested that it was difficult even to get the poles and other stores out of the lorries and wagons. In others, floods interfered very much with the working parties. Stretches of the country had been inundated by the Germans before the retreat, and the essential lines had to be carried forward over the swamped areas by the help of pontoons.

As the advance passed out of the devastated areas into hitherto untouched country, German permanent routes in more or less disreputable state of repair passed into British hands and these were utilized by Divisions and Corps alike. Here, once again, the virtues of co-ordination were seen and, where organization was good, Corps and Division vied with each other in obtaining information about the German circuits in their area and in disseminating such information to anyone to whom it was likely to be of use. The enemy had sawn through most junction poles and much damage had been done to routes where railway trucks had been blown up, or mines had been exploded at cross roads and at the entrances to villages and towns. It was found that routes along main roads had been most destroyed, while time had apparently not permitted of such thorough damage being done to cross-country and railway routes. To a certain extent this played into the hands of the British Signal Service. German bombing planes were operating in swarms along the main roads in Corps and Divisional areas, and the enemy was now shooting almost entirely by the map. If roads and valleys were avoided, it was found that routes were usually safe except from stray haphazard shells.

The reconnoitring of the German routes presented a distinct problem and was dealt with in different ways by different Corps and Divisions. The most normal method was to detail one or two officers of the Corps to go forward on motor cycles and make as rapid a survey as possible of the routes which appeared to run in a suitable direction. A common method employed by Divisions was for a senior signal officer to reconnoitre forward in the O.C. Signal's car. Although the main roads were usually blown up at all road junctions, by-roads had been destroyed much less systematically and often gave access to the areas in the occupation of the most forward British troops. The weather, also, was uniformly good and it was often possible to use field tracks to debouch from one side road to another, while, if the car did by any chance become bogged, there was always a good prospect of help either from troops or from civilian inhabitants who were only too eager to help their deliverers in any way.

A yet more ingenious means used with success by one Corps in favourable weather was an aeroplane survey. Early one morning one of the pilots of the Corps R.A.F. Squadron flew a signal officer over the whole area over which the Corps was advancing. In less than two hours a fairly detailed reconnaissance had been made of the signal communications existing both in the zone occupied by our own forward troops and in that still held by the enemy rearguards. It was a bright sunny morning with an unusually clear atmosphere. The shadows caused by the poles and the light reflected from the wires enabled the whole system to be seen and sketched. It was even possible to distinguish the individual wires and their state of regulation. The sketch which was brought back by the observer was later proved to be correct in every detail and it was quite clear that, given favourable weather and a spare aeroplane, the ideal method of surveying forward routes had been discovered. The saving of time was all-important at this period of the year when the days were short and only a portion of the hours of daylight could be utilized for work owing to the congestion on the roads.

The Corps line system just described was reinforced by a wireless chain which consisted usually of a main directing station at Corps headquarters and an advanced station which was usually at Advanced Corps headquarters or at the headquarters of one of the Divisions in the line. In some Corps an extra station was obtained and manned and used as a Corps message station, thus permitting the directing stations to give their whole time to the control of the forward stations. Wireless was not, however, used to any great extent as an outlet for traffic between Corps and Division except at such times as the advance had outrun the line system. This was not likely to happen in a Corps which was advancing along a Divisional route. A marked exception was, however, provided by the Canadian Corps* who relied upon wireless throughout as an auxiliary system to take surplus

* Another peculiar feature of the wireless system of the Canadian Corps was the use of a Leyland lorry lent by First Army as the Corps Directing station. This was found of great use in regulating the traffic of Divisions who would "ignore the orders of the D.S. unless these orders were backed by considerable surplus power." The lorry was fitted with a special 500-watt spark set.

traffic that could not be accommodated on the Corps lines. An interesting synopsis of the wireless traffic handled by the stations of this Corps is given in Table XII.

TABLE XII.

*Canadian Corps Wireless Traffic during the Advance.*

| Date. | | Corps. | Divisions. | | | | Total. |
|-------|---|--------|------|------|------|------|--------|
| | | | 1st. | 2nd. | 3rd. | 4th. | |
| Aug. 26th | .. | 85 | — | 26 | 2 | — | 113 |
| Aug. 27th | .. | 75 | — | 10 | 62 | — | 147 |
| Aug. 28th | .. | 82 | 9 | 14 | 105 | — | 310 |
| Aug. 29th | .. | 70 | 56 | — | 66 | — | 192 |
| Aug. 30th | .. | 52 | 43 | — | — | — | 95 |
| Aug. 31st | .. | 112 | 22 | 12 | — | — | 146 |
| Sept. 1st | .. | 89 | 0 | 4 | — | 11 | 104 |
| Sept. 2nd | .. | 92 | 68 | 16 | — | 104 | 280 |
| Sept. 3rd | .. | 86 | 50 | 26 | — | 111 | 273 |
| Sept. 4th | .. | 80 | 50 | 32 | — | 115 | 277 |
| Sept. 5th | .. | 69 | — | — | — | 69 | 138 |
| Sept. 6th | .. | 100 | — | — | — | 38 | 138 |
| Sept. 7th | .. | 76 | — | — | — | — | 76 |
| Sept. 8th | .. | 106 | — | — | — | — | 106 |
| Sept. 9th | .. | 65 | — | — | — | — | 65 |
| Sept. 10th | .. | 63 | — | — | — | — | 63 |

Grand Total (Canadian Corps, August 26th to Sept. 10th)    2523

Comparative Totals.

| | |
|---|---|
| Calculated average total per day if Corps and all four Divisions engaged .. .. .. .. .. .. .. .. | 300 |
| Calculated average total per day, Corps .. .. .. | 81 |
| Calculated average total per day, Division .. .. .. | 45 |
| Calculated average total telegraph traffic at Corps head-quarters, same period .. .. .. .. .. .. | 5000 |
| Calculated similar total for Division .. .. .. .. | 660 |
| Calculated daily total D.R.L.S. at Corps .. .. .. | 2200 |
| Calculated daily total D.R.L.S. at Division .. .. .. | 500 |

While mobile warfare exercised a consolidating effect on Divisional artillery and infantry signal relations, the reverse was seen to be the case with Corps heavy artillery and Corps headquarters signals. Two quite different artillery dispositions were made in different Corps. In the one case, the control of certain heavy brigades was decentralized to Divisions and the responsibility for the signals of such Brigades naturally fell upon the already overburdened Divisional signal officer. In the other case, Corps headquarters retained control of all the heavy guns. The tendency with heavy artillery was naturally for the heavier guns to lag behind the more mobile formations in a quick advance, but to collect again when the advance slowed down or stopped before any of the successive lines which the enemy endeavoured to hold. The result of such differential movement was the concentration of the attention of the H.A. signal personnel on the construction, manning and maintenance of a special system of their own. The forward exchange system was utilized in this case also and one main route of four pairs of poled cable or airline was built forward on either side of the Corps area. These were led into forward exchanges which served the various Brigades of the two groups. The inadequacy of the Corps H.A. signal establishment was soon seen and the situation was only saved by the attachment of a cable section from the Army or the Corps. The lines from the C.H.A. central exchange to the forward exchanges were very long and maintenance was very heavy, this being due more to traffic than to enemy shelling. It was only by the utmost exertions of the sections that the trunks between the exchanges could be built and kept through. It was usually necessary to call upon the R.G.A. Brigade signal subsections to lay and maintain the lines back from their headquarters to the forward exchanges, in addition to their normal work forward to the batteries. The inadequacy of the C.H.A. signal section was perhaps the chief lesson of the advance as it affected artillery signals.

The use of continuous wave wireless with heavy artillery was very marked during the advance, and might have been much more so, had the necessary number of stations been available. Where decentralization of Brigades had taken place, it proved impossible to lay lines between R.G.A. Brigade headquarters and C.H.A. headquarters in addition to the necessary command lines to the Divisions under which the Brigades were working. All line traffic had to pass *via* Division and Corps headquarters and was much delayed in consequence. Continuous wave wireless was utilized in such cases to supply the direct communication desired and as many as 30 to 40 messages were passed by this means every day.

While the responsibility for the two signal systems just referred to rested with the A.D. Signals of the Corps, he was fortunately able to delegate this work to two senior officers of his company. The O.C. Corps signal company was usually given charge of the Corps system and the administration of the company. The O.C. Corps H.A. section confined his attention altogether to the heavy artillery signal system. A.D. Signals himself was therefore able to devote a considerable portion of his time and energy to co-ordinating the Divisional communications and assisting the Divisional signal officers to anticipate the line of advance in good time and keep the Divisional route well ahead of the immediate requirements of his Staff.

The problems of forward signals are more susceptible of division into two separate questions for which different solutions were required. Each bound forward, whether long or short, demanded a certain definite signal policy. Each was preceded and followed by an intensive action which resembled more or less closely the battles of position warfare. These questions may be considered separately, the latter being taken first, as it more closely resembles the problems of the preceding years.

The actions of August 8th and September 29th were both of them position battles on a scale that had never before been surpassed. There was, however, this difference from the battles of 1917. There was no comparison between the relative strength of the artillery engaged. From June, 1918, onwards, one of the most comforting aspects of the situation from the point of view of the forward troops, whether infantry, artillery, or engineers, was the fact that for every shell the enemy sent over he received ten or twenty back. In the bombardments which immediately preceded the great engagements of the summer and autumn of 1918, the British artillery dominated the situation to such an extent that the enemy retaliation was largely blind. Shooting by the map was the rule throughout. Even that was smothered to a very great extent by the accuracy of the fire of our own guns and the necessity he was under of keeping his heavy guns far back to avoid capture. This was the one factor which permitted of the survival of the slender ground or poled cable net-work which was the mainstay of the intercommunication system even in the most intense of the engagements subsequent to August 8th.

On this date, the attack was made on a great portion of the British front from a well-prepared defence line, part of the mechanism of which was an efficient and safe buried cable system. The success of the attack quickly carried the Divisions and the Corps off the buries, however, and from that time onward, with one exception, the pauses were never of sufficient duration to permit of buries being dug. Indeed, the conditions were such that the expenditure of labour would not have been warranted. The main enemies of the line system in future—if common sense was exercised in choosing routes—were tanks, traffic and hurried movement.

The solitary exception occurred when a slight pause took place in and about the positions in front of the Hindenburg Line which had been occupied by British troops in the summer and winter of 1917. Here buries existed which had not been destroyed either by our own troops or by the Germans. Exploration of deep dug-outs and shafts revealed testboards and racks which gave promise that the buries might still be in a fair state of preservation. Area detachments were hastened up from their work of salving cables in the rear of the Army areas and pairs were tested out. In many cases, the buries enjoyed a brief and partial revival of use before the final and speedy success of the attack on September 29th took the Divisions in one stride across the Hindenburg Line and well into the unspoilt country beyond.

This very temporary and partial appearance was the last that was seen of buried cable until some months after the Armistice, when the salvage parties, having cleared the greater portion of the airline and cable above ground, commenced to carry out trials as to the possibility of recovering the thousands of miles of valuable wire which underlay the old battlefields.

Although the buried system was eliminated as a characteristic of the forward signal system during an advance, yet line signalling still remained the main method employed. The principle of the single Divisional route was insisted upon and this normally consisted of three pairs of poled cable, usually of twisted " D8," which had by now proved itself to be the best of the twisted cables for use on long main trunks.* These trunks were carried forward by cross country routes, avoiding valleys and other natural features likely to receive attention from the enemy's artillery as possible concentration points for the attacking troops. At or near a common Brigade headquarters the pairs were led into a dug-out or strong point which was fitted up as a forward communication centre, usually with one or two ten-line cordless exchanges and one four plus three buzzer unit.† From here, short spurs ran to the headquarters of the neighbouring Brigades

* It was conclusively proved in all the position battles which punctuated the advance, that the necessary co-ordination in attack could not be obtained without a command telephone system which, to be ideal, must be intact as far forward as battalion headquarters. The essential features of the Divisional telephone system were command telephones at Division, Brigade, and Battalion headquarters, and *liaison* lines between artillery and infantry commanders (when the latter were not in the same headquarters). Superimposed upon the main telephone pairs between Divisions and Brigades were sounders or fullerphones, forward of Brigade messages were passed usually by fullerphone or " D3 " buzzer. All unnecessary Staff telephones were removed from the system when the warfare was mobile, and the administration telephones were also reduced to a minimum, only one " Q " phone being provided at advanced Divisional headquarters.

† The general practice was for the Division to carry at least two, and often three, standard forward offices consisting of what the O.C. Signals considered to be the essential instruments required to provide adequate communication in mobile warfare. The offices used in different formations varied with the experience and the predilections of the officers concerned, but the constituents of a typical forward office used in one Division were as follows :—(See *Plate* XIX.)

| Personnel. | | | Equipment. | | |
|---|---|---|---|---|---|
| N.C.O. lineman | .. | 1 | 10 line cordless exchange | .. | 1 |
| Operators or | | | 4-plus-3 exchange | .. | 1 |
| Switchboard operators | .. | 3 | D3 telephones | .. | 3 |
| Linemen | .. | 3 | Fullerphone .. | .. | 1 |
| | | | Transformer .. | .. | 1 |
| | | | Telephone, P.O. 44 .. | .. | 1 |
| | | | White and blue flag .. | .. | 1 |
| | | | Tags and labels and T13 wire | | |

and to the artillery, though the latter sometimes ran a separate system for themselves. At the main Divisional headquarters there would be a more elaborate office which varied in complication according to the previous experience of the General Staff and the weight exercised by the wishes of the Divisional signal officer. With a slender exposed line system and the greatly increased maintenance burden which was its invariable corollary, it was to the latter's interest to decrease the subscribers on his exchanges to the greatest possible extent. According as he was assisted or hindered by his Staff in the attainment of this object, so his responsibilities decreased or increased. The available personnel was a constant factor in all Divisions and the resultant efficiency of the system therefore depended largely upon the attitude taken up by its users. One division went into action on September 29th with no less than 42 subscribers on the Divisional exchange. Forward of Division, the system was as described above, while six very insecure cable pairs extended rearwards through rear Divisional headquarters to the advanced Corps exchange. It is not surprising that great congestion and friction between departments competing for the use of the telephones reduced the efficiency of the Staff during the battle. It was only a typical case of a Division which had escaped the trials of the earlier portion of the year and was hurriedly adjusting itself with an ill grace to new conditions. The lesson was, however, learnt once for all and a reversion to the slender signal system of mobile warfare completely eliminated friction and ensured efficient control in all the battles which followed.

At Divisional headquarters, personnel and instruments for a second communication centre were held in reserve, and at the communication centre already established, a cable detachment waited to proceed forward immediately the enemy's resistance was overcome. When news of a forward movement was received, the detachment was ordered up to the site chosen for the next station and the forward office was transported either by car, box-car, lorry, or G.S. wagon. The method of transport employed depended upon the speed of the advance, the likelihood of a Divisional move, and the state of preservation of the forward roads. In any case, it was usually possible to establish the next office and connect it up with at least one cable pair and one earthed line, by the time the Brigade headquarters had taken up their new position. If possible, spurs were run by the linemen of the forward centre or by the cable detachment to the Brigade headquarters, but if time did not permit of this, the Brigade signal officer was expected to connect up his office to the new centre himself.*

* This was sometimes unavoidable, but was contrary to the general policy of the Signal Service, which limited the executive responsibility of the signal officer of each formation to the area between his own headquarters and that of the formations immediately subordinate to it.

As the advance continued, the next stage of the proceedings would be the telescoping of the Divisional lines from the rear by the forward movement of Divisional headquarters.  By this time the Corps was usually in a position either to take over the old Divisional exchange or to establish a forward Corps exchange in close proximity. Divisional " Q " was usually left here with a short cable spur to the Corps exchange and the whole of the Divisional signal personnel was thus able to proceed forward to the new headquarters, the lines behind the latter passing to the maintenance of the Corps.

It was essential to the most efficient carrying out of the policy outlined above, that the Divisional artillery headquarters should agree to modify the separate system which it had been their practice to maintain during stationary warfare.  In the more intensive battles, where pauses of some duration took place, the D.A. headquarters exchange, with its radiating lines to its eight or nine artillery Brigades, was still desirable and possible, or, at the least, special artillery lines were included in the divisional trunk route, and separate artillery and infantry exchanges set up side by side at the forward communication centre.   Once movement set in, however, the pooling of all the signal personnel in the Division on one route was the rule, if efficient service was to be given.   This was generally recognized and in the more mobile periods the operators and linemen of the artillery headquarters signal section formed a valuable proportion of the personnel of the forward communication centres.

The building of the line system varied with the circumstances of the advance.  The influence of enemy artillery was almost negligible except as regards the details of the routes followed.  If the country were open, the choice lay between poled cable and ground cable, the latter being laid in ditches or in the open German cable trenches which seamed the country over which the troops were advancing. The former was erected sometimes on the black-and-white service poles, but more often upon rough poles taken from the German dumps or cut from local woods.   At other places, the lines were run along the German permanent routes, one or two pairs being perhaps slung on the poles at sufficient height to be out of the way of tanks, and the other pair run as ground cable with the possibilities of damage localised by tying back the cable to every permanent pole.   On yet other occasions, when the country became more enclosed, cable slung on hedges—familiar to everyone from practice and manœuvre days in England—was rapidly laid and quite safe from traffic.

Three types of country had to be crossed during the advance. The devastated Somme area was an obstacle which confined the cable wagons to the crowded roads as in the retreat.  The open country, which was perhaps typical in the Cambrai area, exposed the cable to danger from all varieties of traffic, but, on the other hand, permitted free passage for cable wagons in almost every direction.  The net-

Y

work of hedges beyond the Sambre-Oise canal presented features alike in every respect to the more enclosed portions of the English countryside.

The methods employed varied with the country, but the outstanding feature of the advance was the free use made of the six-horsed cable wagon. Light cable carts did useful work in difficult country, man and horse-drawn barrows were used to cross the crater-pitted country of the old battlefields, but the six-horsed cable wagon was the main stay of the forward signal officer. The critics of the stationary warfare period were dumb before the reversion to type which now took place. On occasion, during the most speedy phase of the advance, energetic cable detachments carried their lines forward beyond company headquarters. The company commander's " D3," the battalion 4-plus-3 board, and the Brigade ten-line cordless, succeeded each other in the same office as the Divisions advanced, but before the latter arrived, the cable head was once more several miles ahead. On one occasion, at least, a cable detachment commander enquiring for the locality of the battalion headquarters, was obliged to ride back along the line for a hundred yards or so before he could locate British troops. He was then told that the village in which his wagon was awaiting his return was officially in the hands of the enemy and that the N.C.O. to whom he was speaking was in command of an outpost detachment.

Little trouble was experienced in these marvellous days from enemy shelling. There were, however, other menaces to the safety of the lines. As the scene of action was approached from Corps headquarters, one cause of interruption might be seen in the steady advance of the inflated kite balloons along the main roads. Held captive by their wire cables, the balloons travelled at a height of over a hundred feet and buried crossings were, of course, the only means by which the cable could be protected against them. Naturally, also, buried crossings were not the easiest things to achieve across metalled roads during a hurried advance. All poled or slung cables were cut and, often, the men of the kite balloon detachment were too occupied with their own affairs to make good the damage they had caused.

Further forward, damage by tanks was frequent, for more mobile conditions once more prevented efficient *liaison* with this arm. Not only were cables torn asunder, but the light airline routes of the Corps and even the shorter of the reconstructed permanent routes were often destroyed by tanks carrying fascines or supplies. Recommendation was made by sorely harassed signal officers that the height of the loads carried by the tanks should be decreased in order to prevent this constant interruption of signal communication.

Further forward, still, the presence of cavalry once more interfered with the Divisional routes, the experience of Cambrai being repeated on a larger scale. Large bodies of cavalry cannot cross country without destroying ground cables which lie in their path. Too often, they did not take the trouble to avoid or repair the poled cable which should have been safe from their attention. At the same time, it must be admitted that the inconvenience was not always one-sided Badly-slung cables are a menace to horsemen at night and, in the haste of the advance, forward cable routes were not always built at a height which carried them well clear of the head of a mounted man. More care was needed on both sides to produce a cavalry-proof system and to ensure its fair treatment when erected.

One source of damage to the lines which was mainly confined to open country was the ordinary Divisional traffic. In the Cambrai district, especially, the dry weather, the rolling open downs, and the persistent shelling of main traffic routes indulged in by the enemy, all combined to entice the limbers and G.S. wagons of the Divisional transport off the roads. Main cable routes were an obvious guide to cross-country traffic and were used continually for this purpose. In the daytime all went well and the advantage of a short cut was not counterbalanced by damage to the lines, but at night the tracks were widened at the expense of the poled cable that bounded them. Time after time linemen were sent out along the main Divisional route to find from a quarter to half a mile down in the dirt and barked and torn by the wheels of the transport wagons.

A last source of trouble which must be recorded was the wilful cutting or destruction of routes by parties of men not personally interested in their preservation. On a single Divisional front within one month, three such instances caused great trouble. On the first occasion, the night before the battle for the Hindenburg line, two or three hundred yards were cut out of a main Divisional route by a cavalry squadron to make a picket line for their horses. Occurring on a dark foggy night, the damage was not repaired for some two hours and during that time the Division was entirely cut off from all its Brigades. A few days later, a similar happening proved on investigation to have been caused by the infantry of the very Brigade whose lines had been cut, and the missing pieces of cable were found to have been used in the building of bivouacs. Finally, on the evening before the forcing of the Sambre-Oise canal, the whole of the poles from a Divisional route were removed by Australian troops and used for a similar purpose. Such incidents might well make the signal officer despair of human nature. They were far too common and showed a thoughtlessness which was inexcusable. Only by careful education of the rank and file of the Army can their repetition be prevented.

Forward of Brigade headquarters, the main route was sometimes, as has been said, carried forward by the Divisional cable detachment. Much more often, light lines were laid by the Brigade signal section to a forward communication centre of their own, which was later replaced by one of the Divisional centres. From this centre light routes, which were generally of "D2" or "D3" cable, were run to battalion headquarters. Here the line system normally stopped, communication beyond being by visual or runner, as in almost all previous engagements.

The chief lesson of the mobile warfare to the Brigade signal section was, perhaps, the need for some quicker method of laying cable than by man-power. The absence of the Brigade pack animals was severely felt and only by the greatest exertion could the line system be kept complete as far forward as battalion headquarters which were of course constantly upon the move. This was especially the case in heavily wired and enclosed country and the reports of Brigade signal officers testify to the need for more mobility in the transport of their section.

A natural consequence of the hurried movement of the advance was a difficulty in supplying forward units with cable. This had been anticipated and, when the advance commenced, nearly all units were well above establishment and had a considerable proportion of single cable. Artillery cable wagons were filled up and the Divisional ammunition column also usually carried a large supply of "D3" cable. Infantry brigades and battalions were well supplied with "D2" and battalions held in many cases their full establishment of enamelled wire, which, however, they were loath to use except in times of great scarcity. Orders were issued that all possible lines abandoned were to be salved, and the attachment of an area detachment to many Divisions helped them to carry out these instructions very thoroughly. At each pause in the operations, the greater part of No. 1 section of the Divisions was employed sedulously collecting cable from the district in which the section was billeted. Much British cable was lying about all over the country and much German cable of good quality was also available for the trouble of collecting it. The wise Divisional signal officer saw to it that he went into action each time with some 60 to 80 miles of cable, of which two-thirds was probably twisted and one-third single. He was thus enabled, if necessary, to pass over a signal system to a Division passing through his own Division without feeling the loss of the cable or having to exact for it a *quid pro quo*. He knew that in the few days of res t that would be permitted to him he could make good his losses. Thi s was especially the case if there happened to be an abandoned Corps heavy artillery headquarters in his immediate neighbourhood. The Corps H.A. section was so understaffed that it was impossible for them to do much salving. They were also in a better position to replenish their stores from Corps. The network of cable they had abandoned was invaluable to the Division. By means of utilizing all such sources and the occasional finding of a German dump, many Divisions went through the greater part of the advance in September and October without calling upon the Corps for large supplies of heavy cable, though supplies of " D2 " and " D3 " were always useful when they could be obtained.

Once again the question of laterals was of paramount importance for the co-ordination of both advance and battle action. The system built up before any of the great battles included, of course, both Division and Brigade laterals. These were run without difficulty by the cable detachments if sufficient notice was given and notification of the position of flank headquarters was provided by the General Staff.

The case of the Division next the French presented peculiar difficulties, for our allies were not believers in lateral lines between Divisional headquarters and would not trouble to run them. A wise disposition of the Corps in question, however, permitted of the use of the Corps cable section to lay the line from right to left which was normally the duty of the British Division. Little difficulty was then experienced in keeping touch with the French division on the other flank. It was not, however, always possible to use the line when completed. On more than one occasion a " diss " on the line was found to be due to the fact that the French operator had hung the line up on a convenient nail in the office with the intention of attaching it to an instrument only when his own Staff desired to speak to the British General Staff.

Brigade laterals were dispensed with when movement was at all speedy and even Divisional laterals were not always possible under the most mobile conditions. In such cases telegraphic communication with the flank Divisions could usually be obtained *via* the Corps system, but speaking over the long lines involved was usually out of the question.

. The only alternative method of communication of vital importance in rear of battalion headquarters was wireless telegraphy. The main advance in the tactical use of wireless in Division and in Corps was the provision of sufficient extra stations to permit of a complete stepping-up system all along the main line of communication. An extra Wilson set at the Corps gave an advanced station which acted both in this way and as a transmitting station over unusually long distances. The issue of a fourth trench set to Divisions had a similar effect. The extra trench set was erected at the forward communication centre which was destined to become the new Divisional headquarters. The directing station at old Divisional headquarters continued to work until this set had taken over. It then dismantled and proceeded to the new headquarters, or, if movement was very rapid, proceeded straight forward to the next communication centre. In either case, it took over control when it again came into action. Forward of this, the Brigade trench sets—carried sometimes on stretchers, sometimes on pack ponies, sometimes on light Lewis

Gun handcarts—served the Brigade centre or a common battalion
headquarters. By judicious use of the five sets, wireless was always
available, either as an auxiliary to line communication, or as an
alternative when the lines lagged behind the general advance, as, in
spite of all efforts, they sometimes did.

Forward of Brigade or battalion, as the case might be, the " Loop "
sets were often in use up to ranges of 4,000 yards with considerable
success. In actions which at all resembled the position warfare
battles they were of great value between battalion and company
headquarters and between batteries and observation posts. Their
use varied in different Divisions, and in some they were scarcely
employed at all, as visual and runner were found sufficient for the
modicum of communication required within the battalion. Even
so, however, they had almost completely ousted the power buzzer
amplifier sets from favour and it is unlikely that even a return to
trench warfare would have restored the latter more cumbersome
instrument to its erstwhile popularity.

The use of wireless as an integral part of the Divisional chain of
communication had entirely altered its relation to the line system and
much closer touch was kept between the signal office and wireless
office during the advance. The connection of the wireless station
with the former by wire had become a *sine qua non* whenever the
two offices were not in the same building or within easy reach of
each other by orderly.

The traffic now dealt with by the wireless station was of the order
of anything from 20 to 80 messages a day, and another effect of this
great increase was again seen in the partial abrogation of the cipher
restrictions. Clear messages were the rule in the mobile phases of
the advance ; whenever clear messages were forbidden, wireless
traffic dropped at once to very low figures and the forward fullerphone and sounder lines were overloaded in consequence. Never
was it so evident that the chief obstacle to the free use of this method
of signalling was the strangle-hold exercised upon it by the need for
insistence upon the use of cipher.*

* This insistence by the General Staff upon the use of cipher must
have appeared unnecessary and irksome to the majority of wireless
officers whose duty it was to forward the messages to their destination
as quickly as possible. A glimpse of the other side of the picture is,
however, afforded by the reference on page 274, indicating the use to
which intercepted wireless messages sent " in clear " can be put by
an alert enemy.

It is the duty of the General Staff to balance the advantages to be
gained by the unrestricted use of wireless against the value of the
information which is obtained by the enemy from this source, and to
regulate the wireless traffic accordingly.

It is certainly open to consideration whether a more efficient regulation
would not have been obtained if this duty had been delegated by the

The ranges over which the sets worked were often towards the extreme limit of their power and the need of a more powerful set was felt in the Divisions as well as at the Corps. Locally, improvements were made in the Divisional wireless system by the use of continuous wave stations, but this could only be done at the expense of an already insufficient artillery wireless system. The solution of both the range and the jamming problems which have worried the Divisional wireless officer in the past would seem to lie in the direction of the adoption of continuous wave wireless for all purposes, but this was not possible before the Armistice put an end to the war in November, 1918.

A special development of continuous wave wireless which requires some mention was the use of the sets for " flash spotting " and for observation work generally. The general situation as regards cable did not permit of the lavish use of lines between observation post and batteries, and their place was largely taken either by " loop " sets or, more frequently, by continuous wave stations. Fleeting targets could not have been engaged to anything like the extent they were without the help of these sets and a large measure of the difference between the accuracy of the enemy and our own artillery fire must be attributed undoubtedly to the free use of wireless for observation purposes.

Artillery wireless was perhaps hampered more by lack of transport than by any other consideration. The transport of the artillery Brigade signal sub-sections was quite inadequate to their needs and many signal officers who had had no personal experience of the value of C.W. wireless were only too glad to leave their sets behind. In some Corps, an effort was made to provide extra transport for the wireless sets, but this could only be a partial solution of the difficulty, as the rough roads and unsprung vehicles played havoc with the delicate instruments.

Another departure in the use of wireless was its employment on a large scale with Divisional and Corps observers. For this purpose both spark and C.W. stations were employed. Detachments of Lovatt's Scouts and special Observation Sections had been organized in many Corps and Divisions and, while these parties relied on light lines and visual to a great extent, C.W. or spark wireless was a valued supplementary means of communication. Special sets with their

General Staff to the Signal Service, so that the latter was responsible for the regulation of the traffic and the arrangements to maintain secrecy, as well as for the delivery of the messages to their proper destinations.

Possibly the real solution to the problem is to increase the personnel allotted to a wireless station to permit of messages being enciphered or encoded expeditiously at the station itself. A practical well-designed code in preference to a cipher would also assist.

complement of operators were allotted to the Observation Officers and very valuable reports were sent back. These were, indeed, often the only reliable situation reports which the higher command was able to obtain. Although the line system might be intact and the Divisional wireless chain working, these could only deal with messages, if messages were sent to them. Too often, forward commanders were so obsessed with their own plans as to be unable to spare time to keep their superiors informed of the course of operations. It was at such times that the " Divisional Observation Officer "—the Divisional Commander's own " eyes "—was able to keep him informed through his special communication system of much that was essential to a correct appreciation of the situation.

In the summer, when the German long-distance bombing planes were particularly active, a special installation of continuous wave wireless stations had been arranged in connection with a night-flying R.A.F. squadron to assist in combating their activities. One station was established at the squadron headquarters and three outlying stations at selected anti-aircraft defence centres. These outlying stations sent in warnings to the squadron when the approach of hostile aircraft was detected.

The system worked well and was subsequently extended into Army areas. After the commencement of the Allied autumn offensive the enemy bombing of back areas declined considerably. It is an interesting sidelight on the opinion of the anti-aircraft officers on the value of wireless telegraphy as applied to their work that in many cases the sets that had been allotted to them temporarily for a specific purpose were later deliberately stolen and kept in use for general intercommunication purposes during the advance, for which no allotment of C.W. wireless stations had been authorized.

A still further example of the use of continuous wave wireless during the advance was the establishment of eight or nine stations at important railroad junctions to assist in the handling and direction of railway traffic. The Railway Operating Division pronounced these stations to be invaluable. The sets and personnel were found from the equipment and staff of the Central Wireless School, and during their special employment were administered by the O.C. G.H.Q. Wireless Observation Group.

The old difficulties which attended the use of wireless were once again in evidence, but to a much less degree. Brigade Staffs still did not make as much use of this means of intercommunication as they might have done or as the situation warranted. Jamming both by German and by our own sets was very bad, and the poorly trained signalmen " A " with the artillery sets found themselves particularly badly hampered in this respect. Control was much improved, it is true, but with as many as 66 spark sets and 49 C.W. sets working on the ground in the main command system of a single Army—and numerous additional sets serving special needs—a certain amount of interference was inevitable. The German Army, also, relied upon wireless to a great extent for communication forward of Division and their sets added to the confused jumble of sounds from which the operators of individual stations had to select the signals of their own particular *vis-à-vis*.

With both these drawbacks, however, wireless was still of great use and often of vital importance, and the wireless establishments and the time spent on perfecting this method of signalling were absolutely vindicated by the experience of these last months of war.

With the consideration of the line system, and of the auxiliary wireless chain, the principal elements of the main communication system in rear of battalion headquarters have been passed under review. It was only during the initial stages of the fiercest attacks which involved a preparation period comparable in some slight degree to that of the 1917 battles, that other methods bulked at all largely between battalion and Divisional headquarters. Pigeons and messenger dogs were used on occasion, but never regained their former importance in the signal scheme of operations.* Their use, when they were employed, presented no special features of interest other than those already discussed in former chapters. The message-carrying rocket, also, was only occasionally used in those battles which were more of a set-piece nature, and, with them, disappeared also the many varieties of flashlight and rocket signals which had been the most picturesque feature of position warfare.

Motor cycle despatch riders and mounted orderlies were utilized to the same extent as in former mobile campaigns. During the fogs that characterized the early autumn mornings, they were often, though themselves much hampered, the only reliable means of communication to supplement the Divisional wireless stations. Visual on such occasions was impossible, and the maintenance and forward extension of the cables was also extremely difficult and very slow. Runners were, as ever, a reliable means of forward communication, but the use of visual increased at their expense in the comparatively shell-free battles of the advance between the German defence zones.

* The use of parachute baskets dropped from aeroplanes to convey pigeons to troops on the far side of the almost impassable devastated area in front of the Ypres Salient is, perhaps, the solitary exception to this generalization. Pigeons were also exceptionally useful in conveying messages from the fighting tanks, but little other information of interest was sent back by them, owing to the survival of the line system on the greater part of the front. Of those that were sent up the line a considerably larger proportion than usual were released with practice messages. It needs impressing on all forward officers that, if pigeons have to be released and no urgent message is to hand, they should be sent with a situation report, or at least with a duplicate of a former message which may or may not have reached its destination.

A feature of the runner organization in one Division was the organization of a " chain " which was a much exaggerated form of the relay runner system, each man of the chain forming a post in himself and being in sight of the next " link."

Perhaps the most typical of all the message-carrying agencies of the advance was the mounted orderly, and in this respect the establishment of the Divisional signal company was still woefully inadequate. The deficiency was represented to the Divisional and Corps Staffs and was met in various ways, according to the sympathy with which the request for more mounted men was viewed. In some Divisions, officers' grooms and spare chargers were placed at the disposal of the signal officer. For small journeys between headquarters over easily recognizable tracks in clear weather these men were of use, but they were completely lost when it came to making use of a compass or picking up difficult landmarks from a study of the map. A much more efficient system prevalent in many formations was the attachment of a troop of Divisional mounted troops to the signal company, and often, when the whole of these men were required by the Divisional Commander, their place was well filled by a troop from a cavalry unit which happened to be operating with or near the Division. Finally, another measure by which the available orderlies were frequently increased was by the allotment of a section or platoon of Corps cyclists who did valuable work wherever machines could be ridden.

The use of the aeroplane as a despatch carrier was inaugurated in at least one Corps, and aeroplanes were used considerably over the whole front for the collection of reports of the situation as seen from the air. Popham panels were available at Division and Brigade headquarters but were seldom employed, the " aeroplane dropping stations," the establishment of which had by now become part of the usual routine of Divisional signals, being used almost entirely for the dropping of messages from the planes. Much valuable information was passed back in this way and the calling of the Klaxon horn will recall the days of the advance to all ranks who spent any large portion of their time at or near Divisional headquarters.

Men to man the dropping stations were often lent from the Divisional pioneer battalion, and in more than one way the signal section of this battalion had been of the greatest use to the Divisional signal company commander. His resources had already been strengthened by the addition of No. 5 section to the company. In most Divisions the machine-gun signal system had been done away with as a separate system and most of the new section absorbed into the general communication scheme. The pioneer battalion, also, could do without much intercommunication and usually the O.C. battalion was quite ready to fall in with the suggestion that men should be drawn from his signalling section to assist in the Divisional visual chain. It was, indeed, only by means of these men and some of the best visual signallers of the Brigade pool that it was possible to build up anything like an efficient visual system. To the pioneer battalion signallers, themselves, the Signal Service is indebted for very loyal and very efficient service, and whether in charge of the aeroplane dropping station, salving and repairing cable, or engaged upon the more technical work of manning the Divisional terminal or transmitting visual stations, their work was invariably carried out conscientiously and cheerfully.

Visual was again much hampered by the mist and smoke. These decreased visibility in the early morning attacks to such a degree that the whole army was reduced to groping its way forward blindly, keeping direction merely by the aid of the shriek of shells passing overhead, the crash of the barrage on the enemy's lines, and the roar of their own guns behind them. Alternative visual was established in most Divisions, but it is rather questionable if the expenditure of men was always justified by results. It was another case of preparing for the worst. If the lines and wireless were both out of action, visual was of the greatest value. Under the circumstances of the advance, however, it was only through bad organization or quite unusually unfavourable conditions that the visual chain became essential in rear of Brigade headquarters, Even when such cases did occur, it was quite likely that the weather conditions would not permit of visual being employed.

Forward of Brigade headquarters, visual was useful : forward of battalion headquarters it was essential, but no special features of interest marked its use. The conditions were not nearly so exacting as in the position battles and every type of instrument could be used at one time or another without untoward results. The Lucas lamp was an easy favourite, and after this in popularity came the 1918 patterns of disc and shutter. Heliographs could have been much used had more been available, but they were not essential over the short distances which separated the reconnoitring detachments from company or battalion headquarters. Visual was much more used by battery signallers, also, and all observation work was done by this means when cable was short and wireless sets not available. A departure in the tactical employment of visual in the Division was the appointment of an officer especially to control the visual stations. It was found that N.C.O.'s did not usually possess enough initiative and skill to select the best sites, or authority to co-ordinate the Divisional and Brigade schemes. Where a visual officer was definitely appointed the best results were invariably obtained.

The signal system of the cavalry does not call for any particular comment as regards the means employed. Lines were used during the concentrations behind the infantry Divisions ; wireless, visual, and orderlies were predominant, when the cavalry Brigades were working in front of the dismounted troops. Great use was made of the Divisional lines by the officers in command of the cavalry reconnoitring parties who were feeling their way forward in pursuit of the swiftly retreating enemy. In general, a separate line system was not attempted on a grand scale, when the cavalry were operating as an independent force or as individual Brigades attached to the Divisions in the line. The light motor and pack wireless sets proved as efficient as usual, and these and motor cyclists amply sufficed for cavalry Division-Brigade communication while on the move.

The chief lessons that can be drawn from the cavalry action of the advance was the efficiency of the Cavalry Wireless Squadron which had taken the place of the wireless troops of the cavalry Divisional Signal Squadron. All the arguments in favour of the use of wireless in mobile warfare with infantry are, of course, redoubled in the case of cavalry action. As soon as wireless became a practical proposition for Army use, it was quite evident that the direction in which it must first replace lines was with a swiftly-moving force like the Cavalry Corps. This was shown clearly in the mobile warfare of 1914, and the cavalry signal establishments were altered accordingly. The appointment of an A.D. Signals, Cavalry Corps, kept cavalry signals on an equal footing with those of the infantry Corps, but with this exception the signal squadron headquarters—though slightly strengthened—had not been materially altered. The 1914 and 1918 cavalry signal establishments are shown in detail in Appendix I.

---

The mobile warfare, the principal features of the signal practice of which have just been described, continued with accelerating speed until the signing of the Armistice on November 11th brought the war to an end. No particular features arose during the last few days of hurried advance to change the characteristics of the line or wireless system. The Signal Service had adapted itself thoroughly to this fresh type of warfare which was much more in keeping with the temperament of the personnel of the forward signal units. Everybody was working at highest pressure, but all were doing their share cheerfully and ever with an eye to giving a helping hand in other directions than their normal work. This was the day of the forward detachments of the Brigade and Divisional signal units. The men of No. 1 section of the Divisional signal companies, especially, with the memory of the seemingly endless days spent on the buried cable systems of 1916 and 1917, were enthusiastic in the performance of work which they felt was more what they joined the Army to do. These last few days in the van of a victorious Army repaid the cable detachments for all the drudgery of the preceding years. Their days were enlivened by the capture of enemy signal apparatus of every description ; by long trips on horseback or on motor cycles reconnoitring abandoned German telegraph routes ; even, on occasion, by the opportunity of chalking their unit's name as the first discoverers of abandoned German guns and howitzers. One obvious deficiency in the mobile equipment of the Divisional signal company was remedied by the illicit absorption of German field cookers which added much to the comfort of the forward detachments in the last week or two of the war, and of the whole company after the Armistice.* The officers of the Divisional Signal Company, also, were employed in turn on the congenial work of reconnoitring forward along the roads for good cable routes, and searching captured towns for abandoned apparatus and signal offices. Occasional machine-gun, or rifle fire was very little heeded in the absence of shells, which made the war of the last few days utterly unlike anything that had gone before.

No difficulty was experienced in keeping the Divisional system well in front of the demands of Brigadiers. The deciding factor in the speed of the advance was supply and transport, and not signals. The signal companies could meet all demands upon them with a little in hand, and when the advance came to an end well beyond the Belgian frontier, it needed only a few finishing touches to connect up to the Army, Corps and Divisional system everyone who desired, and had any right to a telephone.

* In one Divisional Signal Company an abandoned rear-half of a British cooker, salved and repaired during the 1918 spring retreat, proved invaluable both during mobile work and on night-burying cable. The O.C. Divisional signal company claims a 50% increase of efficiency in his forward Divisional exchanges when first installed, through this fact alone. Any officer who has seen the effect of a hot meal on chilled and overworked operators and linemen will agree that he has not overstated his case. The absence of adequate means of obtaining hot food and drink at short notice for the men has many times proved a distinct handicap to their comfort and efficiency.

## APPENDIX I.

# COMPARATIVE SIGNAL ESTABLISHMENTS.

## DIVISIONAL SIGNAL COMPANY.

| Detail. | 1914. * | 1914. † | 1915. * | 1915. † | 1916. * | 1916. † | 1917. * | 1917. † | 1918. * | 1918. † | Remarks |
|---|---|---|---|---|---|---|---|---|---|---|---|
| H.Q. (excl. attd.) | 1 | 40 | 1 | 50 | 1 | 55 | 3 | 74 | 3 | 167 | * Officers. |
| Ditto (attd.) | | 4 | | 4 | | 7 | | 7 | | 6 | † Men, N.C.O.'s and W.O.'s |
| R.A. Section ... | — | — | — | — | — | — | 2 | 54 | 3 | 57 | |
| No. 1 Section ... | 1 | 48 | 2 | 70 | 2 | 74 | 2 | 72 | 3 | 86 | |
| Nos. 2, 3 & 4 Sections | 3 | 78 | 3 | 78 | 3 | 78 | 3 | 72 | 6 | 75 | |
| Ditto attd. ... | | | | | | | | | | 9 | |
| No. 5 Section | (Created in 1918. Incl. in No. 1 Section figures.) | | | | | | | | | | |
| Total ... | 5 | 170 | 6 | 202 | 6 | 214 | 10 | 279 | 15 | 400 | |

## COMPOSITION IN DETAIL.

| Detail. | 1914. | 1915. | 1916. | 1917. | 1918. | Remarks. |
|---|---|---|---|---|---|---|
| *Headquarters.* | | | | | | |
| Major ... | }† | }† | 1 | 1 | 1 | † Major or Captain. |
| Captain ... | }1 | }1 | | 2 | 1 | |
| C.S.M. ... | 1 | 1 | 1 | 1 | 1 | |
| C.Q.M.S. ... | 1 | 1 | 1 | 1 | 1 | |
| Serjeants ... | 1 | 1 | 1 | 1 | 2 | |
| Shoeing and C. Smith | 1 | — | — | —. | — | |
| Corporals ... | — | 1 | 2 | 2 | 2 | |
| Second Corporals ... | — | 1 | 1 | 1 | 2 | |
| Trumpeters ... | 1 | 1 | — | — | — | |
| Sappers and Pioneers | — | 10 | 15 | 14 | 31 | |
| Drivers (for vehicle) ... | 3 | 5 | 5 | 5 | 5 | |
| Drivers (spare horse) | 3 | 1 | 1 | 1 | 1 | |
| Drivers (spare) ... | 1 | — | — | — | 1 | |
| Batmen ... | 2 | 2 | 2 | 4 | 2 | |
| Motor cyclists— | | | | | | |
| Serjeant ... | 1 | 1 | 1 | 1 | 1 | |
| Cpl. Artificer ... | 1 | 1 | 1 | 1 | 1 | |
| Corporals ... | 12 | 14 | 14 | 1 | 1 | |
| Second Corporal ... | — | — | — | 1 | 1 | |
| Sappers and Pioneers | — | — | — | 12 | 16 | |
| | | | | | | |
| *Wireless Telegraph Section.* | | | | | | |
| Subaltern ... | — | — | — | — | 1 | |
| Serjeants ... | — | — | — | 1 | 2 | |
| Corporals ... | — | — | — | 1 | 3 | |
| Second Corporals ... | — | — | — | 1 | 3 | |
| Sappers and Pioneers | — | — | — | 15 | 50 | |
| Drivers ... | — | — | — | — | 2 | |
| Batmen ... | — | — | — | — | 1 | |
| | | | | | | |
| *Visual Section.* | | | | | | |
| Serjeant ... | 1 | 1 | 1 | 1 | 1 | |
| Corporals ... | 1 | 1 | 1 | 1 | 2 | |
| Second Corporals ... | — | — | — | — | 2 | |
| Sappers and Pioneers | 10 | 8 | 8 | 8 | 32 | |
| Driver ... | — | — | — | — | 1 | |
| | | | | | | |
| *Attached to H.Q.* | | | | | | |
| R.A.M.C. ... | 2 | 2 | 2 | 2 | — | |
| Drivers, A.S.C.M.T. ... | 2 | 2 | 5 | 5 | 6 | |
| Driver, A.S.C. ... | 1 | 1 | 1 | 1 | 1* | * Train transport. (Not counted in total.) |
| Total H.Q. (incl. attd.) | 45 | 55 | 63 | 84 | 176 | |

COMPOSITION IN DETAIL—*continued.*

| Detail.<br>R.A. Section. | | | 1914. | 1915. | 1916. | 1917. | 1918. | Remarks. |
|---|---|---|---|---|---|---|---|---|
| **R.A.H.Q.** | | | | | | | | |
| Captain | ... | ... | – | – | – | – | 1 | |
| Serjeant | ... | ... | – | – | – | 1 | 1 | |
| Second Corporal | ... | | – | – | – | 1 | 1 | |
| Sappers and Pioneers | | | – | – | – | 12 | 12 | |
| Drivers | ... | ... | – | – | – | 2 | 2 | |
| Batman | ... | ... | – | – | – | – | 1 | |
| | | | | | | | | |
| *Sig. Sub-section for R.F.A. Bdes.* (*each*) | | | | | | | | |
| Subaltern | ... | ... | – | – | – | 1 | 1 | |
| Serjeant | ... | ... | – | – | – | 1 | 1 | |
| Corporal | ... | ... | – | – | – | 1 | 1 | |
| Second Corporal | ... | | – | – | – | 1 | 1 | |
| Sappers and Pioneers | | | – | – | – | 13 | 13 | |
| Drivers | ... | ... | – | – | – | 2 | 3 | |
| Batmen | ... | ... | – | – | – | 1 | 1 | |
| Total, R.A. Section | | | | | | 56 | 60 | |
| | | | | | | | | |
| *No. 1 Section.* | | | | | | | | |
| *A and B Cable Sections.* | | | | | | | | |
| Captain | ... | ... | – | – | 1 | – | – | |
| Subalterns | ... | ... | 1 | 2 | 1 | 2 | 2 | |
| Serjeants | ... | ... | 2 | 2 | 2 | 2 | 2 | |
| Farrier Serjeant | ... | | – | 1 | – | 1 | 1 | |
| Shoeing Smith | ... | | 1 | 1 | 2 | 1 | 1 | |
| Corporals | ... | ... | 2 | – | – | – | 3 | |
| Second Corporals | ... | | 3 | 6 | 6 | 6 | 3 | |
| Sappers and Pioneers | | | 26 | 36 | 40 | 36 | 32 | |
| Drivers | ... | ... | 12 | 16 | 16 | 18 | 16 | |
| Drivers (spare horse) | | | – | 2 | 2 | 6 | 4 | |
| Drivers (spare) | | ... | – | 2 | 2 | 2 | 2 | |
| Batmen | ... | ... | 2 | 4 | 4 | – | 2 | |
| Total No. 1 Section | | ... | 49 | 72 | 76 | 74 | 68 | |
| | | | | | | | | |
| *Machine Gun Section.* | | | | | | | | |
| Subaltern | ... | ... | – | – | – | – | 1 | |
| Serjeant | ... | ... | – | – | – | – | 1 | |
| Corporal | ... | ... | – | – | – | – | 1 | |
| Second Corporal | ... | | – | – | – | – | 1 | |
| Sappers and Pioneers | | | – | – | – | – | 15 | |
| Driver | ... | ... | – | – | – | – | 1 | |
| Batman | ... | ... | – | – | – | – | 1 | |
| Total | ... | ... | | | | | 21 | |
| | | | | | | | | |
| *Nos. 2, 3 and 4 Sections.** | | | | | | | | * Each. |
| Captain | ... | ... | – | – | – | – | 1 | |
| Subaltern | ... | ... | 1 | 1 | 1 | 1 | 1 | |
| Serjeants | ... | ... | 2 | 2 | 2 | 2 | 2 | |
| Corporal | ... | ... | 1 | 1 | 1 | 1 | 1 | |
| Second Corporal | ... | | 1 | 1 | 1 | 1 | 1 | |
| Sappers and Pioneers | | | 17 | 17 | 17 | 17 | 17 | |
| Drivers | ... | ... | 3 | 3 | 3 | 1 | 2 | |
| Batmen | ... | ... | 2 | 2 | 2 | 2 | 2 | |
| Attached (Privates) | ... | | – | – | – | – | 3* | * For pigeon stations. |
| Total : | | | | | | | | |
| (Nos. 2, 3 and 4 Secs.) | | | 27 | 27 | 27 | 25 | 30 | |

## CORPS SIGNAL UNITS.

| Detail. | 1914. | 1915. | 1916. | 1917. | 1918. | Remarks. |
|---|---|---|---|---|---|---|
| *Corps Headquarters.* | | | | | | |
| A.D.A.S. ... ... | — | — | — | 1 | 1 | |
| *Corps Signal Company.* | | | | | | |
| Headquarters ... | 4 56 | 5 64 | 4 87 | 6 90 | 6 105 | |
| Ditto attd. ... ... | 7 | 11 | 14 | 17 | 12 | |
| Wireless Section ... | — | — | — | 27 | 31 | |
| Ditto attd. ... ... | — | — | — | — | 3 | |
| Sig. Sect., Corps H.A. | — | — | — | 1 35 | 2 39 | |
| Ditto attd. ... ... | — | — | — | 1 | 1 | |
| Total ... ... ... | 4 63 | 5 75 | 4 101 | 7 170 | 8 191 | |

### COMPOSITION IN DETAIL.

| *Headquarters.* | | | | | | |
|---|---|---|---|---|---|---|
| Major or Captain ... | 1* | 1* | 1* | 1 | 1 | * Majors. |
| Captain or Subaltern | 2† | 3† | — | 1 | 1 | † Captains. |
| Subalterns ... ... | 1 | 1 | 3 | 4 | 4 | |
| Serjeant-Major (W.O.1)) | — | — | — | 1 | 1 | |
| C.S.M. ... ... ... | 1 | 1 | 1 | — | — | |
| C.Q.M.S. ... ... | 1 | 1 | 1 | 1 | 1 | |
| M.M. S.S. ... ... | — | — | — | 1 | 1 | |
| Serjeants ... ... | 3 | 3 | 3 | 3 | 3 | |
| Farrier Serjeant ... | 1 | — | — | — | — | |
| S. and C.S. Corporal ... | — | 1 | 1 | 1 | — | |
| Corporals ... ... | 2 | 3 | 4 | 4 | 5 | |
| Trumpeter ... ... | 1 | — | — | — | — | |
| Second Corporals ... | 2 | 3 | 3 | 3 | 3 | |
| Sappers and Pioneers | 24 | 30 | 53 | 53 | 70 | |
| Drivers ... | 4 | — | — | — | — | |
| Batmen ... ... | 7 | 5 | 4 | 6 | 6 | |
| Motor cyclists— | | | | | | |
| Serjeant ... ... | 1 | 1 | 1 | 1 | 1 | |
| Artificer Corporal ... | 1 | 1 | 1 | 1 | 1 | |
| Corporals ... ... | 9 | 15 | 15 | 1 | 2 | |
| Second Corporals ... | — | — | — | 1 | 1 | |
| Sappers and Pioneers | — | — | — | 13 | 10 | |
| Attached | | | | | | |
| R.A.M.C. ... ... | 2 | 2 | 2 | 2 | — | |
| A.S.C.M.T. ... ... | 4 | 8 | 10 | 15 | 12 | |
| Driver A.S.C. ... | 1 | 1 | 2 | — | — | |
| Total ... ... ... | 67 | 80 | 105 | 113 | 123 | |

| *Wireless Section.* | | | | | | |
|---|---|---|---|---|---|---|
| | * | * | † | | | * No. Corps Wireless |
| Serjeants ... ... | — | — | — | 2 | 2 | Section. |
| Second Corporals ... | — | — | — | 1 | 2 | † Wireless Section part of |
| Interpreter Operators | — | — | — | 9 | 3 | Army Wireless Co. |
| Sappers ... ... | — | — | — | 14 | 23 | |
| Pioneers ... ... | — | — | — | 1 | 1 | |
| Attd. A.S.C.M.T. ... | — | — | — | — | 3 | |
| Total ... ... ... | | | | 27 | 34 | |

| *Signal Section, Corps H.A.* | | | | | | |
|---|---|---|---|---|---|---|
| Captain ... ... | — | — | — | 1 | 1 | 1918—In addition : |
| Subaltern ... ... | — | — | — | — | 1 | 2 Motor Airline Sects. |
| Serjeant ... ... | — | — | — | 1 | 1 | 2 Cable Sections ; " x " |
| Corporal ... ... | — | — | — | 1 | 1 | H.A. Signal Sub-sects. |
| Second Corporal ... | — | — | — | 1 | 1 | (for Est. see Army |
| Sappers and Pioneers | — | — | — | 24 | 25 | Signal Units). |
| Instrument Repairer ... | — | — | — | 1 | 1 | |
| Motor Cyclists ... | — | — | — | 4 | 6 | |
| Drivers ... ... | — | — | — | 2 | 2 | |
| Batmen ... ... | — | — | — | 1 | 2 | |
| Attd. A.S.C.M.T. ... | — | — | — | 1 | 1 | |
| Total ... ... ... | | | | 37 | 42 | |

## COMPOSITION IN DETAIL—*continued.*

| Detail. | 1914. | 1915. | 1916. | 1917. | 1918. | Remarks. |
|---|---|---|---|---|---|---|
| *Corps Signal School.* | | | | | | |
| Commandant (Captain) | – | – | – | 1 | 1 | |
| Asst. Instrs. C.Q.M.S., | – | – | – | 1 | 1 | |
| Ditto, Serjeants ... | – | – | – | 4 | 4 | |
| Total ... ... ... | | | | 6 | 6 | |
| Attached— | | | | | | |
| General Duties ... | – | – | – | 8 | 8 | |
| Clerk ... ... | – | – | – | 1 | 1 | |
| Batmen ... ... | – | – | – | 1 | 1 | |
| Total ... ... ... | | | | 16 | 16 | |

## ARMY SIGNAL UNITS.

| Detail. | 1914. | 1915. | 1916. | 1917. | 1918. |
|---|---|---|---|---|---|
| *Army Headquarters.* | | | | | |
| D.D.A.S. (Colonel) ... | – | – | 1 | 1 | 1 |
| D.A.D.A.S. (Major) ... | – | – | – | – | 1 |
| Clerks ... ... | – | – | 1 | 1 | 2 |
| Batmen ... ... | – | – | 1 | 1 | 2 |
| Total ... ... ... | | | 3 | 3 | 6 |

*Army Signal Company.*

| Detail. | 1914. | 1915. | 1916. | 1917. | 1918. |
|---|---|---|---|---|---|
| Headquarters ... | — | 7 124 | 10 200 | 12 209 | 12 215 |
| Ditto attd. ... ... | — | 18 | 24 | 30 | 28 |
| Wireless Section ... | — | — | — | 1 23 | 2 36 |
| Ditto attd. ... ... | — | — | — | — | 7 |
| W/T Observation Group | — | — | — | — | 1 53 |
| Ditto attd. ... ... | — | — | — | — | 1 |
| Total ... ... | | 7 142 | 10 224 | 13 262 | 15 340 |

## COMPOSITION IN DETAIL.

| Detail. | 1914. | 1915. | 1916. | 1917. | 1918. |
|---|---|---|---|---|---|
| *Headquarters.* | | | | | |
| Lieut.-Col. or Major ... | – | 1 | – | – | – |
| Major ... ... ... | – | – | 1 | 1 | 1 |
| Major or Captain ... | – | – | – | 1 | 1 |
| Captain ... ... | – | 2 | 1 | 1 | 1 |
| Subalterns ... ... | – | 4 | 8 | 9 | 9 |
| Sjt.-Major (W.O.1) ... | – | – | 1 | 1 | 1 |
| C.S.M. ... ... | – | 1 | 1 | 1 | 1 |
| C.Q.M.S. ... ... | – | 1 | 1 | 1 | 1 |
| Serjeants (Supts.) ... | – | 4 | 4 | 4 | 4 |
| Farrier Serjeant ... | – | 1 | 1 | 1 | – |
| Corporals ... ... | – | 6 | 11 | 11 | 11 |
| Second Corporals ... | – | 6 | 10 | 11 | 11 |
| Sappers and Pioneers | – | 75 | 139 | 146 | 165 |
| Batmen ... ... | – | 7 | 10 | 11 | 6 |
| Motor Cyclists— | | | | | |
| Serjeants ... ... | – | 3 | 3 | 3 | 4 |
| Artificer Corporal ... | – | 1 | 1 | 1 | 1 |
| Corporal ... ... | – | 19 | 19 | 1 | 1 |
| Second Corporal ... | – | – | – | 1 | 1 |
| Sappers and Pioneers | – | – | – | 17 | 9 |
| Attached— | | | | | |
| R.A.M.C. ... ... | — | 2 | 2 | — | — |
| A.S.C.M.T. ... ... | — | 16 | 22 | 30 | 28 |
| Total ... ... | | 149 | 234 | 251 | 255 |

Z

## COMPOSITION IN DETAIL—*continued.*

| Detail. | 1914. | 1915. | 1916. | 1917. | 1918. | Remarks. |
|---|---|---|---|---|---|---|
| *Wireless Section.* | | | | | | |
| Captain or Subaltern | – | – | – | 1 | 1 | |
| Subaltern | – | – | – | – | 1 | |
| C.Q.M.S. | – | – | – | 1 | 1 | |
| M.M. S.S. | – | – | – | 1 | 1 | |
| Serjeants | – | – | – | 2 | 3 | |
| Corporals | – | – | – | 2 | 3 | |
| Second Corporals | – | – | – | 1 | 3 | |
| Clerks | – | – | – | – | 2 | |
| Sappers | – | – | – | 13 | 20 | |
| Pioneers | – | – | – | 2 | 2 | |
| Batmen | – | – | – | 1 | 1 | |
| Attached— | | | | | | |
| Drivers, A.S.C.M.T. | – | – | – | – | 7 | |
| Total | | | | 24 | 45 | |
| *Wireless Observation Group.†* | | | | | | † In 1917 this unit was part of the Army Wireless Co. It consisted of one of each type of station only. |
| Subaltern | – | – | – | 2 | 1 | |
| Serjeant | – | – | – | 1 | 1 | |
| Clerks | – | – | – | 2 | 3 | |
| Corporal, Second Cpl. and Sappers | – | – | – | 1 | 8 | |
| Pioneers | – | – | – | 3 | 3 | |
| Batmen | – | – | – | 1 | 1 | |
| 2 Fd. Comp. Sta. (Cpls. and Sappers) | – | – | – | 6 | 8 | |
| 2 Aero Com. Sta. (Cpls. and Sappers) | – | – | – | 5 | 10* | * Includes 4 Pioneers. |
| 2 Fd. Int. Sta. (Cpls. and Sappers) | – | – | – | 6 | 8 | |
| 2 Aero Int. Sta. (Cpls. and Sappers) | – | – | – | 4 | 8 | |
| 1 C.W. Int. Sta. (Cpls. and Sappers) | – | – | – | 3 | 3 | |
| Aero Trans. Sta. | – | – | – | 8 | – | |
| Attached— | | | | | | |
| Drivers, A.S.C.M.T. | – | – | – | 2 | 1 | |
| Total | | | | 44 | 55 | |
| *Airline Section.* | | | | | | * Addition of 8 permanent linemen, May, 1916. |
| Subaltern | 1 | 1 | 1 | 1 | 1 | |
| Serjeants | 2 | 2 | 2 | 2 | 2 | † Telegraphists office disappear, also sappers and pioneers of miscellaneous trades. Replaced by 14 permanent linemen and 14 wiremen. |
| Shoeing and C. Smith | 1 | – | – | – | – | |
| Corporals | 2 | 2 | 3* | 3 | 2 | |
| Second Corporals | 2 | 2 | 2 | 2 | 2 | |
| Sappers and Pioneers | 33 | 33 | 40* | 40 | 29 | |
| Drivers for vehicles | 11 | – | – | – | – | |
| Drivers (spare horse) | 1 | – | – | – | – | |
| Drivers (spare) | 1 | – | – | – | – | ‡ Horsed Section |
| Batmen | 2 | 1 | 1 | 1 | 1 | |
| Attached— | | | | | | |
| Drivers, A.S.C.M.T. | 2 | 10 | 10 | 10 | 7 | |
| Total | 58‡ | 51 | 59* | 59 | 44† | |
| *Cable Section.* | | | | | | |
| Subaltern | 1 | 1 | 1 | 1 | 1 | |
| Serjeant | 1 | 1 | 1 | 1 | 1 | |
| Shoeing Smith | 1 | 1 | 1 | 1 | 1 | |
| Corporals and 2nd Cpls. | 3 | 3 | 3 | 3 | 3 | * Addition of 2 Pioneers to help look after horses. |
| Sappers and Pioneers | 18 | 18 | 20* | 20 | 16 | † Decrease in Tel. Oprs., increase in Fd. linemen at expense of sappers of miscellaneous trades. |
| Drivers (for vehicles) | 8 | 8 | 8 | 8 | 8 | |
| Drivers (spare horse) | 1 | 1 | 1 | 1 | 1 | |
| Drivers (spare) | 1 | 1 | 1 | 1 | 2 | |
| Batmen | 2 | 2 | 2 | 2 | 2 | |
| Total | 36 | 36 | 38* | 38 | 35† | |

COMPOSITION IN DETAIL—*continued.*

| Detail. | 1914. | 1915. | 1916. | 1917. | 1918. | Remarks. |
|---|---|---|---|---|---|---|
| *Area Signal Detachment.* | | | | | | |
| Subaltern ... ... | – | – | – | 1 | 1 | |
| Corporal ... ... | – | – | – | 1 | 1 | |
| Second Corporal ... | – | – | – | 1 | 1 | |
| Sappers and Pioneers | – | – | – | 12 | 10 | |
| Batman ... ... | – | – | – | 1 | 1 | |
| Total ... ... | | | | 16 | 14 | |
| *Signal Sub-section, Army Bde., R.F.A.* | | | | | | |
| Subaltern ... ... | – | – | – | 1 | 1 | |
| Serjeant ... ... | – | – | – | 1 | 1 | |
| Corporal ... ... | – | – | – | 1 | 1 | |
| Second Corporal ... | – | – | – | 1 | 1 | |
| Sappers and Pioneers | – | – | – | 16 | 16 | |
| Drivers (for vehicles) | – | – | – | 2 | 2 | |
| Despatch Riders ... | – | – | – | – | 2 | |
| Batman ... ... | – | – | – | 1 | 1 | |
| Attached— | | | | | | |
| Drivers, A.S.C.M.T. | – | – | – | 2 | 2 | |
| Total ... ... | | | | 27 | 29 | |
| *Heavy Artillery Group Signal Sub-section.* | | | | | | |
| Subaltern ... ... | – | – | – | 1 | 1 | |
| Serjeant ... ... | – | – | – | 1 | 1 | |
| Corporals ... ... | – | – | – | 2 | 2 | |
| Second Corporals ... | – | – | – | 2 | 2 | |
| Sappers and Pioneers | – | – | – | 16 | 16 | |
| Drivers (for vehicles) | – | – | – | 2 | 2 | |
| Despatch Riders ... | – | – | – | – | 2 | |
| Batman ... ... | – | – | – | 1 | 1 | |
| Attached— | | | | | | |
| Drivers, A.S.C.M.T. | – | – | – | 2 | 2 | |
| Total .. .. | | | | 27 | 29 | |

### SIGNAL CONSTRUCTION COMPANY.

| Detail. | 1914. | 1915. | 1916. | 1917. | | 1918. | | Remarks. |
|---|---|---|---|---|---|---|---|---|
| Headquarters .. | – | – | – | 1 | 5 | 1 | 8 | |
| Ditto attd. .. .. | – | – | – | | 5 | | 3 | |
| Two Sections .. .. | – | – | – | 2 | 88 | 2 | 86 | |
| Attd. .. .. | – | – | – | | 16 | | 16 | |
| Total .. .. | | | | 3 | 114 | 3 | 113 | |
| *Headquarters.* | | | | | | | | |
| Captain .. .. | – | – | – | 1 | | 1 | | |
| C.S.M. .. .. | – | – | – | 1 | | 1 | | |
| Sappers and Pioneers | – | – | – | 3 | | 5 | | |
| Batmen .. .. | – | – | – | 1 | | 2 | | |
| Attached— | | | | | | | | |
| A.S.C.M.T. .. .. | – | – | – | 3 | | 3 | | |
| R.A.M.C. .. .. | – | – | – | 2 | | – | | |
| Total .. .. | | | | 11 | | 12 | | |
| *Two Sections (each)* | | | | | | | | |
| Subaltern .. .. | – | – | – | 1 | | 1 | | |
| Serjeant .. .. | – | – | – | 1 | | 1 | | |
| Corporal .. .. | – | – | – | 1 | | 1 | | |
| Second Corporal .. | – | – | – | 1 | | 1 | | |
| Sappers and Pioneers | – | – | – | 40 | | 40 | | |
| Batman .. .. | – | – | – | 1 | | – | | |
| Attached— | | | | | | | | |
| A.S.C.M.T. .. | – | – | – | 8 | | 8 | | |
| Total .. .. | | | | 53 | | 52 | | |

## ARMY SIGNAL SCHOOL.

| Detail. | 1914. | 1915. | 1916. | 1917. | 1918. | Remarks. |
|---|---|---|---|---|---|---|
| Commandant (Major) | – | – | – | 1 | 1 | |
| Instructor (Captain) .. | – | – | – | 1 | 1 | |
| Captains or Subalterns | – | – | – | 2 | 2 | |
| C.S.M. .. .. .. | – | – | – | 1 | 1 | |
| C.Q.M.S. .. .. | – | – | – | 1 | 1 | |
| Asst. Instrs. (Serjeants) | – | – | – | 10 | 9 | |
| Attached— | | | | | | |
| General Duties .. | – | – | – | 13 | 13 | |
| Clerk .. .. | – | – | – | 1 | 1 | |
| Batmen .. .. | – | – | – | 3 | 3 | |
| Total .. .. | | | | 34 | 32 | |

## LIGHT RAILWAY SIGNAL COMPANY.

| | 1914. | 1915. | 1916. | 1917. | 1918. |
|---|---|---|---|---|---|
| Captain .. .. | – | – | – | – | 1 |
| Subaltern .. .. | – | – | – | – | 1 |
| C.Q.M.S. .. .. | – | – | – | – | 1 |
| Serjeants .. .. | – | – | – | – | 2 |
| Corporals .. .. | – | – | – | – | 2 |
| Second Corporals .. | – | – | – | – | 2 |
| Clerk .. .. .. | – | – | – | – | 1 |
| Sappers and Pioneers | – | – | – | – | 45 |
| Batman .. .. | – | – | – | – | 1 |
| Attached— | | | | | |
| Drivers, A.S.C.M.T. | – | – | – | – | 6 |
| Total .. .. | | | | | 62 |

## REPAIR UNIT FOR P.E.L. SETS.

| | 1914. | 1915. | 1916. | 1917. | 1918. |
|---|---|---|---|---|---|
| Officers .. .. | – | – | – | – | 2 |
| Mechanist (machinery) | – | – | – | – | 1 |
| Corporal .. .. | – | – | – | – | 1 |
| Sappers and Pioneers | – | – | – | – | 5 |
| Batmen .. .. | – | – | – | – | 2 |
| Attached— | | | | | |
| Drivers, A.S.C.MT. | – | – | – | – | 4 |
| Total .. .. | | | | | 15 |

## G.H.Q. AND L. OF C. SIGNAL UNITS.

*G.H.Q. Signals Directorate.*

| | 1914. | 1915. | 1916. | 1917. | 1918. | Remarks. |
|---|---|---|---|---|---|---|
| Director of Army Signals | 1 | 1 | 1 | 1 | 1 | |
| Asst. Directors .. | 1 | 1 | 2 | 3 | 4 | |
| Liaison Officer .. | – | – | 1 | 1 | 1 | |
| Clerks .. .. .. | 3 | 3 | 6 | 6 | 9 | |
| Batmen .. .. | 4 | 4 | 5 | 5 | 8 | |
| Drivers, A.S.C.M.T. | 3 | 3 | 4 | 5 | 4 | |
| Deputy Director A.S. | 1 | 1 | 1 | 1 | 1 | |
| Clerks* .. .. | – | – | 5 | 5 | 13 | * Found by signal units |
| Batmen .. .. | 1 | 1 | 1 | 1 | 1 | in 1914 and 1915 |
| Driver, A.S.C.M.T. .. | 1 | 1 | 1 | 1 | 1 | |
| O.C. Signals, G.H.Q. | | | | | | |
| Area .. .. | – | – | – | 1 | 1 | |
| Batman .. .. | – | – | 1 | 1 | 1 | |
| Total .. .. | 15 | 15 | 29 | 31 | 45 | |

*G.H.Q. and L. of C. Signal Companies* (1918—*G.H.Q. Signal Battalion*).

| | 1914. G.H.Q. | 1914. L. of C. | 1915. G.H.Q. | 1915. L. of C. | 1918. Combined. | |
|---|---|---|---|---|---|---|
| At G.H.Q. and on L. of C... | 5 81 | 5 263 | 6 111 | 20 877 | 40 1376 | |
| On L. of C. attd. | — | —* | 11 | 67 | 408 | * Provided from L. of C. transport. |
| 5 Tel. Con. Cos. | — | — | — | — | 15 555 | |
| Ditto attd. | — | — | — | — | 125 | |
| 6 Railway Tel. Cos. | — | — | — | ~ | 18 666 | |
| Ditto attd. | — | — | — | ~ | 102 | |
| Total | 11 385 | | 26 1113 | | 73 3232 | |

### COMPOSITION IN DETAIL.

*At G.H.Q. and L. of C.*

| | 1914. | 1915. | 1918. Combined. | |
|---|---|---|---|---|
| Lieut.-Colonel | - + - | 1 + - | 1 | |
| Majors | 1 + - | - + - | 3 | |
| Adjutant | - + - | -4*+ - | 1 | * Majors or Captains. No Adjutant. |
| Captains | 3 + 1 | - + 7 | 10 | |
| Subalterns | 1 + 4 | 1 + 13 | 25 | |
| R.S.M. | - + 1 | - + 1 | 1 | |
| M.M., S.M. | - + - | - + - | 1 | |
| M.M., Q.M.S. | - + - | - + - | 1 | |
| C.S.M. | 1 + 1 | 2 + 1 | 1 | |
| M.M., S.S. | - + - | 2 + - | 5 | |
| C.Q.M.S. | 1 + 1 | 1 + 2 | 7 | |
| Serjeants | 5 + 12 | 2 + 32 | 41 | |
| Farrier Serjeant | 1 + - | - + - | - | |
| Corporals | 2 + 9 | 6 + 24 | 40 | |
| Trumpeter | 1 + - | - + - | - | |
| Second Corporals | 2 + 15 | 6 + 40 | 43 | |
| Sappers | 31 +210 | 69 +633 | 842 | |
| Drivers | 6 + - | - + - | - | |
| Pioneers | - + - | - + - | 174 | |
| Batmen* | 9 + 5 | 6 + 20 | - | * Duties of batmen performed by Pioneers in 1918 Establishment. |
| Motor Cyclists— | | | | |
| Serjeants | 1 + 1 | 2 + 10 | 18 | |
| Cpl. Artificers | 1 + 1 | 1 + 10 | 15 | |
| Second Cpl. Artificers | - + - | - + - | 4 | |
| Corporals | 13 + 7 | 14 + 84 | 8 | |
| Second Corporals | - + - | - + - | 13 | |
| Sappers and Pioneers | - + - | - + - | 162 | |
| Attached— | | | | |
| R.A.M.C. | 2 + - | 2 + - | - | |
| Drivers, A.S.C. M.T. | 5 + -† | 9 + 67 | 72 | † See note above. |
| Women Telegraphists | - + - | - + - | 336 | |
| Total | 86 268 | 128 964 | 1824 | |

*5 Telegraph Construction Companies (each)*

| | 1914. | 1915. | 1918. |
|---|---|---|---|
| Captain | — | — | 1 |
| Subalterns | — | — | 2 |
| C.S.M. | — | — | 1 |
| Serjeants | — | — | 2 |
| Corporals | — | — | 3 |
| Second Corporals | — | — | 6 |
| Sappers | — | — | 61 |
| Pioneers | — | — | 37 |
| Motor Cyclist (Sapper or Pioneer) | — | — | 1 |
| Attached— | | | |
| A.S.C. Serjeant | — | — | 1 |
| ,, Corporal | — | — | 1 |
| ,, Drivers | — | — | 22 |
| R.A.M.C. Sanitary Orderly | — | — | 1 |
| Total | | | 139 |

## COMPOSITION IN DETAIL—*continued.*

### 6 *Railway Telegraph Companies* (*each*).

| | 1914. | 1915. | 1918. |
|---|---|---|---|
| Captain | — | — | 1 |
| Subalterns | — | — | 2 |
| C.S.M. | — | — | 1 |
| Serjeants | — | — | 2 |
| Corporals | — | — | 3 |
| Second Corporals | — | — | 6 |
| Sappers | — | — | 60 |
| Pioneers | — | — | 38 |
| Motor Cyclist Corporal | — | — | 1 |
| Attached— | | | |
| A.S.C. M.T. Serjeant | — | — | 1 |
| ,,    ,,    Corporal | — | — | 1 |
| ,,    ,,    Drivers | — | — | 15 |
| Total | | | 131 |

## CAVALRY CORPS SIGNAL UNITS.

### *Cavalry Corps Headquarters.*

| | | | |
|---|---|---|---|
| Asst. Director Army Signals | —. | — | 1 |
| Clerk (Serjeant) | — | — | 1 |
| Total | | | 2 |

### *Cavalry Corps Signal Squadron.*

| | 1915. | 1918. |
|---|---|---|
| Major | 1 | 1 |
| Captain | 1 | 1 |
| Subalterns | 2 | 2 |
| Squadron Serjeant-Major | 1 | 1 |
| Farrier Serjeant | — | 1 |
| Shoeing Smiths | 2 | — |
| Squadron Q.M.S. | 1 | 1 |
| Serjeants | 4 | 3 |
| Corporals | 3 | 4 |
| Second Corporals | 3 | 3 |
| Sappers and Pioneers | 39 | 49 |
| Drivers (for vehicles) | 9 | 8 |
| Drivers (spare) | 4 | 1 |
| Batmen | 10 | 8 |
| Motor Cyclists— | | |
| Serjeants | 1 | 2 |
| Cpl. Artificers | 1 | 2 |
| Corporals | 6 | 1 |
| Second Corporals | — | 2 |
| Sappers and Pioneers | — | 18 |
| Attached— | | |
| A.S.C. M.T. Serjeant | — | 1 |
| ,,    ,,    Fitter and Turner | 1 | — |
| ,,    ,,    Drivers | 13 | 17 |
| Vetrinary Officer | 1 | — |
| Interpreters | 2 | — |
| Total | 105 | 126 |

### *Cavalry Divisional Signal Squadron.**

| | 1914. | 1915. | 1918. |
|---|---|---|---|
| Major | 1 | — | — |
| Captains | 1 | 1 | 1 |
| Subalterns | + 2† | 2 | 2 |
| Squadron S.M. | 1 | 1 | 1 |
| Squadron Q.M.S. | 1 | — | — |
| Serjeant | + 2 | 1 | 1 |
| Farrier Serjeant | 1 | — | — |
| Shoeing Smith | + 1 | 1 | 1 |

* In 1914 there was no Cavalry Wireless Squadron. All wireless was in the Divisional Signal Squadron.
† The numbers of "D" troop are shown separate as + numbers.

## Cavalry Divisional Signal Squadron*—continued.

| | 1914. | 1915. | 1918. |
|---|---|---|---|
| Trumpeter | I | — | — |
| Corporals | + 2 | I | I |
| Second Corporals | — | I | I |
| Sappers and Pioneers | 9+35 | 13 | 17 |
| Drivers (for vehicles) | 4+ 1 | 2 | 2 |
| Drivers (for spare horses) | 4 | I | I |
| Batmen | 6+ 4 | 6 | 6 |
| Motor Cyclists— | | | |
| Serjeant | + 1 | I | I |
| Cpl. Artificer | + 1 | 2 | I |
| Corporals | + 4 | 9 | I |
| Second Corporals | — | — | I |
| Sappers and Pioneers | — | — | 9 |
| Attached— | | | |
| Veterinary Officer | I | — | — |
| R.A.M.C. | 2 | — | — |
| Drivers, A.S.C. M.T. | I | — | 4 |
| Drivers, A.S.C. M.T. | I | — | 4 |
| Privates | — | — | 8* |

* From units in Cav. Div. for pigeon stations.

## Cavalry Wireless Squadron.

### Detail.

| | 1914 | 1915 | 1918 | |
|---|---|---|---|---|
| Headquarters | — | — | 1 | 16 |
| Two motor sections | — | — | 2 | 32 |
| Ditto attached | — | — | | 8 |
| Eight Pack Detachments | — | — | | 80 |
| Total | | | 3 | 136 |

## COMPOSITION IN DETAIL.

### Headquarters.

| | 1914. | 1915. | 1918. |
|---|---|---|---|
| Major or Captain | — | — | I |
| Squadron S.M. | — | — | I |
| Squadron Q.M.S. | — | — | I |
| Farrier Sergeant | — | — | I |
| Shoeing Smith | — | — | I |
| Wheelers | — | — | 2 |
| Saddlers | — | — | 2 |
| Pioneers, general duty | — | — | 2 |
| Drivers for spare horses | — | — | 4 |
| Batmen | — | — | 2 |
| Total | | | 17 |

### Motor * Section (each).

| | 1914. | 1915. | 1918. |
|---|---|---|---|
| Captain or Subaltern | 1*† | | I |
| M.M.S.S. | — | | I |
| Sergeants | I | | 2 |
| Shoeing and carriage smith | I | | — |
| Corporals or 2nd Corporals | 3‡ | | 2 |
| Sappers or Pioneers | 16 | | 10 |
| Drivers | 10 | | — |
| Batmen | 2 | | I |
| Attached— | | | |
| Drivers, A.S.C. M.T. | — | | 4 |
| Total | 34 | | 21 |

* 1914 figures are for "A" troop which was a wagon section.
† Subaltern.
‡ One Cpl., two 2nd Cpls.

### Pack Detachments or 1914 Equivalent.

| | 1914. | 1918. |
|---|---|---|
| Subaltern | 1* | — |
| Sergeants | 2 | 8 |
| Shoeing and Carriage Smith | 1 | — |
| Corporals | 2 | } 8 |
| Second Corporals | 2 | } |
| Sappers | 27 | 40 |
| Drivers for vehicles | 7 | 24† |
| Batmen | 2 | — |
| Total | 44 | 80 |

* With Cav. Div. in 1914 one wagon and 3 pack stations.

† Pack sets were carried in limbered wagons specially fitted.

1918 *Establishment*: *Cable Section* (*three detachments*) *with Cavalry Corps.*

| | 1914 | 1918 | |
|---|---|---|---|
| Subaltern ... ... ... ... | 1* | 1 | * With Cavalry Division |
| Sergeants ... ... ... ... | 1 | 2 | in 1914, "B" troop |
| Shoeing Smiths ... ... ... | 1 | 2 | of two detachments. |
| Corporal ... ... ... ... | 1 | 1 | |
| Second Corporals ... ... ... | 2 | 3 | |
| Sappers and Pioneers... ... ... | 19 | 27 | |
| Drivers for vehicles ... ... ... | 10 | 15 | |
| Drivers for spare horses ... ... | – | 4 | |
| Drivers, spare... ... ... ... | – | 2 | |
| Batmen ... ... ... ... | 2 | 2 | |
| Total . ... ... ... | 37 | 59 | |

*Signal Troop with Cavalry Brigade.*

| | 1914 | 1918 |
|---|---|---|
| Subaltern ... ... ... ... | 1 | 1 |
| Sergeant ... ... ... ... | 1 | 1 |
| Shoeing Smith ... ... ... | 1 | 1 |
| Corporal ... ... ... ... | 1 | 1 |
| Sappers and Pioneers ... ... | 14 | 14 |
| Driver for vehicle ... ... ... | 1 | 1 |
| Batmen ... ... ... ... | 2 | 2 |
| Motor Cyclist Cpl. Artificer ... | 1 | 1 |
| Motor Cyclist Corporals ... ... | 2 | – |
| Motor Cyclist Sappers and Pioneers | – | 2 |
| Total ... ... ... | 24 | 24 |

## SUMMARY OF DEDUCTIONS.

THE foregoing comparative tables of Signal Establishments contain only a selection of units which best show the development of the Signal Service during the war. A review of the tables at once betrays certain well-marked changes which may be summarized as follows :—

(1) A great increase due to the increase in complexity of signals caused by technical alterations in methods of warfare, by the growth of the Administrative Services of the Army, and by the progressively greater reliance placed by the General Staff of all formations on the telephone as a medium to facilitate rapid and extensive interchange of information and orders.

(2) These increases were counterbalanced to a very slight extent by the abolition of superfluities such as trumpeters and by the elimination where possible of attached men such as R.A.M.C. orderlies, interpreters, veterinary officers, etc., previously borne on the signal establishments ; the duties of these men being taken over by the various services concerned. The number of batmen was at the same time considerably reduced in proportion to the officers served.

(3) The gradual superseding of horsed by mechanical transport automatically brought about an increase in A.S.C. M.T. personnel attached at the expense of the numbers of horse drivers, many of the latter thus released being remustered in technical trades and forming a valuable source of reinforcement to technical personnel. Farrier-serjeants gave place in many units to shoeing smiths. The latter also were done away with in some small units which still retained a few horses, their duties being relegated to other larger horsed units to which the signal sections were attached.

(4) The general reform in the direction of economy was also seen in the enlistment of Sapper and Pioneer motor cyclists and the consequent disappearance of the bevies of motor cyclist corporals which were an anomaly of the earlier signal establishments.

(5) Finally, the foresight of the makers of the Signal Service as it was in 1914 is demonstrated with remarkable clearness by the way the smaller units, which formed the greater part of the signal companies of the more mobile formations, remained unchanged or little changed throughout the war. Such units are the Infantry Brigade Signal Section and the Cavalry Brigade Signal Troop. Units also little affected by changes except as regards alteration of transport and the technical qualifications of the men composing them were the cable and airline sections, though the final wave of economy somewhat altered the constitution of the latter by transferring the superfluous operators to other units.

---

## APPENDIX II.

## COMPARATIVE TABLES OF TRANSPORT OF SIGNAL UNITS.

### DIVISIONAL SIGNAL COMPANY.

| Headquarters. | 1914. | 1915. | 1916. | 1917. | 1918. | Remarks. |
|---|---|---|---|---|---|---|
| Motor car, 4-seater ... | – | – | 1 | 1 | 1 | |
| 3-ton lorry ... ... | – | – | – | 1 | 1 | |
| 30-cwt. lorry ... ... | – | – | 1 | – | – | |
| 1-ton lorry ... ... | 1 | 1 | – | – | – | |
| P.E.L. lorry ... ... | – | – | 1 | 1 | 1 | |
| Box car, 15-cwt. ... | – | – | – | 1 | 1 | |
| Cart, water ... ... | 1 | 1 | 1 | 1 | 1 | |
| Wagon, limbered, R.E. | – | 1 | 1 | 1 | – | |
| Wagons, G.S., R.E. ... | – | 1 | 1 | 1 | 1 | |
| Wagon, limbered, R.E. (cooks) ... | 1 | 1 | 1 | 1 | 1* | * G.S. |
| Wagon, limbered, G.S. | – | – | – | – | 2 | |
| R.A.H.Q. Detachment. | | | | | | |
| Wagons, G.S., R.E. ... | – | – | – | 1 | 1 | |
| Signal sub-section for R.F.A. Bde. | | | | | | |
| Wagons, telephone ... | – | – | – | 2 | 2 | |
| Wagons, limbered G.S. | – | – | – | 2 | 2 | |
| No. 1 Section. | | | | | | |
| Wagons, cable ... | 3 | 4 | 4 | 4 | 4 | |
| Wagons, limbered R.E. | 3 | 4 | 4 | 4 | 5 | |
| Wagons, cable, light | – | – | – | 2 | – | |
| Nos. 2, 3 and 4 Sects. | | | | | | |
| Wagons, limbered R.E. | 3 | 3 | 3 | 3 | 3 | |
| Carts, Maltese ... | – | – | – | 3 | 3 | |
| Wagon, G.S., for supplies (train) ... ... | 1* | 1* | 1 | 1 | 1 | * Cart, forage. |

### CORPS SIGNAL COMPANY.

| Headquarters. | | | | | |
|---|---|---|---|---|---|
| 1-ton lorry ... ... | – | 1 | 1 | 1 | 1 |
| 30-cwt. lorry ... ... | 2 | 3 | – | – | – |
| 3-ton lorry ... ... | – | – | 3 | 3 | 3 |
| P.E.L. lorry ... ... | – | – | 1 | 1 | 1 |
| Motor car ... ... | – | 2 | 1 | 1 | 1 |
| Motor car with box body | – | 1 | 1 | 2 | 1 |
| Bicycles ... ... | – | – | – | – | 6 |

## CORPS SIGNAL COMPANY—*continued*.

| | 1914. | 1915. | 1916. | 1917. | 1918. | Remarks. |
|---|---|---|---|---|---|---|
| *Wireless Section.* | | | | | | |
| Motor car with box body | – | – | – | – | 1 | |
| Lorry (accumulator charging) | – | – | – | – | 1 | |
| Motor cycles ... ... | – | – | – | – | 2 | |
| *Corps H.A. Section.* | | | | | | |
| Box car ... ... | – | – | – | 1 | 1 | |
| Wagons, cable, light ... | – | – | – | 2 | 2 | |
| Motor cycles ... | – | – | – | 5 | 8 | |
| Bicycles ... ... | – | – | – | 2 | 2 | |
| Wagon, light spring R.E. | 1 | – | – | – | – | |
| Cart, water ... | 1 | – | – | – | – | |
| Vehicles for cook ... | 1 | – | – | – | – | |

### ARMY SIGNAL COMPANY.

| | 1915. | 1917. | 1918. | Remarks. |
|---|---|---|---|---|
| *Headquarters.* | | | | |
| Motor cycles ... ... | 23 | 37 | 26 | |
| Bicycles ... ... | 12 | 33 | 32 | |
| Motor cars ... ... | 2 | 2 | 2 | |
| Motor car, light ... | 1 | 1 | 1 | |
| Box cars ... ... | – | 6* | 4 | * Includes those of wireless section. |
| 30-cwt. lorries ... | 2 | 2 | 2 | |
| 1-ton lorry ... ... | 1 | – | – | |
| 3-ton lorries ... ... | 4 | 6 | 8 | |
| Lorry for Army electric light ... ... | – | 1 | 1 | |
| *Wireless Section.* | | | | |
| Motor cycles ... ... | – | 4 | 4 | |
| Bicycle ... ... | – | 1 | 1 | |
| Box cars ... ... | – | – | 3 | |
| Lorry, accumulator charging ... ... | – | 1 | 1 | |
| Wagons, motor, wireless, light* ... ... | – | 2 | 2 | |
| *Wireless Observation Group.* | | | | |
| Motor W/T lorry* ... | – | 1 | – | * Part of Army W/T Company in 1917. |
| Motor cycle ... ... | – | – | 1 | |
| 30-cwt. lorry ... ... | – | 1 | – | |
| Box car ... ... | – | – | 1 | |
| Special light lorry ... | – | 1 | – | |

### AIRLINE SECTION.

| | 1914. | 1915. | 1916. | 1917. | 1918. |
|---|---|---|---|---|---|
| 3-ton lorry ... ... | 1 | 1 | | | 1 |
| 30-cwt. lorry ... ... | – | 4 | | | 2 |
| Box car, 15-cwt. ... | – | – | | | 1 |
| Motor car, light ... | – | 1 | | | – |
| Bicycles ... ... | 1 | – | | | 6 |
| Wagons, airline ... | 2 | – | | | – |
| Wagons, light spring, R.E. ... ... | 2 | – | | | – |
| Wagons, cable ... | 1 | – | | | – |

### CABLE SECTION.

| | 1914. | 1916. | 1917. | 1918. |
|---|---|---|---|---|
| Wagons, cable ... | 2 | 2 | 2 | 2 |
| Wagons, limbered R.E. | 2 | 2 | 2 | 2 |
| Carts, cable, light ... | – | – | 1 | 1 |
| Motor cycles ... ... | – | – | 1 | 1 |
| Bicycles ... ... | 1 | 1 | 2 | 2 |

### AREA SIGNAL DETACHMENT.

| | 1917. | 1918. | Remarks. |
|---|---|---|---|
| Hand-cart ... ... | 1 | 1 | |
| Motor cycle ... | 1 or 0* | 1 or 0* | * One motor cycle and one cycle to each two Area Detchmt. Offrs. |
| Cycle ... ... | 2 or 1* | 2 or 1* | |

### SIGNAL SUB-SECTION ARMY BDE., R.F.A.

| | | |
|---|---|---|
| Motor cycle ... ... | – | 1 |
| Wagon, limbered G.S. | – | 1 |
| Wagon, telephone ... | 1 | 1 |
| Cart, hand ... ... | 1 | 1 |

### SIGNAL SUB-SECTION H.A. GROUP.

| | | |
|---|---|---|
| Wagon, telephone ... | 1 | 1 |
| Lorry, 30-cwt. ... | 1 | 1 |
| Motor cycles ... ... | 2 | 4 |
| Hand cart ... ... | 1 | 1 |

### SIGNAL CONSTRUCTION COMPANY.

| | | |
|---|---|---|
| Motor cycles ... ... | 2 | 2 |
| Bicycles ... ... | 6 | 6 |
| Motor car, box body | 1 | 1 |
| Lorry, 3-ton ... ... | 1 | 1 |
| Lorries, 30-cwt. ... | 8 | 8 |

### LIGHT RAILWAY SIGNAL COMPANY.

| | |
|---|---|
| Motor cycle ... ... | 1 |
| Bicycles ... ... | 3 |
| Motor car, light ... | 1 |
| Motor car, box body | 1 |
| Lorry, 30-cwt. ... | 1 |
| Lorry, 3-ton ... ... | 1 |

### REPAIR UNIT, P.E.L. SETS.

| | |
|---|---|
| Workshop lorry ... | 1 |
| Motor cars, box bodies | 2 |

### G.H.Q. AND L. OF C. SIGNALS.

| | 1914. | | 1915. | | 1918. | |
|---|---|---|---|---|---|---|
| | G.H.Q. | L of C. | G.H.Q. | L. of C. | Combined. | |
| *At G.H.Q. and L. of C.* | | * | | | | * Provided by L. of C. |
| Motor cycles ... ... | | | | 106 | 249 | organization as required. |
| Bicycles ... ... | | | | | 24 | |
| Motor cars ... ... | 1 | | 2 | 1 | 6 | |
| Motor cars, box body | | | | 13 | 35 | |
| Lorries, 3-ton ... | | | 3 | | 6 | |
| Lorries, 1-ton ... | | | 1 | | | |
| Lorries, 30-cwt. ... | 2 | | | 27 | 9 | |
| *5 Telegraph Construction Companies.* | | | | | | |
| Motor cycles ... ... | | | | | 15 | |
| Bicycles ... ... | | | | | 15 | |
| Motor cars ... ... | | | | | 5 | |
| Motor cars, box body | | | | | 5 | |
| Lorries, 3-ton ... | | | | | 25 | |
| Lorries, 30-cwt. ... | | | | | 25 | |
| Trailers, water cart ... | | | | | 5 | |
| *5 Railway Telegraph Companies.* | | | | | | |
| Motor cycles ... | | | | | 18 | |
| Motor cars ... ... | | | | | 6 | |
| Motor car, box body ... | | | | | 12 | |
| Lorries, 3-ton ... | | | | | 18 | |
| Lorries, 30-cwt. ... | | | | | 18 | |
| Wagons, G.S., R.E. ... | 1 | | | | | |
| Cart, water ... ... | 1 | | | | | |
| Vehicle for cooks ... | 1 | | | | | |
| Side cars ... ... | | | 12 | | | |
| Train— | | | | | | |
|   Wagon, G.S. (for supplies) ... ... | 2 | | | | | |

## CAVALRY SIGNALS.

| | 1914. | 1915. | 1918. |
|---|---|---|---|
| *Cavalry Corps Signal Squadron.* | | | |
| Motor cars, 4-seater ... | | 2 | 2 |
| Motor cars, small ... | | 5 | 5 |
| Motor cars, box body | | 1 | 2 |
| Lorries, 30-cwt. ... | | 2 | 4 |
| Wagons, G.S. ... | | 1 | 2 |
| Wagons, limbered, G.S. | | 2 | 1 |
| Wagons, cable ... | | 1 | |
| *Cavalry Divisional Signal Squadron.* | | | |
| Motor cars, light ... | 2 | 2 | 2 |
| Wagon, limbered, G.S. | — | 1 | 2 |
| Lorry, P.E.L. ... | — | — | 1 |
| Wagons, G.S. ... ... | 1 | | |
| Cart, water ... ... | 1 | | |
| Cart, for baggage ... | 1 | | |
| Wagon, G.S., R.E. ... | 1 | | |
| Wagon, light spring, R.E. ... ... | 6 | | |
| Wagon, cable, 6-horsed | 2 | | |
| Wagon, cable, 4-horsed | 1 | | |
| *Cavalry Divisional Wireless Squadron.* | | | |
| Wagons, limbered W/T | 3* | | — |
| Wagons, limbered, pack, wireless ... ... | 3 | | 8 |
| Wagons, motor, wireless, light ... ... | | | 4 |
| Motor cars, box body | | | 4 |
| *Cable Section, 3 detachments, Cavalry Corps.* | | | |
| Wagons, cable ... | | | 3 |
| Wagons, limbered, R.E. or G.S. ... ... | | | 3 |
| *Signal Troop with Cavalry Brigade.* | | | |
| Wagon, light spring, R.E. | 1 | | 1 |

## APPENDIX III.

## COMPARATIVE STATEMENT OF SIGNAL TRADES.

### DIVISIONAL SIGNAL COMPANY.

| | 1914. | 1915. | 1916. | 1917. | 1918. | Remarks. |
|---|---|---|---|---|---|---|
| *Headquarters.* | | | | | | |
| Office telegraphists ... | — | 12 | 12 | 11* | — | * Telegraphists. |
| Telegraph operators "B" ... ... | — | — | — | — | 14 | |
| Switchboard operators | — | — | — | 4 | 6 | |
| Electrician ... ... | — | — | — | 1† | 1 | † P.E.L. Set. |
| Instrument repairers | — | — | — | — | 2 | |
| Permanent linemen ... | — | — | — | 4 | 4 | |
| Miscellaneous trades ... | — | 2 | 2 | — | — | |
| Pioneers and batmen | — | — | 4 | 10 | 8 | |
| Signalmen ... ... | 11 | 7 | 7 | — | — | |
| Trumpeter ... ... | 1 | 1 | 1 | — | — | |
| Shoeing and carriage smith ... ... | 1 | — | — | — | — | |
| Drivers ... ... | 9 | 8 | 8 | 6 | 7 | |
| Motor cyclist artificer | 1 | 1 | 1 | 1 | 1 | |
| Motor cyclists ... | 12 | 14 | 14 | 14 | 17 | |
| Draughtsmen ... | — | — | — | — | 1 | |
| Clerk ... ... | — | — | — | — | 1 | |

## DIVISIONAL SIGNAL COMPANY—*continued.*

| | 1914. | 1915. | 1916. | 1917. | 1918. | Remarks |
|---|---|---|---|---|---|---|
| *Wireless Section.* | | | | | | |
| Wireless operators ... | – | – | – | 18 | – | |
| Telegraph operators "B" ... | – | – | – | – | 20 | |
| Signalmen "B" ... | – | – | – | – | 36 | |
| Pioneers and batmen... | – | – | – | – | 1 | |
| Drivers ... | – | – | – | – | 2 | |
| *Visual Section.* | | | | | | |
| Signalmen "B" ... | – | – | – | – | 36 | |
| Drivers ... | – | – | – | – | 1 | |
| *R.A. Section (Headquarters).* | | | | | | |
| Signaller linemen ... | – | – | – | 4 | – | |
| Signalmen "A" ... | – | – | – | – | 7 | |
| Airline hands ... | – | – | – | 2 | – | |
| Permanent linemen ... | – | – | – | 2 | 4 | |
| Pioneers and batmen | – | – | – | 5 | 3 | |
| Drivers ... | – | – | – | – | 1 | |
| *Two Signal Sub-sections.* | | | | | | |
| Signaller linemen ... | – | – | – | 24 | – | |
| Signalmen "A" ... | – | – | – | – | 24 | |
| Airline hands ... | – | – | – | 4 | – | |
| Permanent linemen ... | – | – | – | 2 | 6 | |
| Pioneers and batmen | – | – | – | 2 | 2 | |
| Drivers ... | – | – | – | 4 | 4 | |
| *No. 1 Section (Cable Section).* | | | | | | |
| Telegraphists ... | – | – | – | 8 | – | |
| Office telegraphists ... | 12 | 16 | 16 | – | – | |
| Telegraph operators "B" ... | – | – | – | – | 8 | |
| Line telegraphists ... | 12 | 12 | 12 | – | – | |
| Cable hands ... | – | – | – | 20 | – | |
| Field linemen (mtd.) ... | – | – | – | – | 16 | |
| Field linemen (dismtd.) | – | – | – | – | 8 | |
| Signalmen ... | 4 | 8 | 8 | – | – | |
| Wheelers ... | 1 | 2 | 2 | 2 | 2 | |
| Harness makers ... | 1 | 2 | 2 | 2 | 2 | |
| Pioneers and batmen | – | – | 4 | 10 | 4 | |
| Drivers ... | 14 | 24 | 24 | 24 | 22 | |
| Shoeing and carriage smith ... | 1 | 2 | 1 | 1 | – | |
| Instrument repairer ... | 1 | 2 | 2 | 2 | – | |
| *No. 1 Section (Machine Gun Section).* | | | | | | |
| Signalmen "B" ... | – | – | – | – | 12 | |
| Field linemen (dismtd.) | – | – | – | – | 4 | |
| Pioneers and batmen | – | – | – | – | 2 | |
| Drivers ... | – | – | – | – | 1 | |
| *Nos. 2, 3, and 4 Sects.* | | | | | | |
| Signalmen "B" ... | – | – | – | – | 36 | |
| Signalmen ... | 14 | 14 | 14 | – | – | |
| Line telegraphists ... | 5 | 5 | 5 | – | – | |
| Brigade section hands | – | – | – | 36 | – | |
| Field linemen (dismtd.) | – | – | – | – | 15 | |
| Pioneers and batmen | – | – | – | 24 | 12 | |
| Drivers ... | 5 | 5 | 5 | 6 | 6 | |

## CORPS SIGNAL COMPANY.

| | 1914. | 1915. | 1916. | 1917. | 1918. | Remarks |
|---|---|---|---|---|---|---|
| *Headquarters.* | | | | | | |
| Telegrah operators "A" | – | – | – | – | 39 | |
| Telegraphists ... | – | – | – | 22 | – | |
| Telegraphists (office)... | 15 | 19 | 23 | – | – | |
| Switchboard operators | – | – | – | 9 | 12 | |
| Electricians ... | – | – | – | 2 | 1 | |
| Instrument repairers... | 1 | – | – | 2 | 5 | |
| Permanent linemen ... | – | – | – | 6 | 7 | |

## CORPS SIGNAL COMPANY—*continued.*

| Headquarters—*continued.* | 1914. | 1915. | 1916. | 1917. | 1918. | Remarks. |
|---|---|---|---|---|---|---|
| Telegraphists (permanent line) ... | 1 | 1 | – | – | – | |
| Telegraphists (field line) | 4 | 4 | 4 | – | – | |
| Airline hands ... ... | – | – | – | 11 | – | |
| Draughtsman ... | – | – | – | – | 1 | |
| Clerk ... ... ... | – | – | – | – | 1 | |
| Tailor ... ... ... | 1 | 1 | 1 | 1 | 1 | |
| Shoeing and carriage smith ... ... | 1 | 1 | 1 | 1 | – | |
| Pioneers (including batmen and cooks, from 1916 on) ... | 14 | 20 | 26 | 16 | 17 | |
| Drivers and batmen ... | 5 | 5 | – | – | – | |
| Motor cyclist artificer | 1 | 1 | 1 | 1 | 1 | |
| Motor cyclists... ... | 15 | 19 | 23 | 15 | 13 | |
| *Wireless Section.** | | | | | | * In 1915 and 1916 this unit was included in G.H.Q. or army wireless units. |
| Telegraphists ... ... | – | – | – | 5 | – | |
| Wireless operators ... | – | – | – | 8 | 23 | |
| Electrician ... ... | – | – | – | 1 | 1 | |
| Instrument repairer ... | – | – | – | 1 | 1 | |
| Interpreter operators. | – | – | – | 9 | 3 | |
| Pioneer ... ... | – | – | – | 1 | 1 | |
| *Signal Section Corps H.A.* | | | | | | |
| Telegraph operators "B" ... ... | – | – | – | – | 4 | |
| Telegraphists (office)... | – | – | – | 4 | – | |
| Switchboard operators | – | – | – | 3 | 3 | |
| Electrician ... ... | – | – | – | – | 1 | |
| Instrument repairer ... | – | – | – | 1 | 1 | |
| Signalmen "A" ... | – | – | – | – | 6 | |
| Permanent linemen ... | – | – | – | 2 | 5 | |
| Airline hands ... ... | – | – | – | 6 | – | |
| Field linemen (dismtd.) | – | – | – | – | 5 | |
| Signaller linemen ... | – | – | – | 2 | – | |
| Wheeler ... ... | – | – | – | 1 | 1 | |
| Pioneers (incl. batmen and cooks) ... ... | – | – | – | 8 | 4 | |
| Drivers ... ... | – | – | – | 2 | 2 | |
| Motor cyclist despatch riders ... ... | – | – | – | 4 | 6 | |
| Batmen ... ... | – | – | – | 1 | – | |

## ARMY SIGNAL COMPANY.

| Headquarters. | 1915. | 1917. | 1918. | Remarks. |
|---|---|---|---|---|
| Telegraph operators "A" | – | 57 | 73 | |
| Telegraphists (office)... | 43 | – | – | |
| Switchboard operators | – | 22 | 22 | |
| Electricians ... ... | – | 3 | 3 | |
| Instrument repairers... | 1 | 4 | 10 | |
| Fitters ... ... | – | 3 | 3 | |
| Wireless fitters ... | – | 4 | – | |
| Permanent linemen ... | – | 27 | 30 | |
| Telegraphist, permanent line ... ... | 1 | – | – | |
| Airline men ... ... | 8 | – | – | |
| Draughtsmen ... | – | 1 | 1 | |
| Clerks ... ... | – | 3 | 3 | |
| Tailor ... ... | 1 | 1 | 1 | |
| Painter ... ... | – | 1 | 1 | |
| Pioneers (incl. batmen and cooks) ... ... | 33 | 53 | 45 | |
| Drivers ... ... | 7 | – | – | |
| Motor cyclist artificers | 1 | 1 | 1 | |
| Motor cyclists... ... | 19 | 19 | 11 | |
| Shoeing and carriage smith ... ... | 1 | – | – | |

## ARMY SIGNAL COMPANY—*continued.*

| *Wireless Section.* | 1915. | 1917. | 1918. | Remarks. |
|---|---|---|---|---|
| Wireless operators ... | – | 8 | 24 | |
| Telegraph operators " A " | – | 6 | – | |
| Electrician ... ... | – | 1 | 1 | |
| Instrument repairer ... | – | 1 | 1 | |
| Clerks ... ... | – | – | 2 | |
| Pioneers ... ... | – | 2 | 2 | |
| Batmen ... ... | – | 1 | 1 | |

| *Wireless Observation Group.* | 1915. | 1917. | 1918. | |
|---|---|---|---|---|
| Telegraph operators " A " | – | – | 6 | |
| Wireless operators ... | – | – | 33 | |
| Electrician ... ... | – | – | 1 | |
| Fitter ... ... | – | – | 1 | |
| Clerks ... ... | – | – | 3 | |
| Pioneers ... ... | – | – | 8 | |

## AIRLINE SECTION.

| | 1914. | 1915. | 1918. |
|---|---|---|---|
| Telegraphists (office)... | 8 | 8 | – |
| Permanent linemen ... | – | – | 14 |
| Telegraphists (permanent line) ... | 6 | 6 | – |
| Airline men ... ... | 11 | 11 | – |
| Wiremen ... ... | – | – | 14 |
| Wheeler ... ... | – | 1 | 1 |
| Fitter ... ... | – | 1 | – |
| Instrument repairer ... | – | 1 | – |
| Blacksmith ... ... | – | 1 | 1 |
| Pioneers ... ... | 8 | 8 | 3 |
| Batman ... ... | – | – | – |
| Drivers ... ... | 15 | – | – |

## CABLE SECTION

| | 1914. | 1918. |
|---|---|---|
| Telegraph operators ... | – | 4 |
| Telegraphists (office)... | 8 | – |
| Field linemen (mtd.) ... | – | 8 |
| Cable men ... ... | 6 | – |
| Field linemen (dismtd.) | – | 4 |
| Wheeler ... ... | 1 | 1 |
| Harness maker ... | 1 | 1 |
| Pioneers ... ... | 5 | 1 |
| Shoeing and carriage smith ... ... | 1 | – |
| Drivers ... ... | 12 | 13 |

## AREA SIGNAL DETACHMENT.

| | 1918. |
|---|---|
| Permanent linemen ... | 4 |
| Field linemen (dismtd.) | 8 |
| Batman ... ... | 1 |

## SIGNAL SUB-SECTION H.A. BDE.

| | 1918. |
|---|---|
| Signalmen " A " ... | 16 |
| Permanent linemen ... | 2 |
| Field linemen (dismtd.) | 2 |
| Pioneers ... ... | 1 |
| Drivers ... ... | 2 |
| Motor cyclist despatch riders ... ... | 2 |

## SIGNAL SUB SECTION ARMY BDE., R.F.A.

|  | 1917. | 1918. |  |
|---|---|---|---|
| Signalmen "A" ... | – | 12 | |
| Airline hands ... ... | 2 | – | |
| Field linemen (mtd.) ... | – | 3 | |
| Signaller linemen ... | 12 | – | |
| Pioneer ... ... | – | 1 | |
| Permanent linemen ... | 1 | – | |
| Drivers ... ... | 3* | 3 | * One batman. |
| Motor cyclists ... | – | 1 | |

## SIGNAL CONSTRUCTION COMPANY.

1918.

*Headquarters.*

| Blacksmith ... ... | 1 |
|---|---|
| Pioneers ... ... | 4 |
| Batmen ... ... | 2 |

*Sections.*

| Permanent linemen ... | 12 |
|---|---|
| Wiremen ... ... | 24 |
| Wheelers ... ... | 4 |
| Pioneers ... ... | 44 |

## REPAIR UNIT FOR P.E.L. SETS.

1918.

| Pioneer (for store-keeper ... ... | 1 |
|---|---|
| Fitters and turners ... | 3 |
| Electrician ... ... | 1 |
| Instrument repairer (fortress) ... ... | 1 |
| Batmen ... ... | 2 |

## LIGHT RAILWAY SIGNAL COMPANY.

1918.

| Switchboard operators | 3 |
|---|---|
| Instrument repairers | 2 |
| Permanent linemen ... | 8 |
| Wiremen ... ... | 15 |
| Field linemen (dismtd.) | 8 |
| Draughtsman ... | 1 |
| Clerk ... ... | 1 |
| Wheeler ... ... | 1 |
| Pioneers ... ... | 11 |
| Batman ... ... | 1 |

*N.B.*—Signal units with the Armies are alone included in the Tables of this Appendix.

---

## APPENDIX IV.

# TABLE OF SIGNAL ESTABLISHMENTS PROVIDED WITH AN ARMY OF TWO CORPS EACH CONTAINING THREE DIVISIONS AT DIFFERENT STAGES OF THE WAR.

### (1) 1914.

At Mobilization. (At this time the only equivalent of an Army Signal Company was G.H.Q. Signal Company which is therefore shown.)

| Unit. | Each. | | Total | |
|---|---|---|---|---|
| | Off. | O.R. | Off. | O.R. |
| G.H.Q. Signal Company ... ... ... | 5 | 75 | 5 | 75 |
| Two Army Corps Headquarter Companies ... | 4 | 63 | 8 | 126 |
| Five Airline Sections ... ... ... ... ... | 1 | 57 | 5 | 285 |
| Ten Cable Sections ... ... ... ... ... | 1 | 35 | 10 | 350 |
| Six Divisional Signal Companies ... ... ... | 5 | 157 | 30 | 942 |
| Total ... ... ... ... ... | | | 58 | 1978 |

## (2) 1915.

After the creation of the Army Signal Company and the first modifications in the establishments to cope with increasing artillery and position warfare conditions.

| Unit. | | | | | Each. Off. | O.R. | Total Off. | O.R. |
|---|---|---|---|---|---|---|---|---|
| One Army Signal Company ... | ... | ... | ... | ... | 7 | 142 | 7 | 142 |
| Three Airline Sections | ... | ... | ... | ... | 1 | 50 | 3 | 150 |
| Two Cable Sections ... | ... | ... | ... | ... | 1 | 35 | 2 | 70 |
| Two Corps Signal Companies | ... | ... | ... | ... | 5 | 75 | 10 | 150 |
| Two Airline Sections ... | ... | ... | ... | ... | 1 | 50 | 2 | 100 |
| Four Cable Sections ... | ... | ... | ... | ... | 1 | 35 | 4 | 140 |
| Six Divisional Signal Companies | ... | ... | ... | ... | 6 | 202 | 36 | 1212 |
| Total | ... | ... | ... | ... | | | 64 | 1964 |

## (3) 1916.

After the alterations of May, 1916. Increase in constructive power ; addition of area personnel, switchboard operators, etc.

| Unit. | | | | Each. Off. | O.R. | Total. Off. | O.R. |
|---|---|---|---|---|---|---|---|
| One Army Signal Company | ... | ... | ... | 10 | 224 | 10 | 224 |
| Four Airline Sections... | ... | ... | ... | 1 | 58 | 4 | 232 |
| Three Cable Sections... | ... | ... | ... | 1 | 37 | 3 | 111 |
| Two Corps Signal Companies | ... | ... | ... | 6 | 90 | 12 | 180 |
| Two Airline Sections ... | ... | ... | ... | 1 | 58 | 2 | 116 |
| Four Cable Sections ... | ... | ... | ... | 1 | 37 | 4 | 148 |
| Six Divisional Signal Companies | ... | ... | ... | 6 | 210 | 36 | 1260 |
| Total | ... | ... | ... | | | 71 | 2271 |

## (4) 1917.

After the first great re-organization.

| Unit. | | | Each. Off. | O.R. | Total. Off. | O.R. |
|---|---|---|---|---|---|---|
| One Army Signal Company | ... | ... | 13 | 262 | 13 | 262 |
| Three Airline Sections | ... | ... | 1 | 58 | 3 | 174 |
| Two Cable Sections ... | ... | ... | 1 | 37 | 2 | 74 |
| One Signal Construction Company ... | ... | 3 | 114 | 3 | 114 |
| 10 Army R.F.A. Bde. Signal Sub-sections ... | | 1 | 19 | 10 | 190 |
| 22 H.A. Group Signal Sub-sections ... | ... | 1 | 26 | 22 | 572 |
| Two Corps Signal Companies | ... | ... | 7 | 170 | 14 | 340 |
| Two Airline Sections ... | ... | ... | 1 | 58 | 2 | 116 |
| Four Cable Sections ... | ... | ... | 1 | 37 | 4 | 148 |
| Six Divisional Signal Companies | ... | ... | 11 | 281 | 66 | 1686 |
| Eight Area Signal Detachments | ... | ... | 1 | 15 | 8 | 120 |
| Total | ... | ... | | | 147 | 3796 |

## (5) 1918.

At the Armistice. Included amongst the changes are the second great re-organization, the addition of a light railway signal company, and considerable additions to the Divisional Signal Company. Wireless has been absorbed into the formation signal companies.

| Unit. | | | Each. Off. | O.R. | Total. Off. | O.R. |
|---|---|---|---|---|---|---|
| One Army Signal Company | ... | ... | 15 | 340 | 15 | 340 |
| Three Airline Sections | ... | ... | 1 | 43 | 3 | 129 |
| Two Cable Sections ... | ... | ... | 1 | 34 | 2 | 68 |
| Eight Area Signal Detachments | ... | ... | 1 | 13 | 8 | 104 |
| One Signal Construction Company ... | ... | 3 | 113 | 3 | 113 |
| One Light Railway Signal Company | ... | 1 | 61 | 1 | 61 |
| Nine Army R.F.A. Bde. Sig. sub-sections ... | | 1 | 19 | 9 | 171 |
| 17 H.A. Group Signal Sub-Sections | ... | 1 | 28 | 17 | 476 |
| Two Corps Signal Companies | ... | ... | 6 | 105 | 12 | 210 |
| Four Airline Sections | ... | ... | 1 | 43 | 4 | 172 |
| Four Cable Sections ... | ... | ... | 1 | 34 | 4 | 136 |
| Six Divisional Signal Companies | ... | ... | 15 | 400 | 90 | 2400 |
| Total | ... | ... | | | 168 | 4380 |

AA

# INDEX.

PLATE I ᴀ.

# DIAGRAM OF 2nd CORPS COMMUNICATIONS AT
# THE BATTLE OF MONS.

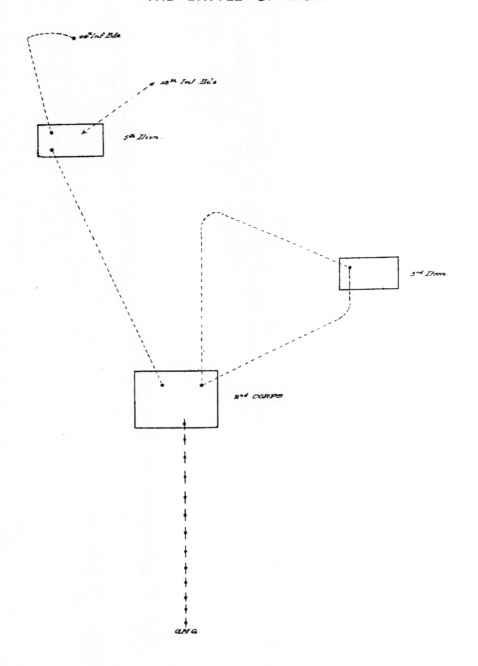

PLATE I B.

DIAGRAM OF 2nd CORPS COMMUNICATIONS
ON 27 AND 28. 8. 14.

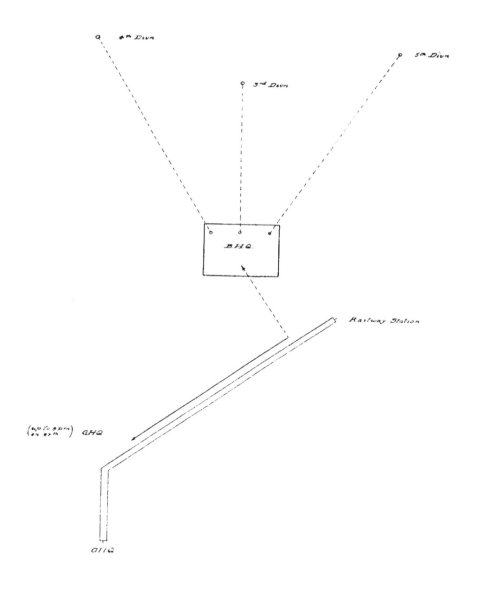

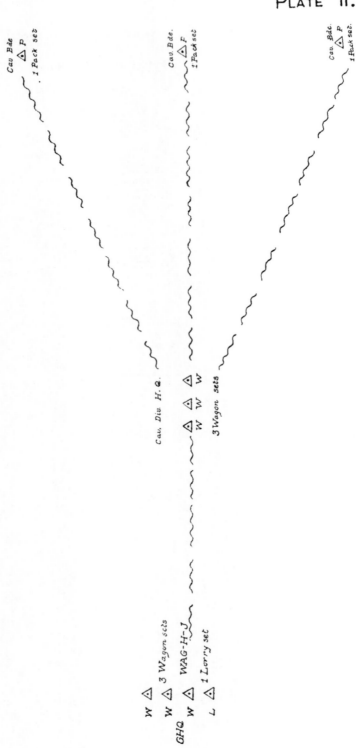

PLATE II.

DIAGRAM OF WIRELESS ORGANIZATION. (AUTUMN, 1914).

PLATE III.

# DIAGRAM OF BRIGADE COMMUNICATIONS AT THE CROSSING OF THE AISNE.

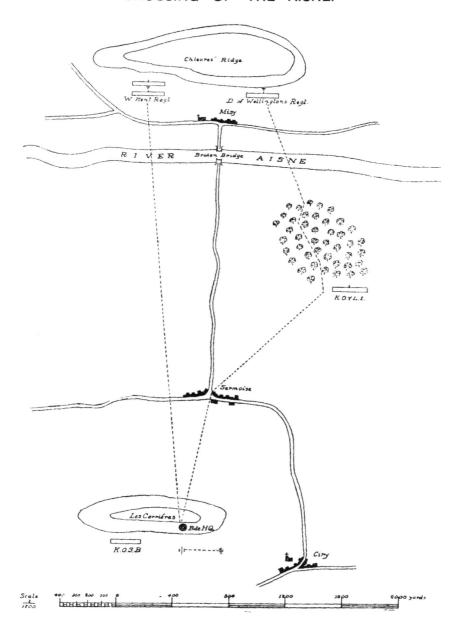

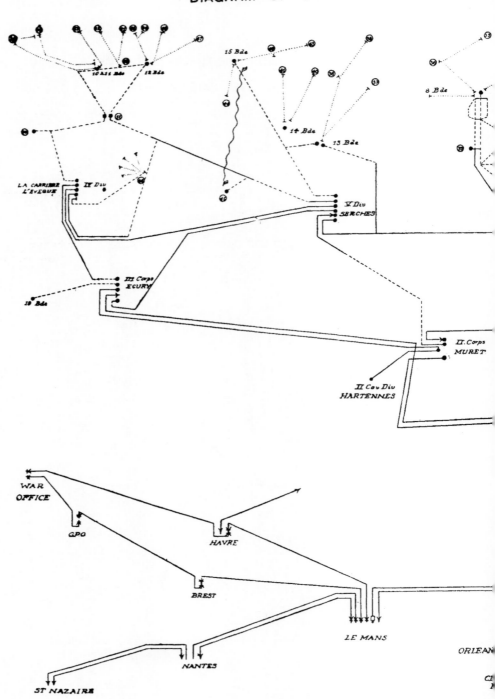

10 & 11 Bde
12 Bde
15 Bde
14 Bde
13 Bde
8 Bde
LA CARRIERE
L'EVEQUE
IV Div
V Div
SERCHES
III Corps
ECURY
10 Bde
II Corps
MURET
II Cav Div
HARTENNES
WAR
OFFICE
GPO
HAVRE
BREST
LE MANS
ORLEAN
NANTES
ST NAZAIRE

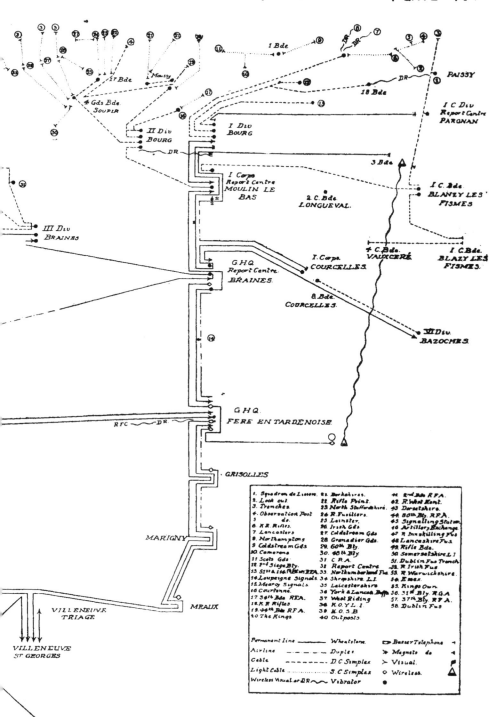

1. Squadron de Liason
2. Look out
3. Trenches
4. Observation Post
5. do.
6. K.R. Rifles.
7. Lancasters
8. Northamptons
9. Coldstream Gds
10. Camerons
11. Scots Gds
12. 3rd Siege Bty.
13. 51st & 116th Bty. RFA.
14. Loupergne Signals
15. Mercy Signals
16. Courtonne
17. 36th Bde. RFA.
18. K.R Rifles
19. 44th Bde RFA.
20. The Kings

21. Berkshires.
22. Rifle Point.
23. North Staffordshire.
24. R. Fusiliers.
25. Leinster.
26. Irish Gds
27. Coldstream Gds
28. Grenadier Gds
29. 60th Bty.
30. 40th Bty.
31. C.R.A.
32. Report Centre
33. Northumberland Fus.
34. Shropshire. L.I.
35. Leicestershire
36. York & Lancs. Bde.
37. West Riding
38. K.O.Y.L.I.
39. K.O.S.B.
40. Outposts

41. 2nd Bde RFA.
42. R. West Kent.
43. Dorsetshire.
44. 80th Bty. RFA.
45. Signalling Station
46. Artillery Exchange
47. R Inniskilling Fus.
48. Lancashire Fus.
49. Rifle Bde.
50. Somersetshire L.I.
51. Dublin Fus Trench
52. R. Irish Fus
53. R. Warwickshire.
54. Essex.
56. 31st Bty. RGA
57. 37th Bty. RFA.
58. Dublin Fus

Permanent line ——— Wheatstone. | Buzzer Telephone
Airline — — — — Duplex | Magneto do
Cable – – – – – D.C. Simplex | Visual.
Light Cable ........... S.C. Simplex | Wireless.
Wireless Visual or DR ∿ Vibrator | ●

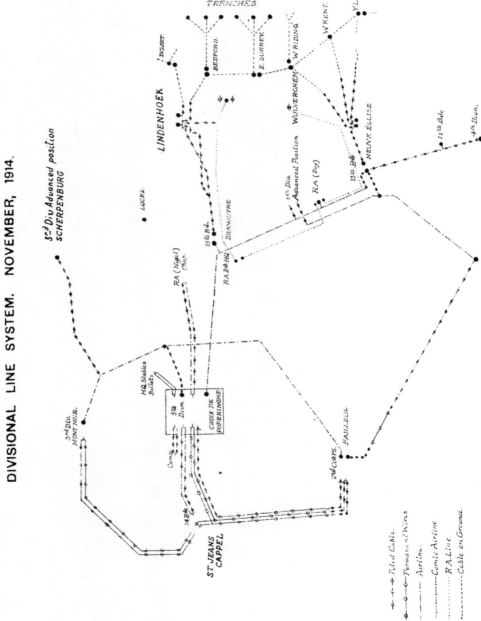

PLATE V.

DIVISIONAL LINE SYSTEM. NOVEMBER, 1914.

PLATE VI.

# DIAGRAM OF COMMUNICATIONS OF THE EXPEDITIONARY FORCE.

## 18TH DEC. 1914.

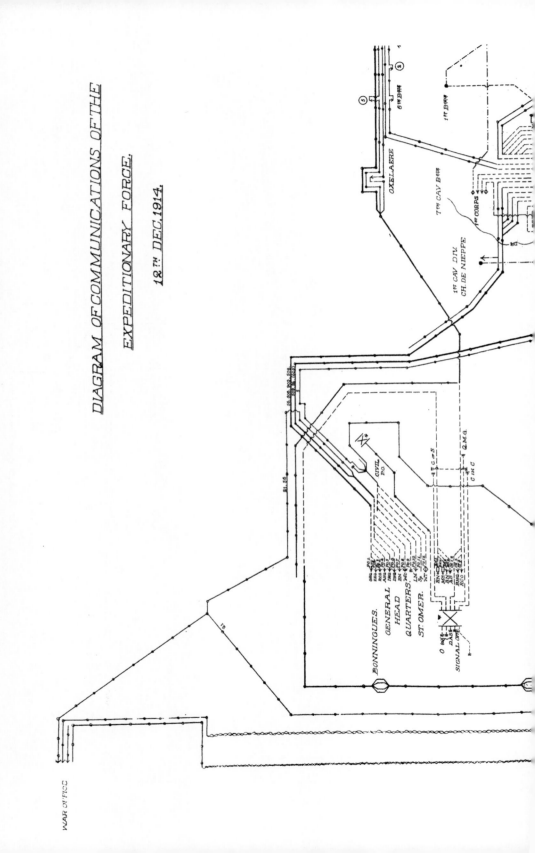

# DIAGRAM OF COMMUNICATIONS OF THE

## EXPEDITIONARY FORCE,

### 12TH DEC.1914.

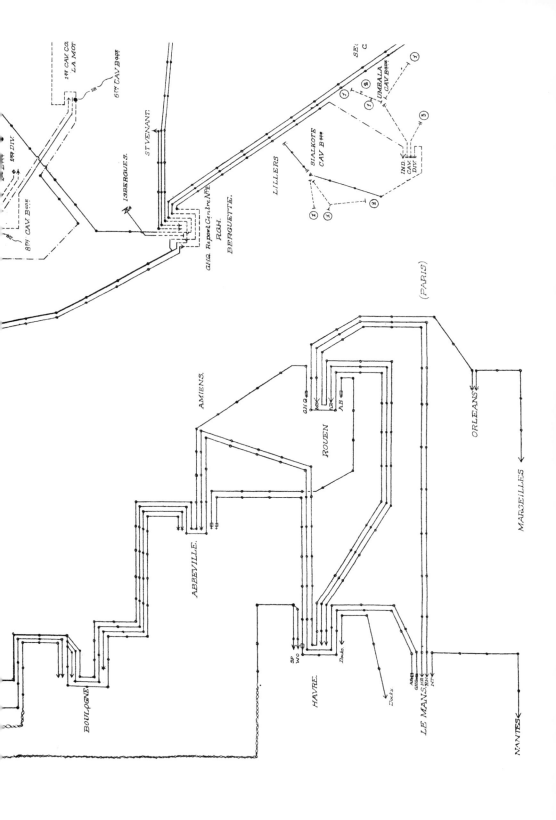

PLATE VI.

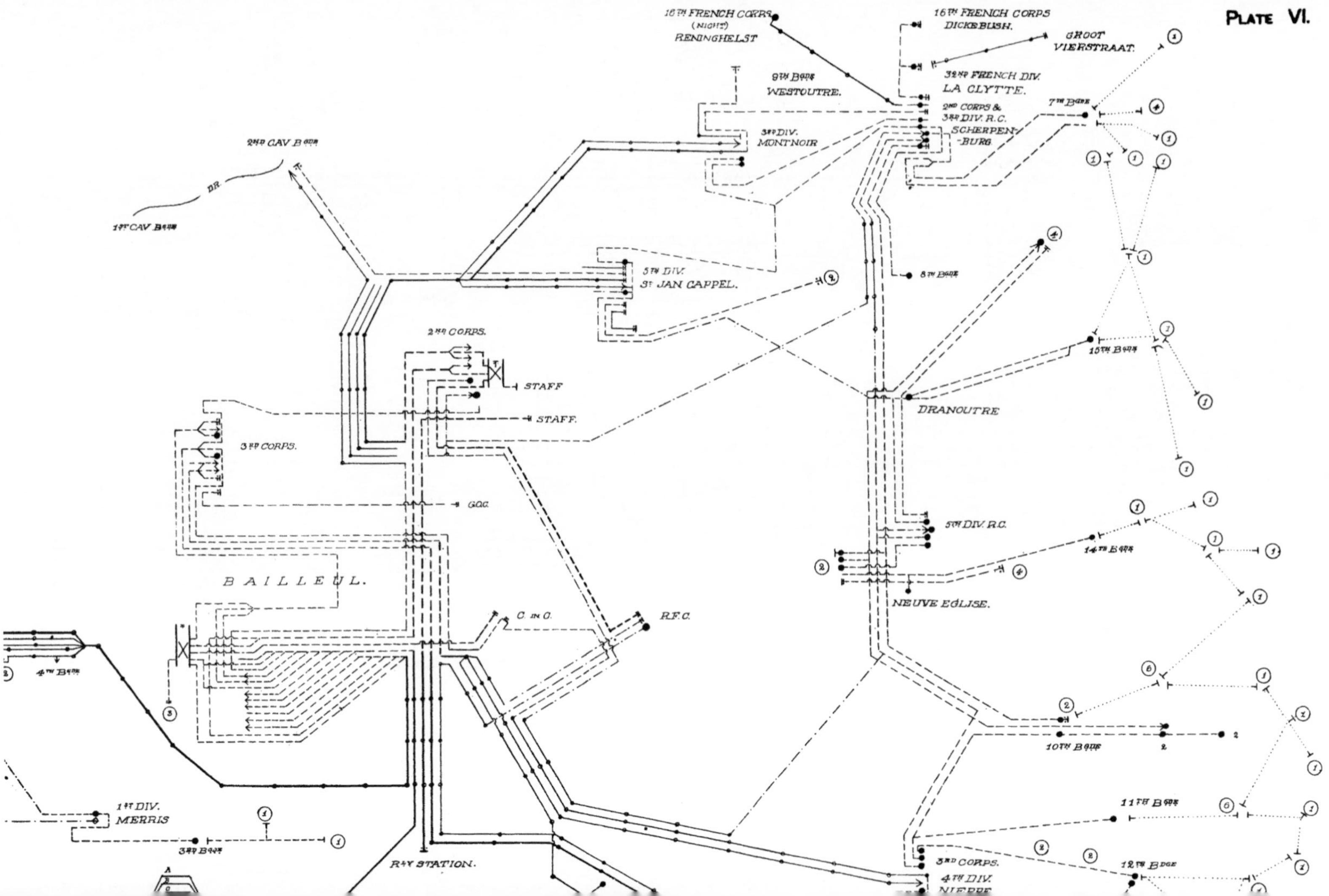

16TH FRENCH CORPS
DICKEBUSH.

GROOT
VIERSTRAAT.

32ND FRENCH DIV.
LA CLYTTE.

2ND CORPS &
3RD DIV. R.C.
SCHERPEN-
BURG.

7TH BDE.

18TH FRENCH CORPS.
(NIGHT)
RENINGHELST.

9TH BDE.
WESTOUTRE.

3RD DIV.
MONTNOIR.

8TH BDE.

DRANOUTRE.

15TH BDE.

14TH BDE.

5TH DIV. R.C.

NEUVE EGLISE.

3RD CORPS.

4TH DIV.
NIEPPE

10TH BDE.

11TH BDE.

12TH BDE.

5TH DIV.
ST. JAN CAPPEL.

2ND CORPS.

STAFF.

STAFF.

G.O.C.

3RD CORPS.

R.F.C.

C IN C.

R.Y. STATION.

B A I L L E U L.

2ND CAV. B.DE.

1ST CAV. B.DE.

1ST DIV.
MERRIS.

3RD B.DE.

4TH B.DE.

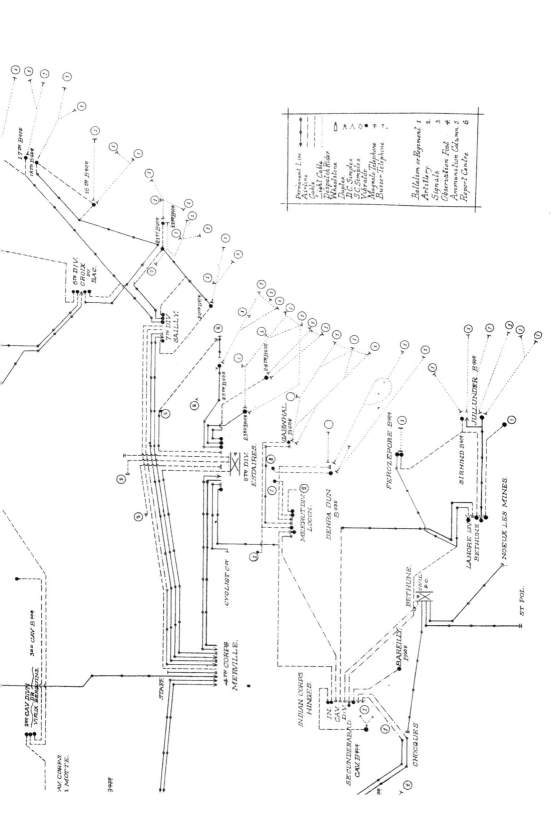

# DIAGRAM OF THE REAR LINE SYSTEM OF THE EXPEDITIONARY FORCE BEFORE THE FORMATION OF THE ARMIES.

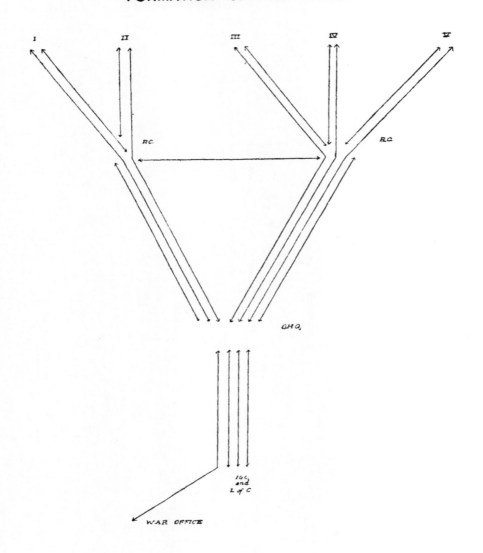

PLATE VIIв.

DIAGRAM OF THE REAR LINE SYSTEM OF THE
EXPEDITIONARY FORCE AFTER THE
FORMATION OF THE ARMIES.

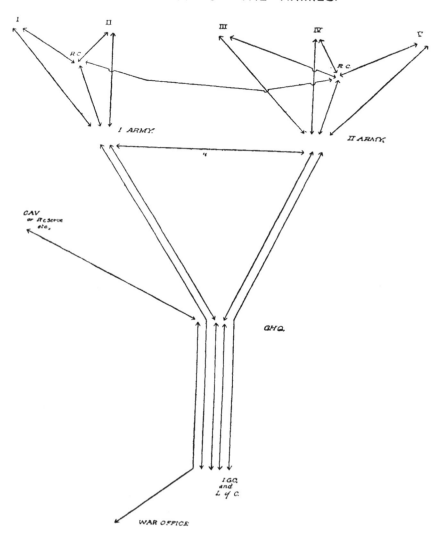

PLATE VIII.

DIAGRAM OF POLES OF TRESTLE ROUTES.

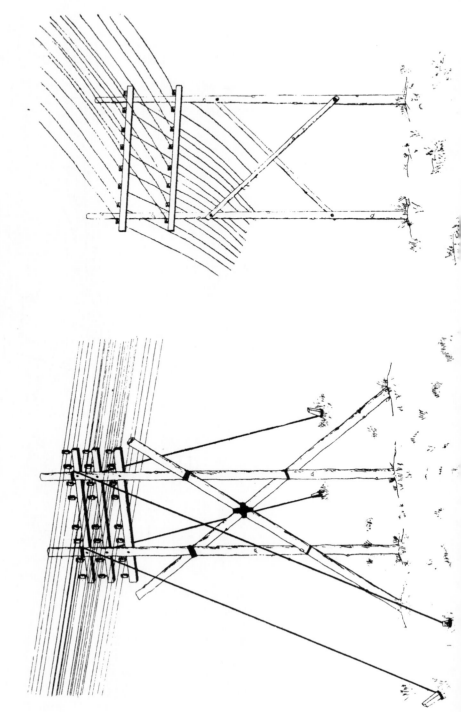

PLATE IX.

DIAGRAM OF FIRST TRENCH WIRELESS SCHEME AND OF AERIAL USED.

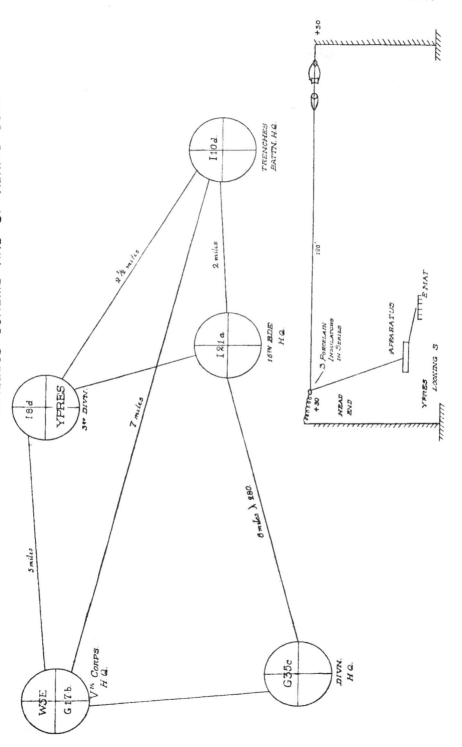

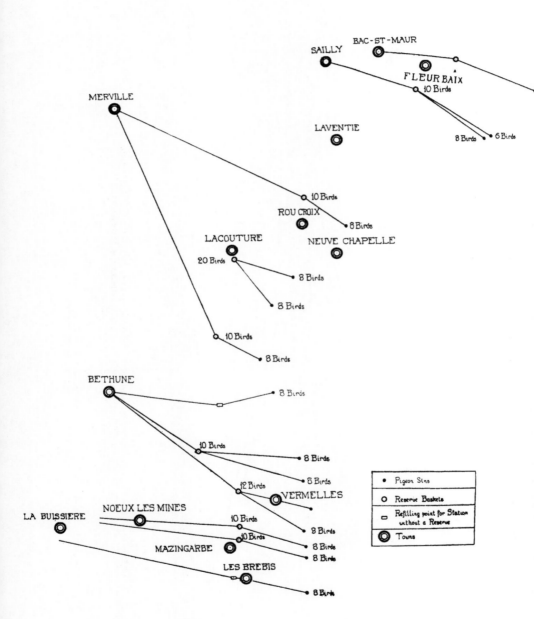

PLATE XI.

DIAGRAM OF FIRST FRENCH LISTENING-POST INSTALLATION.

About 350 metres

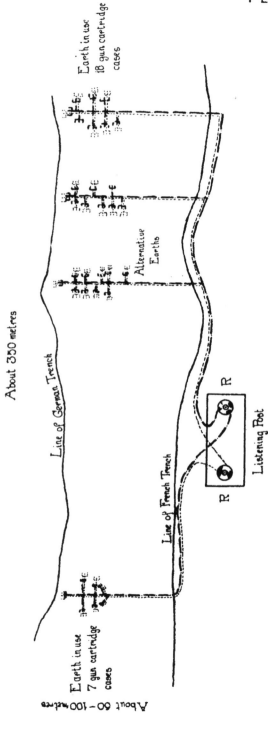

Earth in use
18 gun cartridge
cases

Line of German Trench

Alternative
Earths

Line of French Trench

Listening Post

R

R

Earth in use
7 gun cartridge
cases

About 50–100 metres

The earths are in mine galleries and are believed to be within 15 metres of the German trench.
The gun cartridge cases (of 7·5 cm. gun) are buried in charcoal to prevent oxidation.
The receivers are French Post Office pattern (about 150 ohms).

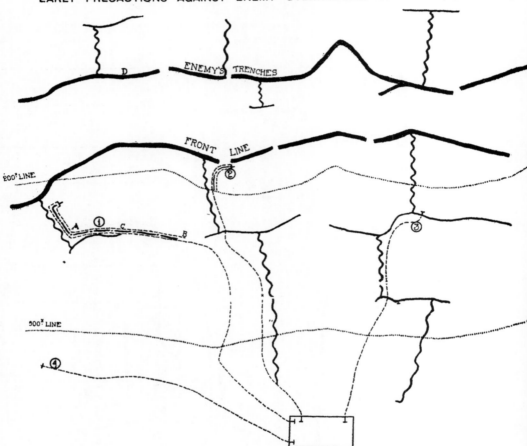

EARLY PRECAUTIONS AGAINST ENEMY OVERHEARING IN 1915. PLATE XII.

ENEMY'S TRENCHES

D

FRONT LINE

200ʸ LINE

② 

A ① C

B

③

300ʸ LINE

④

① Circuit more than 200 yds. from enemy but distance A.B (portion parallel to enemy line) is greater than half C.D. So circuit is made metallic as far as B.

② Metallic to beyond the 200 yard line.

③
④  Ordinary earth returns.

Metallic Twin Cable          Single Cable.

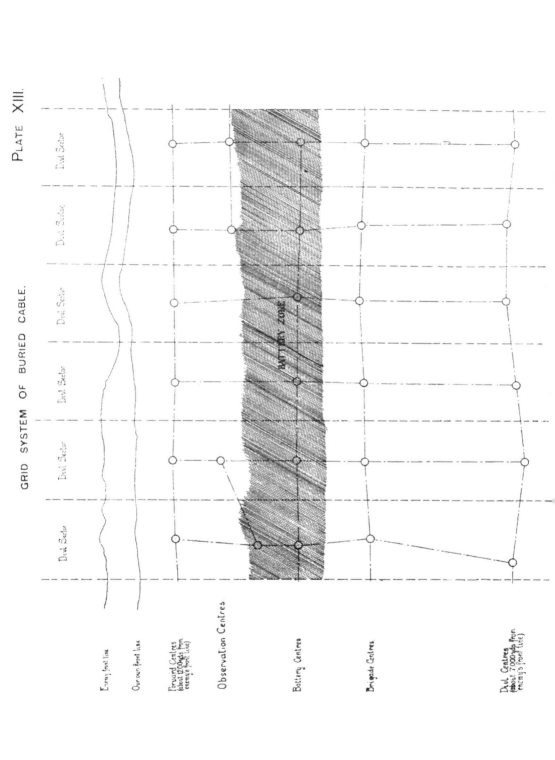

PLATE XIII.

GRID SYSTEM OF BURIED CABLE.

BATTERY ZONE

Enemy front line

Our own front line

Forward Centres
(about 1200 yds from
enemy's front line)

Observation Centres

Battery Centres

Brigade Centres

Div. Centres
(about 7000 yds from
enemy's front line)

Div. Sector

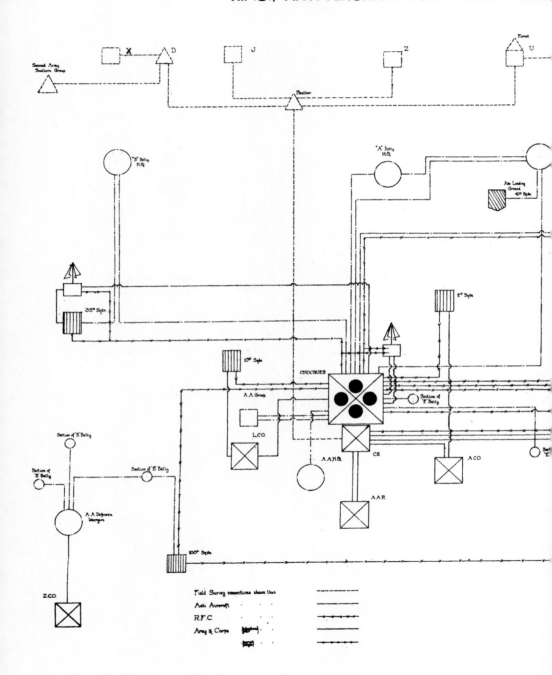

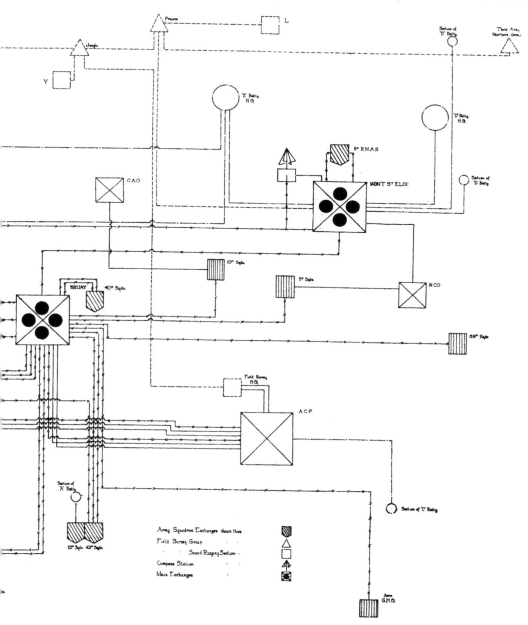

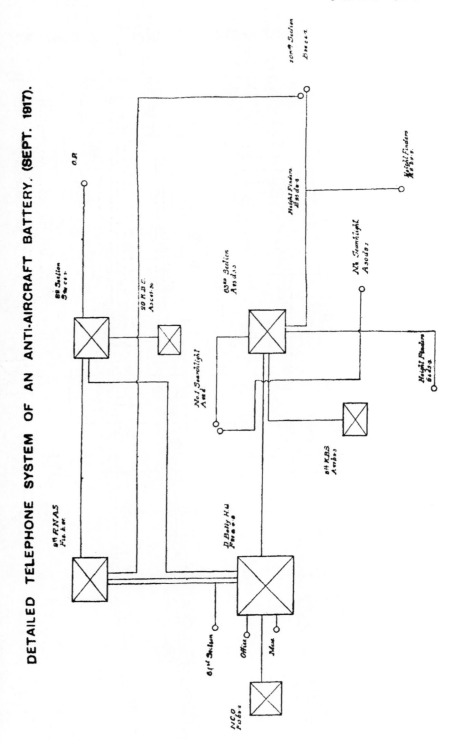

PLATE XV.

DETAILED TELEPHONE SYSTEM OF AN ANTI-AIRCRAFT BATTERY. (SEPT. 1917).

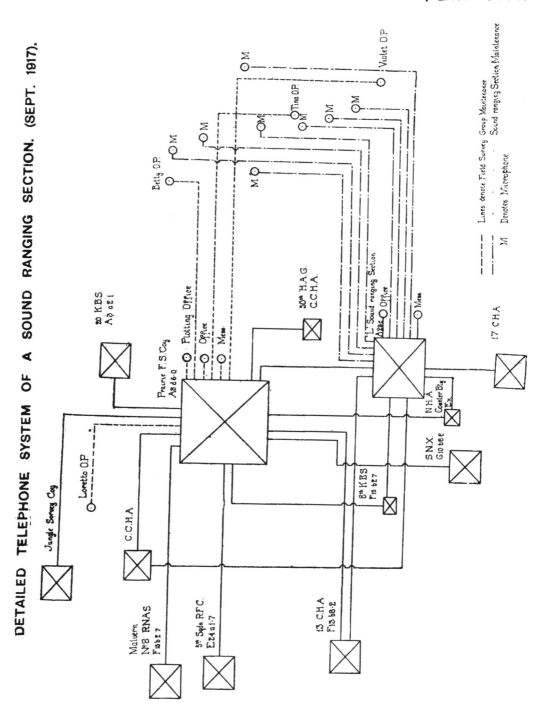

PLATE XVI.

DETAILED TELEPHONE SYSTEM OF A SOUND RANGING SECTION. (SEPT. 1917).

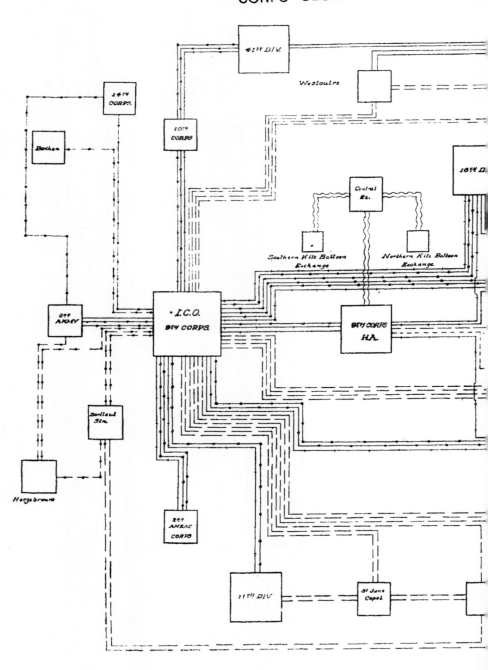

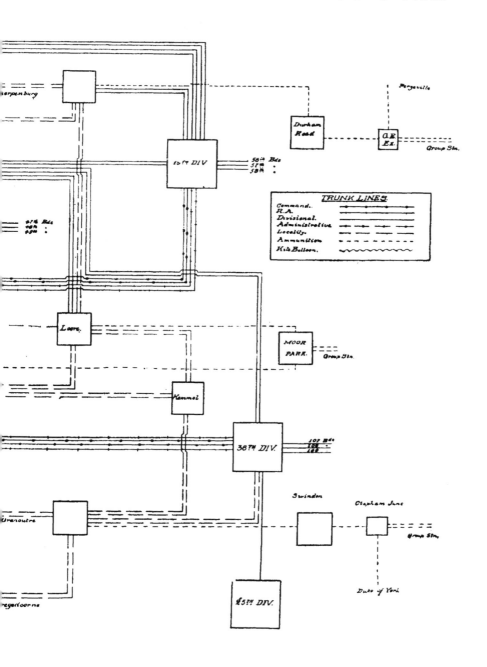

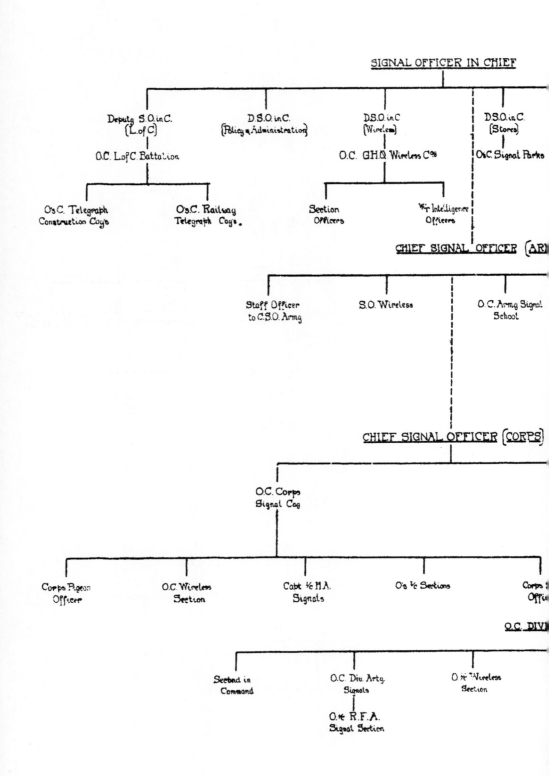

SIGNAL OFFICER IN CHIEF

Deputy S.O.in C.
(L.of C)

D.S.O.in C.
(Policy & Administration)

D.S.O.in C.
(Wireless)

D.S.O.in C.
(Stores)

O.C. L.ofC. Battalion

O.C. G.H.Q. Wireless C^os

O.sC. Signal Parks

O.sC. Telegraph
Construction Coy's

O.sC. Railway
Telegraph Coy's.

Section
Officers

W.T Intelligence
Officers

CHIEF SIGNAL OFFICER (ARMY)

Staff Officer
to C.S.O. Army

S.O. Wireless

O.C. Army Signal
School

CHIEF SIGNAL OFFICER (CORPS)

O.C. Corps
Signal Coy

Corps Pigeon
Officer

O.C. Wireless
Section

Capt. i/c H.A.
Signals

O's i/c Sections

Corps
Office

O.C. DIVI

Second in
Command

O.C. Div. Artg.
Signals

O i/c Wireless
Section

O i/c R.F.A.
Signal Section

PLATE XVIII.

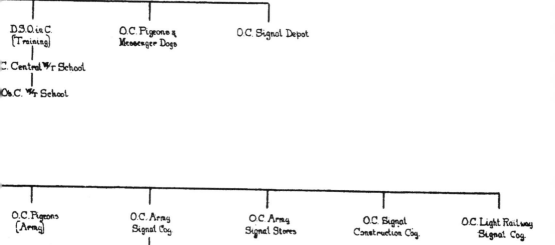

D.S.O. in C.
(Training)

O.C. Pigeons &
Messenger Dogs

O.C. Signal Depot

C. Central W/T School

O.C. W/T School

O.C. Pigeons
(Army)

O.C. Army
Signal Coy.

O.C. Army
Signal Stores

O.C. Signal
Construction Coy.

O.C. Light Railway
Signal Coy.

Adjutant

Section
Officers

O's I/c Area
Detachments

O.C. P.E.L.
Repair Unit

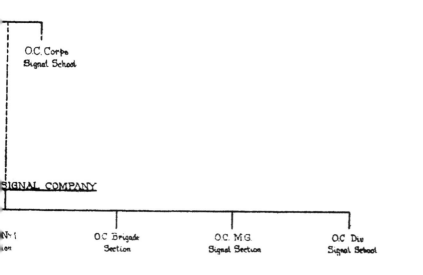

O.C. Corps
Signal School

SIGNAL COMPANY

N: 1
ion

O.C. Brigade
Section

O.C. M.G.
Signal Section

O.C. Div.
Signal School

PLATE XIX.

# DIVISIONAL SIGNAL SYSTEM. (1918 ADVANCE).

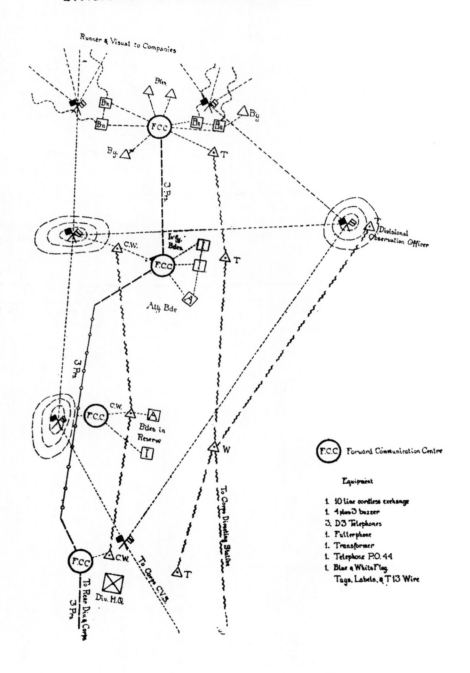

F.C.C   Forward Communication Centre

Equipment

1  10 line cordless exchange
1  4 plus 3 buzzer
3  D3 Telephones
1  Fullerphone
1  Transformer
1  Telephone P.O. 44
1  Blue & White Flag
   Tags, Labels, & T13 Wire

PLATE XXA.

COMPARATIVE DIAGRAMS OF DIVISIONAL LINE SYSTEMS WITH AND
WITHOUT FORWARD COMMUNICATION CENTRES.

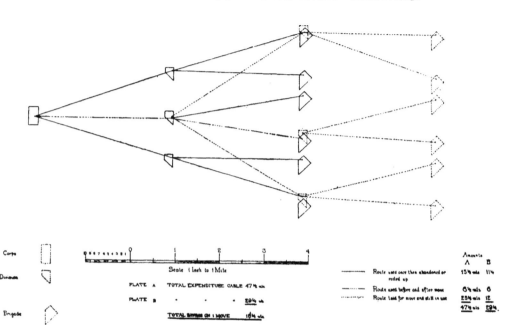

PLATE XXB.

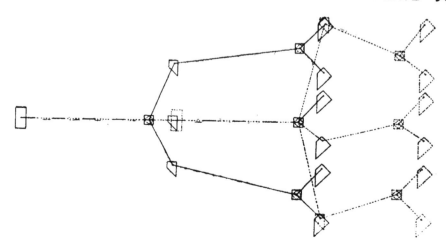